# SAVING YOUR LIFE ~ One Day at a Time

## A DAILY GUIDE TO Easy, Fundamental Coping Skills for Depression

When Nothing is Working ~ Here Are Some Answers

Connie E. Mabry, Ed. S.

# DISCLAIMER

Nothing in this book is intended to constitute medical advice, treatment or specific prescription. Medical diagnosis can only occur between an individual patient and his or her physician.



TUNBY Houghton Publishing

www.savingyourlife.org

**1-800-730-3194**

Printed in the U.S.A.

ISBN: 978-0-941072-79-3

**To my mother, Elizabeth Erika Tunby Hill**
**1919-2003**

**My anchor in every storm**

**With special acknowledgment:**

Timothy P. Kelly, D.C.
The Buckhead Center for Health
Atlanta, Georgia

and

Anthony E. Karpas, M.D.
Institute of Endocrinology & Reproductive Medicine
Atlanta, Georgia

Special thanks to these 'doctors' who helped me along the way:

Robert Yelverton, M.D.
Jim Warren, Ph. D.
Roque Santa Cruz, D.V.M.
Andy Hurayt, M.D.
Emile Risby, M.D.
Michael Lebowitz, D.C.
Saraju Dalsania, M.D.

And in hopes that I am able to make amends to:

Joyce R.
Dorinda T.
Susan D.
Linda S.
Tucker A.
Harry D.
Sloane C.

## Who I Am and Why I Feel Qualified to Write This Book

I actually feel I am an adequate representative to write about coping skills for depression through two different categories. On the one hand, I have some academic credentials. I have an Education Specialist degree in Counseling and Educational Psychology. On the other hand, I have the REAL credential. I have fought depression and several concurrent/somewhat related illnesses for over three decades.

By sharing some of the tools that have made this recovery possible, I am in hopes that even ONE of them will assist you in turning the corner in your life from hopelessness and despair to solid ground and bright, happy days again.

Because I fought multiple illnesses, I doubt that many of my recommendations will be appropriate for everyone. Maybe you can utilize half a dozen of my solutions; maybe you only need one to regain your footing. But, I have also found that what may not be appropriate at this moment, might be the very puzzle piece you need next year or the year after.

So, I have tried to write this as a guide to recovery that you can use and revisit and put away and pick up again. You may be in such a dark, bleak place when you read an idea you really need, that you cannot comprehend the lesson. So, some of the critical theories are summarized at the end of the book for a checklist in time of desperate need.

I have tried to develop this as a resource for the days when you are so low, the gutter looks up. My advisor during my Ed. S. degree work said it perfectly: "This is what you needed and couldn't find when you were struggling." I have searched every single book in print on the topic of depression and have never found anything that remotely touched on how fundamental just surviving this pain was. Just to 'stay above ground' was such an enormous achievement so many days for me.

Little puzzle piece by puzzle piece, I found the information I needed to put the "Humpty Dumpty" of Connie back together again. I would like to save you the energy – the vast expense – the time – the frustration of this research and offer you what worked for me.

Because this is in no way a complete guidebook on tools for coping with depression and recovery from it, I hope to hear from many of you through my website: http://www.savingyourlife.org on strategies that have worked for you.

I would also like to caution you that even though some idea may not work at this time, do not dismiss it totally. As our chemistries change, so does our ability to utilize or tolerate new medications or supplements. So, what may not work for you today, may work next week or six months from now. Just because this is written on a calendar year basis, does not mean it will only be useful information for one year.

One of the reasons I chose this format was because I knew I was capable of absorbing so very little when I was depressed. The overwhelming pain – the black fog that overshadowed my thinking ability – the blankness of my reasoning power - demanded that all material be very simple AND short.

I in no way want to minimize any part of the suffering that is inherent in our illness. So when I appear light or superficial – even joking – about the topic of depression, please know that it is part of the attitude I have adopted in fighting this enemy. Much of what I say will be tongue in cheek and sarcasm was one of the great tools that worked in dealing with depression for me.

I also am aware (as an Instructor of Writing and Linguistics for freshman at a southern university) that I have blatantly violated most every rule concerning punctuation, parallel construction, verb tense shifts, cohesion, etc... I consciously wrote as if I were talking to you. In some instances, reading the selection aloud may make it easier to understand what I am trying to convey.

So, this is not meant to be a literary masterpiece. It is simply a manual for saving yourself from depression. I sincerely pray that you find some peace and hope in these pages.

# A WORD ABOUT THE FORMAT

This book was originally rejected by a publisher because 'daily meditations were not in vogue currently'. I reformatted the text and resubmitted the material, only to be told that they had just published a similar book. I was sent a desk copy of this book and the format was a daily meditation!

What I learned from this was that the format had to suit the READER – not a publishers' specifications.

Immediately, I knew this material had to fit a pattern that someone in the black hole of depression would still be able to read. So – again using my own experience as the yardstick – I knew that we can conquer depression only one day at a time AND that the ideas had to be brief to be assimilated. Any information I had to share had to be in manageable bites.

There was also going to be the need for lots of white space. Being overwhelmed is already too easy when a person is depressed. And if I could give even one ray of hope on any given day, that may be enough to hang on to, until your chemistry righted itself again.

I have intentionally exaggerated punctuation or spacing or used quotes that are not congruent with the daily message above it.

I have done all of this on purpose. I am using visual cues to force you to focus more on what I am saying - OR - I align divergent thoughts as 'brain sparks' that will trigger new neural paths.

# A WORD ABOUT THE FORMAT

# JANUARY

## *January 1*

### BEGIN

> *"A thousand mile journey must begin with one step, a great collection with one object, a landmark preservation with the salvage of one brick, a life story with one captured memory."*
> *Unknown*

Because depression stops us dead in our tracks - wherever we are - it is hard to conceive of momentum. But, as the fresh new slate of a new year begins, think of ONE thing you can do today to move yourself one step forward. Regardless of where you are in your recovery, there is always one more thing that you can do to help yourself.

If we could see the dreams that will be fulfilled, the new people who will enter our lives, the spectacular experiences just waiting for us ahead in this coming year, we would be dazzled by what life has to offer us.

Find just one change to make today ~ one habit to break or maybe reinforce. It could be as simple as cutting the amount of sugar you add to your coffee in half. That is my change this year. It may not sound like much but, I ingest way too much sugar. And that one tablespoon I will leave out 365 times will make for a better year (and a better life) for me.

Do not let this day end without creating some difference in your life. It may not be directly connected to depression. Paint your toenails, dig your golf clubs out of storage, call the Humane Society for a pet, the list is endless.

It is *your* year. Create a series of days that will become one of the best years of your life.

*A Pledge of Trust*
*"Father, during this coming week there may be times when I shall not be able to sense Your presence or to be aware of Your nearness.*
*When I am lonely and by myself*
*I trust you to be my companion.*
*When I am tempted to sin*
*I trust you to keep me from it.*
*When I am depressed and anxious*
*I trust you to lift my spirits.*

*When I am crushed by responsibility and overwhelmed by the demands of people on my time,*
*I trust you to give me poise and a sense of purpose.*
*When I am rushed and running*
*I trust you to make me still inside.*
*When I forget You*
*I trust that you will never forget me.*
*When I forget others*
*I trust you to prompt me to think of them.*
*When you take something or someone from me that I want to keep; when You remove the props I lean on for comfort in place of You; when You refuse to respond to my questions and to answer my selfish prayers, I will trust You even then. Amen."*

*Bryan Jeffery Leech*

*January 2*

## Visualizing the Road Ahead

Boy, did this tool work for me! Not only did I keep snapshots of the 'real me' - the vibrant, upbeat, passionate person I thought I was - on my desk, the dashboard of my car, on my refrigerator door, everywhere - but, these were pictures that showed me with a huge grin reflecting the joy of whatever memory I was capturing on film. Instead of hiding my swollen, sluggish self, I wanted to be 'living life OUT LOUD' as my friend, Sylvia says. Out in the world making memories.

So, the mental image as I was in a dark depression, was superceded by the mental image of who I was when I was all I could be -- when I was 'the real Connie'. The pictures were proof of the joy I had experienced. They were real. I HAD been that happy. If I could do it once, I could do it again. And I always - ALWAYS - saw myself getting back to this place... the truly alive person who was just behind the shadow of this depression, waiting to get back in the spotlight.

Just around the next corner, that image awaited me. I just had to keep going in that direction. I visualized my healthy self and held that as my hope.

And there was always a corner on the horizon. I knew I could, I knew I could, I knew I could... keep putting one foot in front of the other until I rounded that corner. It wasn't an option. It was just a matter of time.

If I could see it, I could BE it.

"Act like you expect to get into the end zone."
Joe Paterno as quoted in *The New York Times*

## *January 3*

## When You Want to Give Up

There are times when all the good advice isn't going to matter.

Sometimes you just can't make anything work. You cannot get it together.

It hurts too much.

These are the days that the only thing you have to do is hold on. Just stay here.

Some days the best you can do is breathe. I had days when just breathing was a huge accomplishment.

You can pick up and get back on track later. Just now the only thing you have to do is not go backward.

If you do not lose ground, it has been a successful day.

Just hold on. This too shall pass.

It always does.

Beyond Our Sight
"The stars are there, however dark the night,
Although we catch no least glimpse of their light
Here in our world where we run in and out
From dreary faith to faith and doubt to doubt;
The stars are there, and they are burning bright!

God's order rules, and we are in God's care,
It matters not that we are unaware;
Beyond our sight, each in its nightly place
Bright witness to God's everlasting grace,
However dark the night, the stars are there!"
James Dillet Freeman

*January 4*

## WHAT MAKES YOU TICK? WHAT MAKES YOU PURR?

*"No one is capable of gratitude as one who has emerged from the kingdom of night."*

*Elie Wiesel*

What makes you want to get out of bed in the morning? I am speaking here of the mornings that you are not depressed. Is it your work, is it your family, is it a project you are engrossed in, is it a shopping spree you have planned...

Stop and think. Right this minute.

This is not HAVING to get out of bed. This is about WANTING to get into the day and this activity. If your heart does not 'sing' with an immediate response - a sure knowing and mental image that brings a smile to your face - then, way beyond the depression, this is something that has to be fixed first.

Every single human needs to have anticipation in their life. This is about an eagerness to get out of bed and begin.... If you honestly have no drive - there is no stimulus in the WANT department -then, you have to find this answer and get it in place in your life.

In the long run, this will help your depression. Because, for a meaningful life, humans MUST have some activity, some hope, some drive above and beyond meeting our basic needs.

I am passionate about teaching. No two classes, no two students, no two lessons are ever the same. It is enriching to meet the challenge of working with young adults. How exciting to be a part of the learning process and the input in this stage of their lives!

Let me be quick to add that there are days when I am certain I would be better suited to selling doughnuts at Krispy Kreme, because none of the material I present seems to be getting learned! But, those are little speed bumps on the road of my life and I go back and revamp my approach to the lesson and go at it from another angle. And usually this works and I can see the growth and progress taking place.

So, I am not talking perfection here. Just passion.

Now, what would make you eager to get out of bed if there was no alarm clock and no financial pressure?

But, ignoring the glass-walled crater of pain that depression can create is to minimize your experience. We can acknowledge our suffering while still moving forward to the light at the end of our tunnel.

*"When you're depressed, the whole body is depressed, and it translates to the cellular level. The first objective is to get your energy up, and you can do it through play. It's one of the most powerful ways of breaking up hopelessness and bringing energy into the situation."*

*O. Carl Simonton, M. D.*

## *January 6*

## Serotonin Solutions

Dr. Judith Wurtman, with her husband, Dr. Richard Wurtman, both former leading research scientists in the study of serotonin activity at NIH (National Institutes of Health), states that some folks will consume sweet, starchy foods - carbohydrates - in an effort to self-medicate. The brain's calming chemical - the neurotransmitter serotonin - is formed when carbohydrates like cake, cookies, bread, chips, pasta is eaten. No wonder we have such massive cravings for these foods!

Dr. Wurtman also says "Insufficient quantities of serotonin sets up feelings of anxiety, inability to focus, and irresistible cravings; whereas, sufficient quantities of serotonin makes people feel less anxious, less depressed, more alert and more emotionally stable."

But, you knew this already, didn't you? Of course, you did. You have intuitively known how to replace inadequate supplies of serotonin in your brain as long as you have been depressed.

Unfortunately, society sees eating a bag of Oreos as binge eating where they would never see a migraine sufferer taking aspirin as odd.

There are ways to supply more serotonin without the excess calories and the sugar high that results from half a dozen doughnuts. One way is to find the correct anti-depressant for your form of depression. Medication is still the foremost way to rebalance our chemistries.

But, lacking the right pharmaceutical intervention, you can try Omega-3 and Omega-6 oils, lecithin, DL - Phenylalanine, or PMS Escape (a powdered drink that Dr. Wurtman has developed to stimulate serotonin activity).

If eating half a cake is what will allow you to get through the last two hours of your work, or to get dinner on the table for your family, or to stay above ground, then by all means EAT IT! Think of it as aspirin until you are able to find a healthier alternative.

You can always lose the extra pounds. You can't always get your job/marriage/life back.

*"The problems of alcoholism and drug addiction have strong links to depression. The search for highs may often begin as a flight from lows."*

Nathan S. Kline, M.D.

## *January 7*

### What Mozart Can Do For You

Any classical music, but most especially Mozart, with its soothing rhythmic patterns, will relax, energize and stimulate creativity says Ann E. Weeks, D.N.S., R.N., from the study conducted at the Center for the Neurobiology of Learning and Memory at the University of California, Irvine.

This study also proved that listening to a mere ten minutes of Mozart can boost IQ by nine points.

Make sure your collection of audio favorites includes some classical favorites. Even as background music, this can enhance your clarity of thinking.

If it is a wild beat with foot-tapping rhythm that improves your mood, then use that to medicate a bad day.

Experiment. Go to a music store and ask a clerk for suggestions. Borrow tapes and CD's from friends.

It really is scientifically proven that music is healing.

*"Some patients feel guilty about achieving recovery with medication. They have been thoroughly indoctrinated in the idea that emotional disturbance must reflect psychic ills, and they expect treatment to require a prolonged, painful search of their unconscious."*

Nathan S. Kline, M.D.

*January 8*

## Transforming at Glacial Speed

There were days - weeks - months, that my recovery was so slow as to be imperceptible. Those were the times that I detached from the outcome.

I remember a bit of sage advice I got when I first started jogging. A runner who had been at this for years told me that rather than focusing on the finish line or a target on the horizon, sometimes he got through a rough run by just looking at his feet. He only thought of putting one foot in front of the other. Taking the next step.

Pretty soon, enough of these steps accumulated and he saw the finish line pass under his stride.

So, to make progress, all I had to do was the next right thing. And when I got there, to do the next right thing again. And so on.

The outcome would take care of itself.

What does the Oriental proverb say... the greatest journey begins with a single step.

*"It does not matter how slowly you go so long as you do not stop."*

*Confucius*

*January 9*

## Becoming Willing

*"You become a winner only if you are willing to walk over the edge."*

*Unknown*

When I received this diagnosis that I faced a lifetime of recurrent, devastating cycles of depression, my immediate response was 'Absolutely NOT!' I had too much I wanted to do, too much life to live to accept these repetitive phases of inertia and pain.

As I began to seek answers in the traditional fields of psychiatry and pharmacology, I was confident I would be one of the sixty percent who responded to anti-depressant medication and would soon be fully functional once again.

However, much as I demanded and shoved and screamed for the magic pill, the respite eluded me. I have been prescribed lithium seventeen times, Prozac on nine different occasions and so on. Nothing was working. Polypharmacy (the blending of a bit of this and a bit of that - multiple medications for the same illness in varying dosages) didn't work either.

So, then I began to sniff and prowl around the fringes of traditional medicine. And some of my efforts took me way out on the edges. But, I became open and willing. Open to ANY possibility of relief and willing to experiment in the non-traditional medicines.

If I thought a 'health intuitive' - a psychic who was successful in diagnosing intractable illnesses - would help, I tried that. If I thought some New Age 'expert' could offer relief, I followed their suggestions.

The great majority of these efforts produced nothing but frustration and a dent in my wallet. But, what they did offer was hope - and forward momentum - and advancement. Because, each door I opened as another avenue for healing, led to another option and so on.

And ultimately, the handful of theories that did work for me, in combination and varying amounts, created a formula for recovery.

But, let me tell you, some of these attempts were pretty desperate. None were illegal but, boy, were they weird. However, it was the "I will do WHATEVER it takes" attitude - the willingness to step over the edge - that eventually brought me back to a full and productive life.

I am not recommending that you fling judgment and common sense out the window. I am asking that you keep all your options open. What - really - do you have to lose?

*Expect the best of life and it will meet your expectations!*

## *January 10*

### **"When You Get Into a Downward Spiral, Hit the Ground Running"**

Howard Kaminsky and Alexandra Penney in *Magic Words*

This philosophy is not always applicable. But, if you can see your 'fighter self' - the karate expert dealing a death blow to the opponent, depression - this might work for you.

I have always seen my illness as an opponent. And like any fight, one party will be victorious and the other side will lose. And - NO MATTER WHAT - I was going to win.

If you see yourself as 'down for the count' or immobilized and powerless when the depression begins, then you are going to be the loser. Staying down for the count is exactly what your opponent wants.

So, I used anger for energy - even if it was just mental energy - and fought with my heart and soul every time I stepped into the ring with depression.

And I kept the image of myself - exhausted maybe, sweating, yet still on my feet - with the referee holding my arm aloft and declaring me the winner - every single time.

When I could sense a cycle approaching, I armed myself for battle. I was never going to take a passive stance against depression.

I have won. Every single time.

So can you.

*"I have failed over and over again in my life. And that is why I succeed."*

*Michael Jordan*

## *January 11*

### **Whatever Works**

I heard an astonishing revelation one night at a support group meeting. It turned out to be an invaluable piece of information.

A man said that he had been so depressed, he literally did not have the strength - the will- to get out of bed. But, he found a solution. He found he could always roll out of bed onto the floor. Once there, it was too uncomfortable/cold/hard to stay there. And once he got to his feet, he walked directly into his shower and stood under the running water. Clothes and all.

The benefit of the negative ion release of a shower lightened his mood significantly. Any movement - even shuffling a few steps - creates adrenalin. And no one will stay in soaking wet clothes all day. So, by this time, his mood was improved. He put on any clothes - except pajamas- and the day evolved from there.

I can guarantee that by this point, you would be in a far different mental state than you were fifteen minutes ago. I know for a fact this works. I have had to use it.

*"Every moment of one's existence, one is growing into more or retreating into less."*

*Norman Mailer*

## *January 12*

## YOU HAVE TO CHANGE YOUR CHEMISTRY

Keep in mind this is a chemical imbalance in the delicate, miraculous circuitry of our central processing unit - our magnificent brain. So, shifting a few things will get the teeter-totter back in line - but, just like all teeter-totters, this is an ongoing pattern.

Everyone's chemistry shifts - constantly. Cortisol levels reach near fatal levels when we get over-stressed; hot flashes and wild cravings are body signals that our hormones are not in line; a toothache tells us we have bacteria in our mouth.

Depression is a flashing neon sign that we are way out of balance in the fragile neurotransmitter system of our brain.

And sometimes we have to fix this error as best we can, until the right pharmaceuticals are prescribed. If you crave a yeasty, sugary doughnut, go eat it - or eat six. You are probably deficient in B vitamins if you crave yeasty breads. Soothing creamy ice cream may be just what you need because of its high mineral/calcium content.

Salty French fries are boosting adrenal deficiencies. Carbohydrates create more serotonin.

But, although others may chastise you for eating what is not good for you or bingeing on low nutrient food, remember YOU live in the laboratory that is your body and YOU are the chemist in charge.

Your body will tell you what it needs. Fix the chemistry in whatever temporary way you need but, remember what it was you HAD to have and then research it when the depression passes. There is a chemical stimulus behind every craving. And depression is a chemistry that has gone out of kilter.

There are myriad supplements and dietary adjustments (like getting enough caffeine) that will balance your system. It is a process of trial and error. But, the tools are out there. You just have to find what works for you.

*"The better life cannot be imposed from without – it must grow from within."*

*Mrs. Humphrey Ward*

## *January 13*

## LIFE

*"It is wise to keep in mind that no success or failure is necessarily final."*

*Source Unknown*

If today is a tough day, the best you may be able to do is to read this quote as frequently as you can throughout the day.

If you are having a good day today, take a moment to let your imagination capture the little glimpses of pleasure that make life brighter for you. For me, it is the scent and softness of clean sheets at night, gorgeous fresh flowers on my dining room table, snuggling with my dog, finding personal mail between the bills, any time with my nieces.

These are the flashes of joy that give meaning to the dullest, darkest day. Think of what makes you believe in life. Keep these images in your heart. These are the free anti-depressants that all of us need.

*"Dear Lord, I need your peace today.*
*I have crooked places that need to be made straight*
*and rough places that need to be smoothed.*
*I'm facing mountains I can't climb and valleys I can't cross.*
*I need help.*
*I release into your hands all the worries and anxieties and struggles of life."*
*Dr. Suzan D. Johnson Cook*

## *January 14*

### Primary Cycle

There are mixed reactions to acknowledging your cycles and/or primary cycle. For diagnosis, it is imperative. Sometimes that is the only way a correct diagnosis is achieved.

Most all folks who are diagnosed bipolar will have a fairly obvious primary depressive cycle. The reason for a particular time of year provoking a depression is unknown. There are studies being done on everything from lunar influences, to genetic markers, to circadian rhythm.

If you are diagnosed with major depression, you may be aware of certain times of the year that are dark for you. Seasonal Affective Disorder (SAD) is recently recognized due to the lack of light during the winter months. Then, there are those who have the opposing cycle - as I do - of the summer months being our primary cycle.

Although the triggers are not known at this time, you may want to be aware of this more fragile time, so that you can lighten your schedule or learn to plan around this time.

Because of my work as a teacher, my schedule dovetails with my need for extra solitude and rest in the summer. You can save yourself so much aggravation and downplay your obligations if you can recognize your primary cycle.

*"Live in each season as it passes; breathe the air, drink the drink, taste the fruit and resign yourself to the influences of each."*
*Henry David Thoreau*

*January 15*

## WHAT A DEADLINE DOES TO ME

Having had a multitasking sort of life long before that became vogue, deadlines were a helpful and necessary way to structure the multitude of simultaneous projects I had going at any one time. Deadlines gave a light at the end of the tunnel kind of culmination to the various projects; a 'point on the horizon' to focus on to schedule everything necessary for completion, a point of ending and letting go.

Deadlines have been a relief, an aid, a tool and more.

Now deadlines are very different for me.

Because of the rapidity in which I used to cycle from functioning to vegetative, deadlines created enormous anxiety. I never knew when the debilitating phase would strike or how long it would last. So, a deadline would strike fear in my heart. It appeared almost self-defeating, as the anxiety created by a deadline froze me into immobility.

Eventually I found numerous creative ways to avoid deadlines. I 'non-commit' now. When asked for a time to have something completed, to meet someone else's requirements or agenda, to wrap up a task, etc... I use vagueness and non-response to buy myself some time. An "I'll get back to you on that" response has become second nature to me.

Of course, this is not foolproof as the bank, the IRS or your landlord will not be as flexible.

But, if at all possible, I buy some time and make the deadline work for me and not against me. Occasionally, I find myself plunging right into the duty/project/task and accomplishing what I can. Sometimes the momentum alone will carry me quite a distance toward completion. Then, having taken the bulk of the pressure off the deadline, I can get back to the person and quasi-commit. Something on the line of "I believe I can have most of what you need by that date; I'll do what I can and then we can re-evaluate". Then if nothing else gets accomplished by the deadline, I have at least got something to offer and am not apologetic and defensive.

A step back is really helpful here. Try to see the project/task in a general perspective. How very little of what we agitate over is really important in the greater scheme of life. I use the mental visualization of 'if there were a medical emergency or catastrophe in my family at this moment, where in my priorities would this task stand?' I think back to when I have had something on this scale happen, and life and all it's busyness went on without me and my input. So much of what I took on as enormously important in the past was because someone else had put that importance on it - it was their agenda. Sit back and take an objective look at the big picture.

Get a grip on what is really important to you and let other stuff roll off your back - 'the duck philosophy of life'! I am not advocating irresponsibility. You still have to pay your bills. But, maybe you could plan to sit down and write them out on the 20th of the month if they are due by the 1st. Then if you have a couple of bad days, they still get paid on time because you've bought yourself a grace period. Or some folks like to pay each bill as it comes in. I use direct deposit and automatic withdrawal/payment on what I can, and that helps.

Experiment. Find what works for you. Stay open. What works today may not be best next month. Be flexible. Deadlines aren't as cast in stone as we tend to make them. Even the IRS allows a six-month extension!

*Normal is a cycle on the washing machine.*

## *January 16*

## IN JUST ONE GENERATION

There is little that can restore your hope faster or more steadfastly, than to look at the miraculous progress of the last twenty to twenty-five years in the field of neurobiological disorders. Let me do some of the research for you - but, also, feel free to use your library, the Internet or literature available through your physician to assure yourself.

The recent strides in depression recovery are breathtaking. If ever we could be classified as 'lucky' to have this illness, now is the time. Prior to the early 1960's, the only treatments available for mental/ brain disorders were primitive restraints like the infamous straight-jacket or even chains. Other 'treatments' were complete isolation and imprisonment or extremely painful options like packing a person in ice for days at a time.

You may feel despondent today, but you are NOT without hope. Not only has major improvement been made in healing options available to you, but even the stigma of chemical imbalance in the brain is being reduced.

Scientists now see through Magnetic Resonance Imaging (MRI) the actual chemical reactions of the brain to various stimuli and can treat depression according to this understanding of neuro-pathways. Many alternative healing options are available through acupressure, massage, amino acid supplements, etc...

We live in an age of discovery. Take whatever time you need to discover what works for YOU.

*"In the depth of winter, I finally learned that there was within me an invincible summer."*

*Albert Camus*

## *January 17*

## Self - Reliance

"Trust thyself: every heart vibrates to that iron string.

The voices which we hear in solitude grow faint and inaudible as we enter the world. ...the virtue in most request is conformity. Self-reliance is its aversion. It loves not realities and creators, but names and customs. Whoso would be a man must be a nonconformist...nothing is as sacred but the integrity of our own mind. Absolve you to yourself, and you shall have the suffrage of the world.

I do not wish to expiate, but to live. My life is for itself and not for a spectacle. What I must do is all that concerns me, not what the people think....it is the harder, because you will always find those who think they know what your duty is better than you know it. It is easy in the world to live after the world's opinion; it is easy in solitude to live after our own; but the great man is he who in the midst of the crowd keeps with perfect sweetness the independence of solitude.

We must go alone. Isolation must precede true society. But your isolation must not be mechanical, but spiritual, that is, must be elevation. At times the whole world seems to be in conspiracy to importune you with emphatic trifles. Friend, client, child, sickness, fear, want, charity, all knock at once on the closet-door and say, "come out unto us." but keep thy state; come not into their confusion. The power men possess to annoy me, I give them by a weak curiosity. No man can come near me but through my act.

I must be myself. I cannot break myself any longer for you, or you. .. I will not hurt you and myself by hypercritical attentions. If you are true, but not in the same truth with me, cleave to your companions; I will seek my own. I do this not selfishly, but humbly and truly.

But so you may give these friends pain. Yes, but I cannot sell my liberty and my power to save their sensibility. Besides, all persons have their moments of reason, when they look out into the region of absolute truth; then they will justify me and do the same thing."

Ralph Waldo Emerson, Excerpts

*"Since we cannot change reality, let us change the eyes which see reality."*

*Nikos Kazantzakis*

## *January 18*

## Helping Your Doctor Help YOU

Initially, even getting the proper diagnosis is critical. Most of us suffer for an average of a decade before the symptoms and repetitive cycles are recognized. Often a diagnosis comes only after a two to three hour intake interview. The best doctors ask the best questions and can ferret out the distinctive features of our illness.

However, if you have a doctor that is not directing your recovery in the way you feel is meeting your needs, assist them. Write down specific issues or problems that you experience between appointments. Don't wait to be led - mention these areas at the beginning of your appointment.

Keep in mind that you both have the same goal - your recovery - although you may not have the same agenda. The better equipped you are to educate your doctor concerning YOUR particular symptoms, the more adept he/she will be in medication options and healing tools.

This is a partnership between you and your doctor. Hold up your end of the equation. If a physician is not receptive to this philosophy, you have the wrong doctor.

Be accountable for your recovery. It is YOUR life that hangs in the balance.

## *January 23*

## Those Little Birds on the Beach

Now why did God create those little white birds who spend 98% of their waking time scurrying frantically up and down the shore pecking miniscule scraps of food out of the sand?

What purpose could SHE/HE possibly have had in mind?

Other than to be a chink in the greater food chain of life, and they are rather quaint and amusing to observe, I really can't think of one.

So, if SHE/HE made this tiny creature with its tiny organs and its tiny purpose, what was I created for?

Being objective, I really hope there is a greater good to my life although it does seem like most days I spend 98% of my time with my head in the sand trying to just find enough sustenance to make it one more day.

So, I will choose - just for today - to do one thing above what that little bird can do. I will hug someone who needs it, I will let someone ahead of me in traffic, I will send a card to a friend, I will speak to a neighbor, I will return something I borrowed and I will be grateful.

This title says it all... *No Such Thing...*

*NO SUCH THING AS A BAD DAY: A MEMOIR* a book by Hamilton Jordan

## *January 24*

## Sometimes Your Worst Personality Traits Can Save Your Life

This is tongue-in-cheek advice: I have found that my obstinacy and fierce determination (God forbid anyone or anything gets in my path when I make up my mind about something) have been invaluable in my recovery.

I never let a doctor dismiss my feelings or concerns or give up on myself. So, this was actually a healthy use of those potentially negative characteristics.

I have found that my insatiable curiosity about life and everything and everyone has been of enormous help in seeking solutions for my depression. However, those folks who find my questioning annoying would see this asset in a negative light. And it CAN be negative - but, I can also learn to use it for my good.

Although my humor may be dark at times, I *always* benefit from a good laugh.

What are some of your positive/negative traits? What do others comment on about you? I truly feel that ANY negative can be used in a positive direction. If you are aggressive - terrific! Use that. If you are sarcastic - good for you! This can be your weapon against indifferent doctors or judgmental folks. If you are sloppy - hurray! The little annoyances of life will not bother you.

Think of your less admirable traits in a new light. And use these assets to help heal yourself.

*Fragment*
*"You cannot harm me,*
*you cannot harm*
*one who has dreamed a dream like mine."*

*North American Dakota Indian poem*

## *January 25*

## "UNCOOPERATIVE PATIENTS"

Kathleen Lindner, MLS, RN, of Englewood, NJ, quotes a study for the *Journal of the American Medical Association* (JAMA) that 'uncooperative patients' get better faster. To a doctor, 'uncooperative' means asking too many questions, being persistent, researching one's own illness and examining one's own medical records. Yet patients who are more knowledgeable about their health and participate in the decision-making process state they receive better care from their physicians.

Be uncooperative if that is what it takes. Some physicians need a gentle nudge. Some physicians' egos cannot tolerate input from the patient. Fire them. Find someone who will work WITH not AT you.

*"Once we give up searching for approval, we often find it easier to earn respect."*

*Gloria Steinem*

*January 26*

## To Believe In Life

"To believe in life is to believe the sun will always climb the stairway in the sky and bring us morning.

To believe in life is to plant seeds so there will be flowers to cover the hills and fill our vases.

To believe in life is to know that life itself is a risk, and the only time our chances run out is when we no longer take a chance."

flavia

Everything I need to know about life, I learned from Noah's Ark...

1. Don't miss the boat.
2. Remember we are all in the same boat.
3. Plan ahead. It wasn't raining when Noah built the Ark.
4. Stay fit. When you're 600 years old, someone may ask you to do something really big.
5. Don't listen to critics; just get on with the job that needs to be done.
6. Build your future on high ground.
7. For safety's sake, travel in pairs.
8. Speed isn't always an advantage. The snails were on board with the cheetahs.
9. When you're stressed, float a while.
10. Remember, the Ark was built by amateurs; the Titanic by professionals.

*January 27*

## Screaming in the Car

There were times that I needed to let off some steam. My life was a pressure cooker about to blow and I needed relief. Exercise is fabulous for getting rid of stress. But, if exercise was not an option, I would find other alternatives. Because I lived in Atlanta for over a decade, traffic nightmares were a daily occurrence and I found that I could just scream to my heart's content (as long as my windows were rolled up!) in my car. I didn't harm anyone and I felt better immediately.

I have friends who go pound a tennis ball against their garage wall. One inventive woman stored her old glass jars and because she lived on an isolated farm, she could go throw these with all her might and wail and rage when she needed to. Joining a softball league might provide a regular outlet.

Do what you need to maintain your equilibrium. The alternative is a heart attack.

"Embrace life. Life contains much that is noble and elegant, much that is drab and distasteful, and much that is somewhere in between. Life is a vast mix, and we must embrace it all."

Stephen E. Broyles in *The Wind That Destroys and Heals: Trusting the God of Sorrow and Joy*

*January 28*

## We Are Spiritual Beings Having a Human Experience

Be gentle with yourself. There is a bright, shining eternal light within you. That is your true self. This is your perfect nature. Your higher self.

But, the necessities of life push at us from all directions at all hours. We can be irritated, frustrated, petty, hurtful. There are too many demands on us too much of the time.

If you find yourself being hurried and coerced, take a quiet moment to find your center again. Even if this means leaving a tense discussion or meeting to find some privacy in the restroom, try to calm the tensions placed on you. These are human demands. Everyone feels this. Just keep coming back to that still, perfect place that is your spiritual center.

This is so helpful. So simple. So necessary.

"The greatest thing in the world is to know how to belong to oneself."

Montaigne

## *January 29*

### Will-Power

*"Belief creates the actual fact."*
*William James*

Do you have the will to change? If even one molecule of your being responds "YES!" then decide that you CAN be your real, vibrant, healthy self again.

Remember that ultimately, healing from depression is about changing your chemistry. You can achieve this!

Can you think of a single goal you have achieved in the past? Getting that job? That degree or credential? That new car? Then, if you have succeeded once, you can succeed again.

Put all your will behind this determination and it is yours.

*"To accomplish great things, we must not only act, but also dream; not only plan, but also believe."*
*Anatole France*

## *January 30*

### HAVING AT LEAST A DOZEN TOOLS IN YOUR TOOLBOX

No carpenter would work on a project with just a hammer. He needs at least a saw, measuring tape, pencil, level, nails, sandpaper, screwdrivers, etc...

We also must have multiple tools in our recovery toolbox. I never have less than one dozen tools working for me at any given time.

The mandatory and minimum tools for me are: adequate sleep and rest, minimal stress, something to look forward to, proper medications, nutritious eating habits, lots of love, laughter, warmth and touch and exercise on a regular basis, a haven or place of private retreat and a goal.

Some days you will barely meet your sleep requirements. You may need to add extra laughs or contact with loved ones to compensate. As long as you have multiple avenues of recovery, if one should fail at any given time, you are still able to maintain being in a pretty good place.

There will be days when you need to depend on every tool at your disposal to just keep afloat.

The dozen minimum rule also applies to phone numbers for support. Please write down the names and phone numbers of twelve people you can call in a crisis. If there aren't twelve folks you can count on now, join a support group or church and find them. Keep this list in your wallet. Having just one or two people to call on when you are in need is not prudent. Have as many support contacts as possible and just keep calling until you reach a friendly voice.

Do not limit your recovery resources. Keep your toolbox full.

*"Having at least one other with whom we are intimate heals us, keeps us honest, and strengthens us for whatever lies ahead."*
*Unknown*

## *January 31*

## Being There – Staying Here

If today is a 'death-defying day' and the pain is overwhelming, here is what you do:

1. cancel all plans for the day (call in sick to work, whatever...)
2. change your chemistry; you may crave carbohydrates - eat them; if it is chocolate you crave - eat that. Remember to keep DLPA, Tyrosine, Omega 3's and lecithin available for these times.
3. distract yourself. If you are capable of sitting up and watching television - do that. If all you can do is sleep - do that.

If I have been able to add back to my chemistry what it is lacking, usually within a few hours I am back to a semi-functioning level. But, just because you feel better, keep today on a low-key. This is not the time to go back to full speed.

Do not fight a really bad day. Accept that it is a rough day and let go. You will actually benefit from this letting go because trying to force your normal activity will only create more tension and alter your chemistry even further.

Let yourself do whatever it takes today. Tomorrow you can begin again.

"'It doesn't happen all at once,' said the Skin Horse. 'You become. It takes a long time. That's why it doesn't often happen to people who break easily, or have sharp edges, or who have to be carefully kept. Generally, by the time you are Real, most of your hair has been loved off, and your eyes drop out and you get loose in the joints and very shabby . But these things don't matter at all, because once you are Real you can't be ugly, except to people who don't understand.'"

Margery Williams, *The Velveteen Rabbit*

# FEBRUARY

## *February 1*

## Cranial Tension

Here is an area that is not exclusive to depressives. All folks who sit at a desk and especially those who type on a keyboard and stare at the computer monitor for multiple hours a day, will develop muscle tension in their shoulders and neck. This eventually translates into tension headaches.

Have you ever felt like your scalp was too tight? Try this - right where you are this minute - scrunch your shoulders up to your ears. Now, do it again.

Did you hear or feel any cracking? Good.

Now, turn your head and try to gently touch your shoulder with your chin. Do this on your other side.

Now drop your head down to your chest - keeping your shoulders back. Clasp both hands at the base of your neck and pull gently downward to the count of five or six.

If you tense up, do these quick exercises again.

You can eliminate headaches before they start this way.

Why not copy this page and tape it where you will see it throughout the day?

*"Stress is an ignorant state. It believes that everything is an emergency."*

*Natalie Goldberg; from Wild Mind*

## *February 2*

## Benefits of Treating Yourself to a Massage

Even the scientific and medical communities have funded studies that prove the many benefits of massage. You can lower anxiety, increase blood circulation and lymph flow, increase white cell productivity, lower blood pressure and relax your muscles with a massage.

Sometimes the greatest benefit is the quiet hour. Sometimes it is the fact that nothing is required of you but to lay there. And sometimes it is the beauty of giving yourself something you really need instead of waiting for someone else to give it to you. (We really expect a lot of others when we wait like this. There are few mind-readers in the world.)

If there is a massage school in your area, the hour can be pretty inexpensive.

Massage can activate those powerful, feel-good endorphins we are so desperately in need of when we don't have the energy to exercise.

Treat yourself to an hour once in a while. You may find this becomes a part of your ongoing recovery.

*"This art of resting the mind and the power of dismissing from it all care and worry is probably one of the secrets of energy in our great men."*

*Captain J.A. Hadfield*

*February 3*

## I Am My Own Worst Enemy

If I am forced to be in public on a day of severe depression, for some odd reason I feel self-imposed to put on a mask of normality. I feel obligated to be 'on'. It seems I absolutely must convince those I come in contact with that I am feeling perfectly fine. I will use caffeine, sugar or simple adrenaline to go all out.

Why in the world would I betray myself like this?

Who am I trying to prove what to?

No wonder others think I am lying when I describe how excruciating the pain of depression I am feeling is. My actions are not matching my feelings.

Am I perpetuating denial?

To be true to myself is one of the hardest parts of this disease. But, if I am to be authentic, then I must reflect visibly what I am experiencing inwardly. If I am not honest with myself, then who else can be honest with me?

"It's hard to beat a person who never gives up."
Babe Ruth

## February 4

## First Thing in the Morning

One of the clearest indicators of depression is early morning wakenings - usually 3 or 4 a.m. After a period of insomnia of an hour or two, folks can usually go back to sleep for several more hours.

Here is what I have found that works for me: if I wake up in the still-dark hours of early morning, I will go ahead and take my medications and supplements. I don't drink too much water, as I don't want my bladder to wake me up again once I am sleeping peacefully.

But, it seems to give me a headstart on the day if I can get these meds into my bloodstream early. When the alarm goes off, I have some momentum already - even before my feet hit the floor.

I don't recommend forcing yourself to get up to facilitate this advantage, but if you are already awake, try it. Even though anti-depressants can be stimulating, I don't seem to have trouble eventually falling back to sleep. So, that when I eventually get up, my head sure seems clearer and my mood is more optimistic if I have made the early morning insomnia work to my advantage.

"You cannot measure a subjective experience. It would be like trying to find the square root of a sonnet."
Unknown

## February 5

## The Anatomy of Hope

Dr. Jerome Groopman in his book, *The Anatomy of Hope*, says, "Hope, I have come to believe, is as vital to our lives as the very oxygen we breathe."

As a senior-level physician in Boston, he is naturally a skeptic. But, in working with very ill patients for decades, he now distinguishes between the power of despair and the power of hope. He defines hope as "the elevating feeling we experience when we see - in the mind's eye - a path to a better future. Hope acknowledges the significant obstacles and deep pitfalls along that path. True hope has no room for delusion."

When I am depressed, I find I need tangible proof to hang on to as hope for a better day. So, I read inspirational material like *Guideposts* magazine or the Before and After Success stories of *Shape* and *Weight Watchers.* I will post on my mirror a picture of myself when I looked and felt terrific. I need to really 'get it' that change is real and I can change my chemistry and get out of this depression.

Without hope, I would never have kept trying. And I wouldn't be thriving and happy as I am now.

*"An intense anticipation itself transforms possibility into reality; our desires often being precursors of the things which we are capable of performing."*

*Samuel Smiles*

## *February* 6

## How Is Your Moment?

A friend with great spiritual awareness used to greet me with "How is your moment?"

Not - "How are you?", "How have you been?", "How are you doing?"

But, "How is your moment?" It never failed to stop me dead in my tracks. I could blur through life - and the thousands of moments that are here and gone - and not really assess how I was NOW. This instant. This second. And the irony was that so very many times, if I stopped to reflect on that ONE moment - that instant of my life - that snapshot of time was not really so bad.

No matter what it had been the night before with the endless, sleepless hours or any hour before when I couldn't quit sobbing, THAT MOMENT would often be free of headaches, aching toothaches, nausea - the bills could get paid later, the ironing could continue to be put off another day, I wasn't actively fighting with anyone at that second - in truth, that moment often was not too bad.

And if I could get myself to do this internal inventory, from time to time throughout some of the rougher days, I could intersperse these moments of blue sky into an otherwise bleak day and put a little perspective into the process.

How is YOUR moment?

*"Practice hope. As hopefulness becomes a habit, you can achieve a permanently happy spirit."*
*Norman Vincent Peale*

## *February 7*

## A New and Unique Approach to Vibrators

I suppose I watch too much *Saturday Night Live* in my quest for humor. They certainly mock any and every thing. And recently they harpooned the vibrator.(pun intended)

But, I have found a fabulous use for my industrial strength vibrator - this one pound unit I purchased at a discount store for less than twenty dollars - that may not work for everyone, yet it works for me, most especially when I am at my bleakest.

We tend to think of our cranium as the one piece skull that we see in cadavers. But, in truth, the head has at least twenty-two bones that move and shift! I have become very aware of how 'locked down' my skull can seem at times. The tightness is almost unbearable.

So, I will use the vibrator on my scalp and unlock those glued-together areas. I push as hard as I can all over my head. When I find the most tender areas, those are the ones I concentrate on. Usually I can get this awesome relief within a minute or less. Whatever loosens up in my skull creates waves of relief throughout my body.

If you try this, go to the area just above your ears - just below the temples - and the whole area at the bottom of the back of the head. You will be amazed how much better you feel.

I have occasionally found it necessary to use this technique more than once a day. But, the relief is so dramatic that once is usually enough.

Many of you will not have the symptom I am speaking of. But, if you do experience this tension in your head, a vibrator ceases to be something to laugh about.

*"The brain is a wonderful organ. It starts working the moment you get up in the morning and does not stop until you get into the office."*

Robert Frost

## *February 8*

### Find Your Heroes

I will use *Reader's Digest's* Heroes in Action section or *Guideposts* magazine's Profiles in Courage series to find my inspiration. There are hundreds of books available - biographies and autobiographies - on everyday folks made extraordinary by crisis.

Some have gained fame by their courage alone. A great example is the story of Joni Ericsson, a snowskier who suffered severe injury and ultimately, paralysis, who uses her mouth to paint. Her spirit refuses to follow her body into decline.

The stories of strangers who risk their lives to save others - people who but for the fate of being in the same place at the same time, would never have met. The Helen Kellers and Corrie Ten Booms of the world.

I will look for someone who has beat the odds. The person who never accepted the disability or horrific circumstances they were given as a death-knell.

If you have never read the *Diary of Anne Frank*, it is a place to start. This child never had normal schooling, friendships, household chores, typical play - even life in the sunshine we take for granted. Locked away from the world for twenty-five months, she nevertheless has moved hundreds - maybe thousands or tens of thousands - to see themselves and their world differently.

You need maybe only go so far as your local church, the Salvation Army, or a neighbor to find inspiration. But, be open to inspiration wherever you can find it. Do not let the horror and pain of your situation build emotional callouses on your heart so that you are numb to what others have experienced and overcome. Focus on that overcoming - that success of others to know that if they did it, YOU CAN, TOO.

I have felt for quite some time now that Christopher Reeve played Superman prior to his paralysis for a reason. Who could fly through the air and stop speeding trains, yet function as a normal man but our cosmic hero, Superman? To have been elevated to that height only to later find his real self in a wheelchair. It is this dichotomy that makes his courage even more spectacular. Not just any screen hero, but Superman - the mightiest of all; he steps off the screen to truly become the mightiest in his day-to-day courage.

Winston Churchill suffered severe depressions throughout his life. And one of the stories I like best about him is one he told of a trail in the desolate mountains of South America. A group of travelers were hiking in this area using local guides. They were climbing single file along a narrow trail, moving slowly. Rounding one curve they came to a section of the trail, not wide enough for both feet even. It looked impassable. They were ready to turn back, until they noticed the sign tacked crudely into the side of the mountain: "You can do it, thousands before you have."

So, on the days I feel crushed by depression, I will lock onto the example of someone before me who is a HERO. Someone who beat the odds. If they could do it, SO CAN I.

*"I am not judged by the number of times I fail, but by the number of times I succeed; and the number of times I succeed is in direct proportion to the number of times I can fail and keep on trying."*

*Tom Hopkins*

*February 9*

## Minimizing a Binge

If I know that eating handfuls of cookies, a quart of ice cream, a bag of M and M's is inevitable and the serotonin created by these unhealthy carbohydrates will pull me out of a current depression, then I will eat whatever I am craving with no remorse. However, there are times when eating some of this junk food is a frantic effort and becomes a binge. At these times I have learned to minimize what damage is done. I will still medicate with sweets or potato chips, but, I have learned to:

a. eat something nutritious first, thus minimizing the capacity of my stomach AND/OR

b. eat some form of protein before the sugar binge; this levels blood sugar spikes to more manageable ranges.

Another technique I have learned the hard way is to seek to identify if this craving is better satisfied with a nap rather than a sugar rush. Am I actually craving rest and seeking sugar to give me energy or am I depressed and needing to change my chemistry? I will sit with the feeling a moment and often, I can use delayed gratification just enough to convince myself that I am really only tired and that if I really do want to have a sugar 'fix', then I will allow myself that if I feel I still need it after a nap. Usually, it really is sleep I am needing. That is a more appropriate 'fuel' then.

If you are hit with these cravings during work and can ascertain that it is a nap you really need, I have been known to 'have an errand' and go sleep in the back seat of my car briefly. I will park in a corner of the parking lot and nap for twenty or thirty minutes. No one is the wiser; I have hurt no one and I am refreshed and a better-functioning employee when I get back to my desk. Or, if a break is not an option, I will go ahead and eat the candy and do the best I can to get through the rest of the day. Again, if you can MINIMIZE the damage, you will not have a sugar crash later.

On the days I am this chemically altered, I usually go straight to bed after work and recharge those worn-out batteries. I am not telling you that there are not times that a junk food binge is not EXACTLY what you need. What I am advocating is that you minimize the damage if at all possible.

*"You don't drown by falling in the water; you drown by staying there."*

*Edwin Louis Cole*

## *February 10*

## Hydro - therapy

Water, water everywhere.... You won't believe how the use of this readily available element will benefit your mental attitude.

Take a shower - negative ions are released when water strikes a surface. Just stand there in your clothes under the water if you have to. I have been too weak and lifeless to even take my nightgown off. But, if I just stood under the water for a bit, I ALWAYS felt better.

Drink lots of water - being dehydrated will make anyone lethargic. Keep one of those little fountains on your desk. Same theory as the shower.

My favorite hydro-therapy - a walk on the beach.

I also own at least two twenty-nine cent water pistols at any given time. Talk about bringing some levity to a situation! Water pistols are not just meant for kids.

How about a bubble bath?

Use water to help yourself. You have nothing to lose by trying this.

*Keep in mind: Henry Ford, Thomas Edison nor the Wright Brothers were trained engineers.*

*Another way to keep things in perspective: Remember that the Ark was built by amateurs and the Titanic by professionals.*

## *February 11*

## Being An Observer To Yourself

There are times when you will be able to step back and 'see' yourself and your behavior as if you are another person objectively watching. A rather negative view of this might be that it is a form of disassociation. But, rather than being an unhealthy state of mind, this actually can be a terrific tool.

I have experienced this - completely unbidden - on several occasions and now I employ it consciously when needed. When I am in a depression, I walk and talk as if enclosed in fog. The environment around me is very unclear and my sight very shortened. Every task needs immediate resolution and I have trouble seeing options.

And the times this 'step back and see yourself objectively tool' may best be utilized would be in situations of very heightened emotions. I have found that in an escalating conversation with someone - especially when I am in the extreme irritability of depression and I am dealing with an inept sales clerk, for example - I can apparently pass an emotional marker of sorts and detach immediately. I feel as if I had left my body ranting and raving while my true self watches this scene rationally from an elevated spot. I always am looking down at myself when this happens.

Have you ever experienced this? It is hard to grasp if you have not. But, it can be a learned skill and a fabulous tool for reigning in unchecked emotions.

Because it never fails - I see how out of control and unreasonable I am in these settings. I honestly see the part I am playing in this little drama and immediately drop my emotional range - way down into neutral - and resurrect a potentially embarrassing and fruitless exchange.

If you have spent any time with meditation or other therapeutic altered states, this will not be difficult to accomplish. Chances are, you can successfully 'save yourself' on your first try.

One of the greatest benefits for me, is that the power of self-recognition is exponentially greater than being chastised by someone else. The lesson seems to penetrate deeper somehow. And it certainly saves on embarrassment. In the minute it takes for this shift in perception, I take a cleansing breath and pause. Sometimes I even will take a physical step back as I regroup. And then, in a neutral, calm tone, I can reshape the encounter. Never - and this is not hyperbole - have I failed to achieve my original goal and I have the satisfaction of my heart in knowing I did not harm another person.

*"By three methods we may learn wisdom; first, by reflection, which is noblest; second, by imitation, which is easiest; and third by experience, which is the bitterest."*

*Confucius*

## *February 12*

## Employers Are Catching On

Depression costs employers $44 billion per year according to a study published in the *Journal of the American Medical Association (JAMA)* in 2003. Workers with depression lost 5.6 hours per week compared to 1.5 hours of non-depressed workers.

This does not take into account the incredible health care costs associated with the illness.

The good news is that *Medical Care* reported in 2004 the results of a two-year study in which depressed employees were treated by their primary care physician. Not only did their productivity increase six percent, but their absenteeism decreased twenty-two percent. This meant huge savings to the employer and the benefits to the employees health were immeasurable.

Mid-America Coalition on Health Care has developed a model surveying tool that is being used to identify depression in the workplace. This is being adopted by more and more corporations as a means to increase productivity.

From BankOne, Union Pacific and PPG Industries to even the recent $100 million the Pentagon has budgeted to screen returning troops for depression, corporations across America are removing the stigma and beginning to see depression as just another illness that needs attention.

Everyone will benefit from this. Everyone.
(some material taken from article by Alana Semuels, *Pittsburgh Post-Gazette* 2005)

*"To array a man's will against his sickness is the supreme art of medicine."*

*Henry Ward Beecher*

*February 13*

## Circular Thinking

There is a place I have found, in the depths of depression, where my thought pattern is that of a broken record. The same two or three thoughts - always bleak and negative - circle round and round in my head.

I don't always find it is the same two or three thoughts, but they are always similar in tone and content. Instead of the passing thoughts that are constantly filtering through our mind, like 'that blouse needs ironing', ' there is not a cloud in the sky', 'I better quit eating so much sugar', etc... I will hear 'you will never get better', 'everyone else has a better/easier life', 'I can't'... And these ugly, untrue ideas keep their repetitive pattern like a drumbeat in my head.

There are these phases I find from time to time where I can cycle through the same deadly thoughts for hours.

To break this rigid series of ideas that lead nowhere, I have to consciously become aware of them first. This happens pretty readily. And then I have to detour my brain waves through television or reading. But, I stop the monotony with new words/new thoughts/better philosophy - even if they are forced at first.

I do not know how common this problem is with other depressives, but it is self-defeating and useless. And the sooner it is interrupted, the better you will start to feel.

The mind can only hold one thought at a time. You CANNOT simultaneously think 'I have a nice nose' and 'I will never get a raise.' It is one or the other. But, not BOTH.

Replace the circular negative litany with a positive mantra.

*"As a man thinketh in his heart, so is he."*
*Aphorism popularized by James Allen,*
*English philosopher*

## *February 14*

## Trust Yourself

It took years of therapy for me to do this. Hopefully, you are light years ahead of me in self-knowledge. I let other people tell me how I felt for the first thirty years of my life. But, once I found my center and learned my own reality - who I really was, warts and all - I found I had a great intuitive sense, if only I got still enough to hear it.

If I heard remarkable accolades about a psychiatrist and but found he/she to be non-responsive, then I had to believe my intuition and move on. Others' experience was not MY experience.

If a certain new product or medication was enormously beneficial to fellow sufferers, then it was not a given that it would work for me. Only I could judge the severity of the side effects versus the benefits of the medication.

I have learned to trust myself above anyone - regardless of their authority. There are no perfect humans - and that includes psychiatrists and other physicians, therapists and parents.

If you have spent the time and energy to get to know yourself, go the extra step and learn to trust your judgment.

*"Take the first step in faith. You don't have to see the whole staircase, just take the first step."*
*Martin Luther King, Jr.*

## *February 15*

### Where Does It Hurt?

My anxious mother asked me this frank question once while I was desperate for relief. And, it was an eye-opener as I really had to think to answer her.

Yes, I did have specific, localized pain in my head and abdomen, but mostly it is a psychic pain that decimates me. I hurt not only physically, but emotionally. My soul is in agony. My spiritual life is in shreds and hemorrhaging. The pain is so intense that my aura hurts.

I know another depressed person will know this pain, but I don't have the words to tell my mother.

Keep in mind that during the dark hours, it is not your job to educate; it is your job to survive.

*"History has demonstrated that the most notable winners encountered heart-breaking obstacles before they triumphed. They finally won by their defeats."*
*B. C. Forbes*

*February 16*

## The Will to Change

*"There's a part of every living thing that wants to become itself:*
*the tadpole into the frog,*
*the chrysalis into the butterfly,*
*a damaged human being into a whole one.*
*That is spirituality."*

Ellen Bass from *No Ordinary Moments*
*- A Peaceful Warrior's Guide to Daily Life by Dan Millman.*

You can become the butterfly. It need not be soon. Do not force the river. But, never lose sight of the broken cocoon of depression left in your wake. If you can summon the will to know you are the butterfly and NOT the caterpillar, you CAN and WILL change. Emerging into the sunlight is worth the effort to break free.

*"It is this hard, inexorable passage of time that, I believe, is the one great surprise in every human life."*

Pat Conroy in *My Losing Season*

*February 17*

## Three Basic Areas to Check

Three non-invasive, but often enormously beneficial areas to check out are: have your thyroid checked, have hormone levels checked and find a competent acupressure specialist.

Be aware, however, that the scale for 'normal' thyroid covers a wide range and is open to diverse interpretation. So, if you have a less than ideal physician, he will check you off as having normal thyroid function. Well, I am here to tell you that a good diagnostician will see that you are barely within the range of acceptable and connect this finding with your symptoms and often find that a small dose of thyroid medication can make you function on a much higher level.

A wise endocrinologist once told me that a study of mental patients who were screened for low thyroid function, enabled close to eighty percent to be discharged from inpatient status once their thyroid imbalance was treated adequately. There are physicians who are not attuned to looking at multiple factors or multiple screenings to decipher marginal function. You might try to educate your doctor if he/she falls into this category or you may have to seek out a more competent physician. Always get a copy of your lab results. By law, you are entitled to copies of all lab work you have done.

Hormone imbalances are responsible for such notorious disorders as postpartum depression. It is simple to eliminate hormonal abnormalities as a factor in your depression with some easy bloodwork. Again, ask for copies of your lab results and learn how to read these documents.

A source of immediate relief for me has always been acupressure. Practitioners of this protocol rely on the ancient acupuncture meridian mapping of the body to find energy blockages. Acupressure is acupuncture without the needles. Usually it is a chiropractor who administers this treatment. Look for therapists in your Yellow Pages.

One of these three - if not all three - will bring you some relief. I guarantee it.

*"Every now and again take a good look at something not made with hands, a mountain, a star, the turn of a stream. There will come to you a wisdom and patience and solace and, above all, the assurance that you are not alone in the world."*

*Sidney Lovett*

## *February 18*

## Understanding the Vagaries of Travel

The nature of how travel affects us slipped up and caught me flat-footed. It did not occur to me that: the tedium, stress and exhaustion of travel would induce shifts in my chemistry; that changing even one time zone would shift my chemistry; that lacking access to clean water, a good night's rest, my usual medications would throw all my carefully balanced chemistry into turmoil.

A change of scenery can do wonders for our morale. Seeing beloved friends and family can light the heart with joy. But, being prepared for the stresses of travel is imperative in order not to have a relapse into the dark well of depression.

By allowing yourself an extra day coming and going to adjust helps; by doing your homework as to services and options in accommodations helps; by keeping a flexible itinerary that accommodates delays will maintain your serenity.

Sometimes getting into a new milieu can be radically beneficial. It is the preparation - both physically and mentally - that will create either a healthy retreat or a step back into hell. Go - but, do not go without cautious planning.

*"Writing and travel broaden your ass if not your mind and I like to write standing up."*
*Ernest Hemingway*

## *February 19*

## Your Body Has Never Read the Textbooks

How many times have you had a pharmacist, physician or fellow sufferer inform you that your response to a medication could not have happened? Our chemistries are sensitive, exquisitely balanced miracles and not only are not even identical twins chemically aligned, WE are different chemically in different periods of our life.

I learned to respond laughingly and dismissively when someone tried to convince me that my experience could not possibly be real. But, my body had not read that textbook! The other person often had lofty credentials, but I learned that the ultimate authority for me was what I knew to be true for me. I was the only one 'living in the laboratory'. Just because a textbook said it was so, did not make my chemistry any different.

If you find yourself taking unusual dosages or having unlikely responses to medication, confide only in an understanding physician or keep the information to yourself. You know what is true for you. And that is good enough.

*"It were not best that we should all think alike; it is a difference of opinions that makes horse races."*
*Samuel Langhorne Clemens*

## *February 20*

## White-Knuckle Living

Some of you will understand this term. I hope most of you don't. White-knuckle living refers to those days you feel you are hanging on by your fingertips. It means those days it takes one hundred percent of your undivided attention and one hundred percent of your energy just to stay above ground.

I wish I had the magic answer for these days. I do know how to pull myself back from the very bottom or what I call Level 1 days (Level 10 being euphoria) and the tools to do that with are what I share with you here in this book (see the Desperate Days Checklist at the back of this book). But, what works for me may not work for you.

If today is a white-knuckle day for you, give yourself permission to take care of yourself. Do whatever it takes. Dawn will bring a new day and a new beginning.

*"To act with common sense according to the moment, is the best wisdom I know...*

*Horace Walpole*

## *February 21*

## Treating Multiple Health Issues Simultaneously

It is rare that depression is the lone illness a person faces. In my case, I had two harsh hormonal diseases to overcome before the symptoms of depression became clear-cut enough for diagnosis even.

It is imperative that you define what you are dealing with. Each illness has its own protocol and medication. There will be large areas of overlap, but finding your optimal level of recovery in each illness is vitally important.

Finding a physician who does not dismiss multiple problems is critical.

This isn't as complicated as it sounds. Often fixing a low thyroid can eliminate depression. Just make sure that you check with a good pharmacist to verify that medications you are prescribed don't conflict with each other.

Awareness of your body and your chemistry will direct your recovery.

*"The truth is that our finest moments are most likely to occur when we are feeling deeply uncomfortable, unhappy, or unfulfilled. For it is only in our discomfort, that we are likely to step out of our ruts and start searching for different ways or truer answers."*
*M. Scott Peck*

## *February 22*

## The Power of Daydreaming

I will speak of the power of daydreaming in several installments. For now, I want to expose you to a creative tool of immeasurable benefit.

By now you have discovered one of the greatest survival tools I use is distraction. I really want to capitalize, underline and bold print that word. If you can't get through the tough times any other way, you move your mind away from the distress your body and soul are suffering. You have control over your thoughts when you have control over nothing else.

So, here is how it works:
I was a strong enough student that I got bored in class pretty easily. I could hang on for the fifteen minutes of a sermon usually, but that was pretty much my limit. A forty-five minute class of straight lecture was beyond my capacity.

So, I would spend moments when I was restricted physically - as in a meeting I didn't want to be in, or a lecture I was attending - by unrestricting my mind. By daydreaming.

This habit began with a well-liked but, homely English teacher my senior year of high school. She just could not hold my attention (it is likely she will read this and be taken aback - I always looked so attentive?!). But, I frequently drifted into a reverie. I wasted great amounts of classtime pondering the question: if I had $20,000 for plastic surgery for this woman, how would it best be spent? Believe me, I had enough raw material here to work with that this one thought-trend kept me occupied an entire semester! I would maintain eye contact - always a good thing in class - and I would imagine what a difference a nose job or face lift would make in this woman's life. If it was a really dull class, I would divide the daydream into repairs above the collarbone and repairs below the collarbone. Usually, the bulk of the time was spent in one region alone. She was that bad. I tried out different imaginary noses, I moved her hairline forward and back, I lifted various features - it is amazing how many possible combinations are available if you really concentrate.

And remember, you only have to APPEAR to concentrate. You never harm a soul - you just entertain your bored-out-of-your-mind self and keep a smiling visage.

From time to time, you may find you need to do a whole body makeover before the time has elapsed, but if you are creative enough, this tactic for distraction will never fail you.

When I am immobilized with the blackest of depressions, I allot myself a whopping tax-free lottery win of $50,000 and daydream away. I mentally cut and stitch and improve my face and body beyond recognition. It is really quite entertaining. Or I travel to Bora Bora, Greece, Morocco or Alberta on the ultimate fantasy holiday. If I cannot get away from the depression physically, then I will get away from it mentally.

You can daydream about the perfect partner, dream a day spent with some famous person, a life free of monetary worries.

Daydreaming doesn't hurt anyone. But, it can save your life on a day that is unbearable to face head on.

*"I will trust today's experiences, secure in the knowledge that they are meant for me, at this time."*
*Unknown*

## *February 23*

## Sleep – The Great Healer

Before anti-depressants and modern therapy, there were 'rest cures'. I use this in my recovery, too. When all else fails, I believe fervently that the magnificent power of the body to be in balance will prevail if we quiet it for a long enough period.

Our bodies were designed to rest one-third of our existence. That is planned into our blueprint. Of the eight hour trio that makes up every day, one third of it is meant to be in complete hibernation.

So, extend that metaphor and heal yourself with a rest cure. Similar to electric shock when all the broken pieces are allowed to fall back into homeostasis, sleeping can sometimes restore us back into chemical balance.

Take the phone off the hook and snuggle deep in the covers.

*"The best bridge between despair and hope is a good night's sleep."*

*Unknown*

## *February 24*

## Loneliness

Have you ever been so lonely that your whole body ached? Literally. That physical ache is one of the worst pains on earth.

Ironically, I was more lonely when married than I have ever been single. Being in a crowd brings no reassurance or guarantee against loneliness. You might be one of thousands screaming at a concert or in the middle of a busy mall or seated with your family at Thanksgiving dinner - and you might still be achingly lonely.

I have no great remedy to offer you here. Because of the nature of depression, I believe we can be at greater risk for loneliness than the general population.

There isn't a quick fix nor a cheap one for loneliness. Sometimes my disconnectedness from myself created my loneliness.

I can honestly say I have not felt that cavernous hollowness in years now. I know of some quick, cheap ways to connect - from going to a support meeting to even picking up the phone and calling someone I trust.

The same relief may not work every time so have several alternate plans for loneliness-relief available.

I don't encourage you to be patient with this one. Loneliness is different from alone-ness. There is no good to come from that soul-empty place. Find your way to move out of it and do it.

*"It is essential we realize that control is not outside of us but within."*

*Barbara Harris, editor of Shape Magazine*

## *February 25*

## Bequeathing Indian Names

Now, here is a tool I use for a distraction that really borders on the fringe of utterly ridiculous.

I heard the really rude joke about Native American parents naming their children according to something they saw during the child's birth. Of course, 'Two Dogs Mating' wasn't the exact terminology used in the joke, but you get the point.

I began using this technique for salvation when in really boring circumstances. Now I use it all the time.

For instance, I name drivers who irritate me (that is practically everyone on the road; I heard it summarized once as 'everyone else drives either too fast or too slow to suit me'). A male might be 'Had a Fight with his Wife this Morning' or 'Thinks He Owns the Road' (this is a big family). Females can be 'She Thinks She is so Important, She has to be Attached Always to her Cell Phone'; or 'I Guess Blue is an Acceptable Hair Color'. Both sexes fall frequently into 'Drives Like an Idiot' - it is like the Smith of Indian naming.

The name I give myself most frequently is 'Head Like a Sieve'. When I blank out, it is easier to pull this little ditty out of the air and give myself a moment's more thinking time than to own up to how little gray matter is functioning in my brain. I will regroup to come up with the appropriate response and also divert the other person with humor - so a lot gets accomplished if I can pull this trick out of my bag of tools.

Pompous folk are my largest target. 'Head Up His Ass' and 'Thinks He Can Do No Wrong' are quite common nomenclatures.

The real beauty of this little tool is how wonderfully smug it allows you to be. You can keep an alert and interested countenance while having a field day mocking someone. And NO ONE GETS HURT.

Isn't this terrific? Bet you use it in the next twenty-four hours.

"I thoroughly disapprove of duels. If a man should challenge me, I would take him kindly and forgivingly by the hand and lead him to a quiet place and kill him."

Samuel Langhorne Clemens

## February 26

### Finding a Place of Peace

"...people develop in aloneness and are only led to the truth after being disillusioned."

From *A Year by the Sea: Thoughts of an Unfinished Woman* by Joan Anderson

This is something that only you will know the solution to. At different times in every life there is a need to get quiet and alone with your thoughts. I imagine this could be accomplished window shopping in a large mall with hundreds of people around you. Or driving alone with the stereo screaming. But, solitude is necessary in EVERY life.

I know the greater the tension in my life, the more frequently I seek this. It is the teeter-totter of balance that keeps me sane. The more demands and chaos frame my days, the more I will go to the polar opposite for silence and tranquility.

My preference is always the ocean. At one point, when I was a stockbroker working frantic thirteen or fourteen hour days, I found just driving on the beach road near my home with all the windows down inhaling huge lungfuls of salt air could slow my pulse and calm my nerves. If I felt indulgent, I would sacrifice my pantyhose and let that childhood-returning toe scrunch in the sand be my tranquilizer. I would return to my car with shredded pantyhose and a tranquil soul.

If the seashore is not an option, a swingset in a park will do. I ignore any errant looks. It is not for others that I free my restricted heart like this. These are my moments. My freedom from structure. My gift to my soul.

And odd as it may sound, I love to wander in cemeteries. The peacefulness in rows of headstones; the solemnity of knowing these lives are missed - wondering what each stone represents in joys lived, milestones accomplished, hearts broken. There is a stillness in graveyards that is majestic to me.

When I was in college, it was still possible to wander into a church. Doors were left unlocked then. I could enter any cool, dim sanctuary, kneel briefly and return to the sunlight restored.

Now, I find that the chapel of any airport or hospital offers the same refuge.

You alone will know what equalizes you and when you need it. It need not be broadcast or advertised. It does not have to be structured or scheduled. But, brief moments stolen away are nourishment for every soul.

"Nothing can bring you peace but yourself."
Ralph Waldo Emerson

## *February 27*

## Spring Comes Every Year

"I know from many years of experience that spring follows winter. The oak will sprout new leaves, the wildflowers will bloom, and the bulbs will push up their noses. I also know, from long experience, that God hears my prayers and His faithfulness surrounds me."
Mary Jane Clark

Some days this will be all you have to hold on to. Just to know that spring will come again - no matter what.

"With every colored egg and gentle raindrop, every fragrant breeze and fresh bouquet, comes a promise. This is April's gift to us: Inspiration to begin anew, right along with the rest of the world – no catching up, and no looking back. Spring after spring, nature suggests that everything is possible, and makes it all look easy."
Unknown; from April 2002 *Country Living*

*February 28*

## Think of Your Refrigerator as a Medicine Cabinet

There will be times when nothing pharmaceutically is working to heal your depression. These are the times that you will have to use 'alternative' medicine. You can replace serotonin with cheap food as carbohydrates will create it for you. This is not a permanent solution, but junk food CAN get you through a tough spot.

There are some items you might want to keep in your kitchen at all times. I make sure that I have carbohydrates in many forms available no matter what.

In my cabinets and refrigerator there are always several cereals (and I keep Parmalat milk in the little boxes that do not need refrigeration), microwave popcorn, instant grits, couscous packages, Triscuits, several types of bread in my freezer, pretzels, crackers, microwave stuffing mixes, cake mixes and ginger snaps.

*"Science is not a sacred cow. Science is a horse. Don't worship it. Feed it."*

*Aubrey Ebe*

# MARCH

## *March 1*

### Hobbies

Do you have something that you are good at or like to do? Ideally, you enjoy something that is stress-free and leaves all the cares of the world behind.

I once took a watercolor class. The only real benefit was that I got to spend an hour a week with some other folks who wanted to dabble, too. And I learned that what I painted was exactly right and there was no one true way to watercolor.

Having permission to be fabulous according to my own artistic ability was liberating. Every instructor, I have subsequently found, usually has several 'never do' and 'always do' guidelines and they always contradict each other! So, my way is always correct, too.

I will spend a couple of thoroughly pleasant hours creating some pictures - mostly as note cards with matching envelopes. But, I am distracted for some pleasant hours and depression has not entered my mind. I also play the piano and garden. I know fishing and woodworking are hobbies that lend themselves to this creative distraction.

There are only certain levels of depression where you have the energy to do these things. But, from time to time, a hobby may be your temporary medication.

*"My personal hobbies are reading, listening to music and silence."*

*Dame Edith Sitwell*

## *March 2*

### Brain Metabolism

When I get discouraged, I remind myself of the marvels the scientific community is making in their ability to examine a living brain. The brain only 'lives' twenty-four hours after death as deterioration begins immediately. So, to be able to study a working brain in recent years has moved the study of neurobiological disorders ahead light years.

It has now been replicated in several studies that there is significant difference in brain metabolism in depressed individuals. Well, I could have told them that decades ago! It is so obvious to me that my brain has slowed, that nothing is working right, that it actually physically hurts and I can feel that my 'wires are crossed'. None of the normal signals are getting through like they should. (see March 12 One Hard and Fast Rule)

Some of the studies find on PET (Positron Emission Tomography) that there is decreased frontal blood flow and cerebral hypometabolism (hypo is Latin for under and hyper is Latin for over). There are also blunted responses within the TSH (Thyroid Stimulating Hormone) and TRH (Thyrotropin-Releasing Hormone) so it would make sense that we would have weight gain during depression. There are even structural differences in the pituitary and adrenal glands.

Our hope is so realistic - almost tangible - when we know that so much research is breaking new ground every single day.

*"The important thing in science is not so much to obtain new facts as to discover new ways of thinking about them."*
*William Lawrence Bragg*

## *March 3*

## What You Can Ask of Others and What You Can Offer Others

It recently struck me how intensely frustrating it is to want to be able to help another person in the throes of depression and not be able to do much.

It became very clear how hard our illness must be on others who love us.

But, when I found myself unable to take away the pain my friend was suffering, I tried to think of the times when I was in that dark pit and what I would want someone to offer me.

Primarily, I did not want any offers that required a response. I did not want a visit or a phone call. I had nothing to say to anyone. But, what would have helped (and so many friends and family did offer this) was a note or a card or an email or a message on my answering machine. Just to know that I was in the thoughts of those who loved me and that they were rooting for me to return to the land of the living lightened my heart. I mattered to someone, even if I did not matter to myself at that moment.

To find a bag of cookies on my doorstep was fabulous. Sometimes a note on my windshield was an unexpected boost. I have two friends that are notorious joke tellers. They would leave these outrageous stories on my answering machine for me to find whenever I was able. Although many of these were not screamingly funny, they were a welcome lift.

I know that we tend to give what we like to receive. So, I will drop off bags of M & M's, or a silly card or one of those sentimental 'I believe in you...' - type cards when I attempt to help someone else. Sometimes, leaving a video (not one that has a deadline to return) can be just the right thing.

Acknowledging your frustration is fine, but keep your focus on what you can do.

A simple gesture can be priceless.

*"Love begins at home, and it is not how much we do...*
*but how much love we put in that action."*
*Mother Teresa*

## *March 4*

## Choosing Our Reactions

Joan Lunden says in the Foreword to *Stressed Is Desserts Spelled Backwards*, "we, in fact, have the power to choose not to react at all to that which happens around us."

Now stop and read that sentence again. "We, in fact, have the POWER to choose not to react AT ALL to that which happens around us."

Can you just imagine? Being so completely confident in who you are, what your beliefs are, what you do and do not stand for, that others' opinions, tantrums, demands, rejections or needs are simply like water running off a duck's back? It does not penetrate. Therefore, it cannot harm or alter us in any way.

Visualize yourself coated in Vaseline - nothing gets in. You are hermetically sealed from damage. And all you have to do is build this magical mindset around yourself. You may have to apply and re-apply your shield - especially around family it appears to me - but, you have the power to protect yourself. Not power in that you injure others. Not power to make others abide by your actions or reactions. Just an invisible barrier to the force of what others say and do. And all you have to do is decide to choose this. You can arm yourself a hundred times a day, if that is what it takes.

Our true strength is always in acting out of our own volition, not reacting to others.

*"...it is the way I choose to see the world that will create the world I see."*

*Joan Lunden*

## *March 5*

### Hiding Our Depression

"Not rarely, we hear about someone who has committed suicide, and we are astonished, because he seemed fine, he was pleasant, he went to work every day. We all have read about or know someone like that. It's amazing how well you can hide depression - how horrible you can feel, getting not a wink of sleep, and still get up and go to work. You may sit on a Board or do charity work, and even though you're depressed, your makeup will be on straight, and you'll be well dressed. People who are astute may notice that your zest is gone, but they usually won't ask. Or let's say you've lost your appetite, which is very typical, and you've lost weight. People will tell you how fabulous you look."

Nada Stotland, M.D., M.Ph., Chairman,
Department of Psychiatry,
Illinois Masonic Medical Center, Chicago, IL

This is a double-edged sword. Sometimes hiding our illness might salvage a job or performance, but do cancer victims hide their suffering? Sometimes. This is something that you alone can answer. And it is a moving target. You may choose to share your pain some days and to disguise it others. And you can disclose to some people some days and hide the bulk of your symptoms from the rest of the world.

This is strictly your decision.

*"Think for yourself. Whatever is happening at the moment, try to think for your self."*

*Jean Riboud*

*March 6*

## YOU Are the Captain of the Team

"'Many of us would just as soon have our choices made for us.' she said. 'But, the heroine, when at a juncture, makes her own choice – the nonheroine lets others make it for her.'"

Joan Anderson, *A Year by the Sea: Thoughts of an Unfinished Woman*

Do not give your power away. Even at your weakest. Be true to yourself. YOU are the only one living in 'the laboratory'.

You are the CEO, CFO, captain, president, whatever of your healing. Not one other person - not your mother, not your doctor (doctors), not your minister or your spouse or your best friend - has the power to get you out of your depressions. If you are to conquer this illness, YOU are going to be the one who orchestrates your healing.

You can enlist a whole squad of professionals and loved ones to help you, but ultimately it is YOU that sets up the plays, decides the offense, develops and implements the strategy. If you are in bleak place today, this is not what you need to hear. So, skip this and find other words that meet your needs for today. Come back to this tool when you are stronger.

For me - most of the time - being in charge of my own recovery was a great comfort. I like steering my own course. I could just drop sail and anchor where I was for awhile without needing permission to just let the world pass by temporarily; I could embrace life at any speed at any given time; I could sit in idle or go full-speed ahead if I wanted.

And I was free to add or drop players on my team any time I wanted to. It was MY team and only if every one in my squad was beneficial was I going to make any progress.

No two of us are alike. No two of us have the same chemistry. No two of us will heal the same way. But, we can adjust plays and players in our game plan - at our rate, in our own way - until we win.

And when we crush this illness, the credit is all ours, too.

"Never regret. If it's good, it's wonderful. If it's bad, it's experience."

Victoria Holt

## March 7

## The Wisdom of Dr. Kay Redfield Jamison

From *An Unquiet Mind* - by Kay Redfield Jamison, M. D.

"I had, ever since I could remember, inclined in the direction of strong and exuberant feelings, loving and living with what Delmore Schwartz called 'the throat of exaltation'.

Inflammability, however, always lay just the other side of exaltation. These fiery moods were - at least initially, not all bad:......It did not seem consistent with being the kind of gentle, well-bred woman I had been brought up to admire and indeed, continue to admire.

Depression, somehow, is much more in line with society's notions of what women are all about: passive, sensitive, hopeless, helpless, stricken, dependent, confused, rather tiresome, and with limited aspirations.

But it was a tidal existence. When I was depressed, nothing came out of me. When manic, or mildly so, I would write a paper in a day, ideas would flow, I would design new studies, catch up on my patient charts and correspondence, and chip away at the mindless mounds of bureaucratic paperwork that defined the job of a clinic director.

Time finally did bring relief. But it took its own, and not terribly sweet, time in doing so.

I drew into myself and, for all intents and purposes, shuttered my heart from the world.

My moods were still intense and my temperament rather quick to the boil, but I could make plans with far more certainty and the periods of absolute blackness were fewer and less extreme."

Dr. Jamison is a living witness to the power of recovery. There can't be many more demanding careers than the one she lives and she determined that she could and would beat depression and she has.

Is she can do it and I have done it, YOU can do it.

"You are the product of your own brainstorm."
Rosemary Konner Steinbaum

## *March 8*

## Safe Environments

"Another part of loving care is to develop safe environments to be in. The community I choose to surround myself with is a choice I make for myself. I can choose to be in the company of people who nurture the feelings I have and the choices I make."

People who dismiss your feelings or experience have no place in your world. This includes physicians and therapists.

This includes family.

Populate your world with those who have the same high goals and dreams of success that you do.

*"No matter where we go, our bodies are where we live."*
*Barbara Harris, editor in chief, Shape*

## *March 9*

## Making Your Insides Match Your Outside

Are you familiar with this term? It is used frequently in recovery circles.

When we feel ugly, unlovable, wretched, unwanted - it is hard to understand how people can't see that. But, they see our nice clothes, a good haircut, intelligent conversation and polished manners.

When we hurt so badly, it is amazing that others can't see it. But, it is to our benefit to use this discrepancy to our advantage. We can get through a day of work or a meeting by keeping the reality of our insides to ourselves. No one is the wiser.

We can keep our jobs and keep from worrying our children, our parents, spouse, friends. So, think of it as a tool and use it to help yourself.

The time will come that your inner self will be as beautiful as your outside self.

*"Being defeated is often a temporary condition. Giving up is what makes it permanent."*
*Marilyn vos Savant*

# *March 10*

## More Minutia

I can grasp at the slimmest straw or most outrageous analogy if it works - at least for that moment.

Here is an example -

I noticed my fingernails for some reason the other day. I have always liked my hands - the long, slim fingers and their graceful appearance. I even wore those artificial nails the various salons apply for years.

Now that I can no longer afford that luxury or tolerate the primer used in the process, I am back to my own, somewhat fragile, fingernails.

But, in 'seeing' the nails last week, it occurred to me that I could use these oft-overlooked parts of myself for emotional strength. The cycle our nails go through can be related to the cycles we weather in our moods. Sometimes my nails are strong, long and gorgeous. Other times they are brittle, hang-nailed and short.

But, they function in so many ways - opening a cap on a prescription bottle, scratching a fierce itch, lifting pages one at a time, etc...

So, my depression cycles wax and wane, but I (what I think of as the REAL ME) continue to function. If I can keep that perspective - that just as this depression 'came on little cat's feet', so will it depart. It never stays. It never remains static. It WILL go away.

Just as I don't notice the change in my nails until the results are visibly evident, neither am I aware of what progress is being made in lightening my mood until the results are very evident.

You are getting better - even if you don't see it.

*"Faith is not something to grasp, it is a state to grow into."*
*Mahatma Gandhi*

## *March 11*

# Do Not Get Stuck Where You Can't Get Home

While I was at a conference in Dallas once, I rode with colleagues to a Division party. Huge mistake. I was not feeling great when we left for the party and then an hour of inhaling secondhand smoke, trying to converse over screechingly loud music and dodging drunks while cold sober shoved me right over that precipitous edge into a very dark place.

I have certainly put my time in as the loud, overly obnoxious party-person. But, this night I was an unwilling observer. If I had driven myself to the occasion, I could have put in a respectable, brief appearance and then taken myself back to the hotel and some tranquility and relief.

But, the colleagues I rode with were in the mood to seriously party and I did not want to spend the $75 plus for cab fare. By the time we did finally leave five hours later, I was really feeling bad.

I have made it a practice from that point on to make sure I have an escape route. If I am depressed to the point that I do not feel I should be behind the wheel, then I stay home.

*"The way out of trouble is never as simple as the way in."*
*Edgar Watson Howe*

## *March 12*

# Don't Call Me a Recluse

I have often found that others see my self-protective behavior as reclusive. I never seem to have to explain my temporary behavior from those who are in the same boat. They instantly comprehend.

What appears to be isolation to some, is really:

Recharging my completely depleted batteries

Nesting in a safe haven

Keeping silent when the words I feel like saying would do irreparable harm

Marshalling the shreds of energy that I do have to eat, take my meds, do minimal maintenance living - trying to avoid hospitalization

Focusing 100% on recovery.

Do you find people accusing you of isolating? Their solution is for you to get out and do something. Sometimes they are right. Sometimes they are wrong.

You decide.

*"I tolerate with the utmost latitude the right of others to differ from me in opinion."*

*Thomas Jefferson*

## *March 13*

## Making It Through Today

I knew the minute my eyes opened this morning that today was not going to be an easy one. Yesterday was stellar. I got so much accomplished and felt genuinely good all day. So, here I am back in the gray area. It is not a black day, but it is going to be a struggle nonetheless.

So, here is how I am going to approach it. I have heard alcoholics say that they consider any day a success that they don't take a drink. So, bizarre as it may sound, my goal today is to stay above ground and go to sleep in my bed tonight.

I give myself permission to do anything I need to do between now and then to accomplish this.

So, I will survive today. I will not sink lower into depression. I will coddle myself. I will set severe boundaries. If that means hanging up on someone who feels impelled to give me advice on how to handle my illness or what I 'should' be doing, they get a shut door or a dial tone. I am ruthless on these days, because it often feels like it is 'me or them'. I will do whatever it takes to protect myself during this fragile time.

Sometimes that means spending money I don't really want to spend. If I need the distraction of a video or to have Chinese food or pizza delivered to my door, then I need to do that. I focus on THESE twenty-four hours. I do not think about what needs to be done tomorrow or this week or deadlines. I get tunnel vision. I see only pampering for today and a night of restful sleep.

Now, if you must show up at the office today, put on your invisible armor (see April 20). You can do it. Protect yourself throughout the day. Take yourself to lunch. Make ten personal calls to friends who support you. Surf the Internet and distract yourself. Do only the bare minimum, then get yourself home. Eat whatever you need, try a candlelight bubblebath or whatever works for now and get to bed. You can get back on your path tomorrow.

*"No one ever won a chess game by betting on each move. Sometimes you have to move backwards to get a step forward."*

*Amar Gopal Bose*

*March 14*

## One Hard and Fast Rule

I have one absolute rule that I follow. I will not drive a car when depressed to the point that I know my reflexes are delayed. I have asked neighbors to drive me to doctor's appointments or other commitments I am unable to postpone or miss. I have paid many a food delivery tip and I have even gotten a no-delivery pharmacy to deliver. Even though this incurs extra expenses I really couldn't afford, the cost of an accident was much higher.

But, for me to get behind the wheel of a car when I am severely depressed is deadly. The electrical impulse from my brain to my foot is broken. So, when I see a red light, I am practically through the intersection before my foot connects with the brake. Not only are some of my circuits broken, every physical effort is sluggish and impaired.

So, I keep non-perishables in my cabinets and rely on others, but I don't, under any circumstances, drive when severely depressed. The consequences just aren't worth it.

I won't put innocent strangers or myself at risk. It may be hard for you to ask for help, but this is the time to ignore that.

*"True hope dwells on the possible, even when life seems to be a plot written by someone who wants to see how much adversity we can overcome."*

*Walter Anderson,*
*The Confidence Course*

## *March 15*

### Productivity

I think it is the complete lack of having anything to show for my day - my week - sometimes my month - that makes me really frustrated with depression sometimes. What a waste of time. I will never get this time back! I give it away forever! I hate this passionately.

But, I have learned to remind myself that Nelson Mandela spent decades in jail and no one would ever consider his life wasted. What about the hundreds - could it be thousands? - of prisoners of war who have lost years of their lives? Nothing wasted about those lives. What more poignant legacy than the twenty-five months Anne Frank gave up of her life?

So, I reframe my thinking and ask God for the greater/bigger picture and to bring me perspective.

*"What we see depends mainly on what we look for."*
*John Lubbock*

## *March 16*

### Some Words of Inspiration:

Expect a miracle.

"What lies behind us and what lies before us are tiny matters compared to what lies within us." Ralph Waldo Emerson

I believe in the sun even when it is not shining,
I believe in love even when I do not feel it
I believe in God even when He is silent.

*"Life is a series of new beginnings."*
*flavia*

# March 17

## Yoga

Have you ever tried any yoga exercises? I don't mean the human pretzel type where you stand with your leg next to your ear. Just some of the gentle poses that are the most common.

Of the many types of ancient yoga now found to be popular in American culture, the one usually meant when folks refer to 'yoga' is hatha yoga. Hatha emphasizes renewed vigor through breathing exercises and special postures called asanas. During the 1960's, this form of yoga became popular as a means of relaxation as well as exercise. Some practice it as a consciousness technique as focused thought and awareness of breathing are a part of all yoga techniques.

I do two Sun Salutations each morning as both a form of stretching and also, moving oxygen into my muscles. Many yogis see this particular asana as the most important to do if you have limited time as it stretches and strengthens every major muscle group in the body as well as exercises the respiratory system.

In a fluid sequence, you move through twelve simple positions. From position 1, which focuses the thought and brings concentration and calm to positions 3 through ten which aids in digestive conditions, reduces abdominal fat and limbers the spine among other benefits, I can accomplish both sequences in less than five minutes.

I recommend any reputable book or Internet site that will walk you through these simple exercises. Considering how easy this is - no equipment (I am in my nightgown on the carpet in my bedroom), no fees or memberships - and the benefits to my mobility and metabolism, I never skip these short, but critical five minutes. Why not give this a try?

A place to start:
www.holistic-online.com/Yoga/hol_yoga_pos_sunsal.htm

*"Those who think they have not time for bodily exercise will sooner or later have to find time for illness."*
Edward Stanley

## *March 18*

### More Indulgences

Okay, so you are getting better at giving yourself uncensored permission these days. No little voices in the subconscious telling you not to...

So, how are you doing with the bubble baths in candlelight with the 'do not disturb' sign on the doorknob and the door locked? How about buying salad already washed and chopped because you will actually eat it that way and if you purchase the economical version, you never get around to cleaning it and end up tossing the whole package out spoiled in the end anyway?

How about those 'to me - for me' purchases ? Don't know what that is? Oh, this is one of my favorites. I truly love giving gifts to my friends and family. I buy Christmas gifts throughout the year whenever I see something that perfectly suits a loved one. But, I have also learned to give gifts to myself. Wow, was that a novel idea at first!

But, if there is a book, a perfume, a hat that I really, truly want, I give it to me from me. And I thank me, too, for such a thoughtful gesture!

We deserve to give ourselves what we give to others.

*"It is good to have an end to journey towards; but, it is the journey that matters, in the end."*
*Ursula K. LeGuin*

## *March 19*

### Energy Must Flow

*"Energy must flow. I am convinced that if we do not move forward, we are first nudged, then pushed by some unseen, yet divine, force."*
from *Stressed is Desserts Spelled Backward*- by Brian Luke Seaward, Ph. D.

Isn't this the awful truth? I just hate it when I have decided to finally give up - I lay like a slug - eyes closed so that blinking isn't even necessary - and damn, if my bladder doesn't start sending "I need attention" messages to my brain! Now, here I am trying to just die - I have had enough of this misery! I do not want to deal with my body and this suffering ONE MORE MINUTE and my bladder is needing attention!

When I can ignore the call of nature no longer, it is amazing how those few steps to the bathroom can propel me into the kitchen to answer another of nature's needs. Then, that leads me to the couch, to the television (remote powered only, of course), and maybe even to the possibility of considering answering the phone! And not ten minutes ago I was immobilized with not a shred of energy in sight.

Wow. And to think the universe can speak to me through my kidneys! Now that is amazing.

*"My will shall shape the future. Whether I fail or succeed shall be no man's doing but my own. I am the force; I can clear any obstacle before me or I can be lost in the maze. My choice; my responsibility; win or lose, only I hold the key to my destiny."*
*Elaine Maxwell*

## *March 20*

## Relaxing Is Hard Work

If you push yourself to get through every day, you will experience this same effort in trying to slow down and rest. The enormous determination that gets most of us through the worst days of fatigue and misery, drain all reserves we have in our energy bank.

So that unwinding becomes as difficult as work is. I have days that it will take hours for me to ease out of the overdrive function I have had to use to keep going through a series of dark days.

I mean, I am WORKING at relaxing! But, hard as it may seem to just BE - just rest - I can only recharge my batteries by going into idle mode.

If you have been forcing yourself through some tough days, realize that it will be difficult at first to let go and rest.

*"The finest workers in stone are not copper or steel tools, but the gentle touches of air and water working at their leisure with a liberal allowance of time."*
*Henry David Thoreau*

## March 21

### Unclutter Your Mind

If you are in a depression, do not make vacation plans; do not make major purchasing decisions; do not make promises just because you feel obligated; do not work on your taxes - file for an extension (and if you are too depressed to even fill out that form, call or have someone else do it for you); do not apply for new jobs or change careers.

Your full time job when you are depressed, is getting undepressed.

And it WILL take all your time and energy to do that.

Then, when you are 'in your right mind' again, tackle all those other jobs. But, clear the slate when you are depressed and have one thought only. Getting out of the depression is the only thing that matters now. Even the IRS can wait. Other people use extensions, why can't you?

*"You're not obligated to win.*
*You're obligated to keep trying to do the best you can every day."*

*Marian Wright Edelman*

## March 22

### Successful Meds That Quit Working

This is so hard to accept. If you have struggled for years to find a medication that works for you and finally gotten stabilized, it may take a while to actually recognize your symptoms again if they resurface. It may take weeks even for you to grasp the fact that although you are taking your meds as directed, they just aren't doing the job anymore.

The only solution for this is to a) recognize that your symptoms are returning
and b) immediately see your physician to re-evaluate your medication.

The sooner the better. Sometimes this just happens. Don't waste time wondering why. Just go find another prescription that works for you.

*"Let me tell you the secret that has led me to my goal;
my strength lies solely in my tenacity."*
*Louis Pasteur*

## *March 23*

## Distraction Will Always Work

I will repeat this tool several times because it is the one non-invasive, non-chemical alternative we have that will ALWAYS work.

The one fail-safe method for me of coping with the glass-walled well of depression is distraction. It has never failed to lift me - even if only one level or so- out of the misery. Better yet, there are no side effects and it does not matter if the pharmacy is already closed or your doctor is on vacation. And the benefits are immediate.

Having never been a television-watcher, I was loathe to shell out the forty or fifty dollars a month for cable. But, I rationalized that I paid far more than that monthly for prescriptions and I was 'medicating' with the idiot box, so actually it was cheap therapy in the long run. Without cable, I could receive several stations, but, it was for the dire days that I had to have as many options as possible. Also, the sit-com reruns and the Comedy Channel were musts and I needed a service provider to receive those.

I also kept a stash of videos that I had on loan from neighbors and friends. Usually, if the depression was dark enough, a two or three hour movie was too much for me to sustain interest in. But, it worked at times.

You may find other resources for distraction. I could delve into the pile of *People* magazines that I stored for just this type of emergency. An all-photo format was just perfect for distraction. I found doctors' offices were grateful to give me their old magazines if I picked them up several times a year and promised to recycle them to the Assisted Living Centers in our area. So, money wasn't the issue here.

Maybe music can be a distraction for you. For me, it was not 'attention-grabbing' enough - within moments, my negative thinking was louder than the music and I had accomplished nothing. But, it might work for you.

It would be nice to zone out with an exercise video or a rollerblade session. But, the level of depression I am talking about made physical activity ludicrous.

Eating chocolate always made me feel better, but it did not distract my thoughts. Remember: the mind can hold only ONE thought at a time. So, if you are involved in watching Ted and Dianne on *Cheers*, there is no room for the deadly thinking of suicide. Eating chocolate fills the mouth - not the mind.

In some instances, I flipped channels for six or eight hours before I felt sufficiently better to move on. Many times I was noticeably better in just one hour. You cannot limit yourself with a deadline in these circumstances. Just think of this as therapy and it will work when it will work - you cannot force a solution.

But, I can promise you. Distraction ALWAYS works.

*"Use what talent you possess; the woods would be very silent if no birds sang except those that sang best."*
*Henry Van Dyke*

*March 24*

## Self-imposed Hospitalization

Sometimes we have no choice but to have someone else take over for awhile. I have had two thirty-day hospitalizations. Both out of desperation and both milestones in my recovery. I like to think of these as merely adult 'time-outs'. Not in a sense of punishment, but a genuine time away from the world - a time of reflection, protected solitude and growth.

I literally had to say, "I think I need to be in the hospital". When I explained to my doctor what had transpired the previous seventy-two hours, my wish was immediately granted. I don't think he would have recommended this and yet, I knew I needed it.

Sometimes, you really do need to let go and let someone else make the decisions. You would be surprised at how easy it can be to put control in someone else's hands temporarily.

Those sixty days meant vivid, significant turning points for me. Something I would not have had if I had not known that I really needed medical intervention at those times. What gifts those breaks were.

Believe me when I say I know this is really, really hard to accept. But, if you need to be in someone's care twenty-four hours a day, get yourself there.

"The ultimate measure of a man is not where he stands in moments of comfort and convenience, but where he stands at times of challenge and controversy."

Martin Luther King, Jr.

## March 25

## Resiliency

"Resiliency is a unique spiritual muscle. Like a special flower, it is a hybrid of several coping skills which combine to overcome the winds of change, the odds against us. The fibers of resiliency are humor, creativity, persistence, and optimism, and their roots reach well below the surface, ready to rise again and again when needed. Perhaps its greatest facet is the ability to stay focused in the present moment, rather than stuck in the past or focused on the future. We enhance our resiliency when we galvanize these resources in the face of adversity. Each time we rise from the metaphorical fall, we come back stronger; what was once considered a mountain now becomes a molehill."

from *Stressed is Desserts Spelled Backward* by Brian Luke Seaward, Ph. D.

"We do not grow absolutely, chronologically. We grow sometimes in one dimension, and not in another; unevenly. We grow partially. We are relative. We are mature in one realm, childish in another. The past, present and future mingle and pull us backward, forward, or fix us in the present. We are made of layers, cells, constellations."

Anais Nin

## *March 26*

## More from Stressed is Desserts Spelled Backward

"The dark night of the soul is only a night, not a lifetime. Just as winter turns to spring, so too does night become day."

It is so easy to forget this.

Such a simple truth. But one that can save us. If you are so deep into the dark place that linear thinking is beyond you, try this mantra: "this too shall pass". This too shall pass. This too shall pass.

And it always does. Always.

*"Defeat doesn't finish a man – quit does. A man is not finished when he's defeated. He's finished when he quits."*
*Richard Milhouse Nixon*

## *March 27*

## Some Days

*"Some days it is clear sailing. Other times just holding course requires all our skill. It is at the close of such days – days of intensity and drama – that we most welcome the chance to drop anchor in a snug and familiar harbor."*
*Author unknown*

If today is a hold onto your rudder and make it to shore kind of day, remember:

- to let the wind work with you; don't fight it
- you work better if you have a crew to help you
- the weather ALWAYS changes
- putting our anchor down is only temporary.

If the harbor you found is only a crisis intervention, get your map out tomorrow and figure out where you are going. Set sail again and return to your journey.

*"If you're going through hell, keep going."*
*Winston Churchill*

*March 28*

## PSYCHONEUROBIOLOGY

Psychoneurobiology is a mind-body-spirit approach to healing. It scientifically uncovers the relationship between the psyche (spirit, emotions), neurons and the body. Some define it as a scientific reframing of traditional Chinese medicine. There are several forms of this type of healing. One I have had success with is experiential psychotherapy. Several disciplines - like Feldenkrais - work with awareness of the body to improve movement and human functioning.

The emotional component is inherent in all these protocols and for me that was essential. Much of this work deals with traumas from childhood. The Menninger Clinic in Topeka, KS. (moved to Houston in 2003) has practioners of psychoneurobiology and psychoneuroimmunology (includes stress as a factor in the mind/body connection). There are some fabulous practioners in these fields. The best way to find someone to work with is ask for references from psychologists, chiropractors, friends.

We know from yogis in India how much control we can exert over heart rate, blood pressure, blood flow and temperature regulation using our minds. Biofeedback can be highly successful in pain management, as well.

Biofeedback was one road that appeared to have no success for me, but the benefits are fabulous for some. Clinical kinesiology is a non-invasive technique that can provide immediate relief for many.

I will caution, though, that any of the mind/body connection work stirs up a lot of pain and feels like you are taking a big step backward. Also, be sure you feel a gut comfort with the practitioner you choose, as you must utterly trust anyone who works with your subconscious.

Many folks dealing with depression never need to work on this area of healing. Some do. You decide if you could benefit from this type of healing.

*"People, even more than things, have to be restored, renewed, revived, reclaimed, and redeemed; never throw out anyone."*
*Audrey Hepburn*

## March 29

## Practice Healthy Deafness

I love my imaginary hearing aid. When someone is certain they know more about my illness than I do or can remedy my situation in three short sentences, my eyes glaze over and I mentally hum the *Star-Spangled Banner* to myself to drown out their noise.

It amazes me how some folks want to advise you because of the recent article they read in *Reader's Digest* or what their nephew's doctor just prescribed for him. Because I know the intention is one of healing and aid, I listen politely, murmuring and nodding appropriately. But, I change the subject as soon as possible and move on as I do not want to engage this person in a discussion of what I know is best for me.

This goes for someone telling me how much happier I would be if I cut my hair, wore certain colors, went back to school, whatever. I just turn that little imaginary hearing aid on and smile benignly.

"When we honestly ask ourselves which person in our lives means the most to us, we often find that it is those who, instead of giving much advice, solutions, or cures, have chosen rather to share our pain and touch our wounds with a gentle and tender hand. The friend who can be silent with us in a moment of despair or confusion, who can stay with us in an hour of grief and bereavement, who can tolerate not knowing, not curing, not healing, and face with us the reality of powerlessness, that is a friend who cares."

Henri Nouwen

## March 30

## One Description of Depression

"... when the tide swept back over her ankles and sucked the sand down under her feet... that sensation... that slight and unsettling imbalance, that feeling of having the ground shift under you no matter how firmly you planted your feet."

Excerpted and adapted from *Sanctuary* by Nora Roberts

This is exactly how depression feels to me. That imbalance with the world. The ground not being solid under my feet.

Maybe that is why I lay down so much when I am depressed? It sure feels a lot more stable and steady.

What does it take to feel like you are on solid ground? Find it and do it.

*"Confidence, like art, never comes from having all the answers; it comes from being open to all the questions."*
*Earl Gray Stevens*

## *March 31*

## Self-Preservation

I am using self-preservation as a kind and benevolent way of giving you perspective on your survival. You will need to arm yourself with some special talents to help you on this journey of recovery to a fully functioning life. If you are not a fighter by nature now, you will need to learn to fight. I am a lover - not a fighter - but, I have become a ferocious combatant when I am fighting depression. You don't need to put your armor on in every situation and you won't need to wear it everyday. But, you are going to need to have it ready at a moments' notice in your closet.

This is a critical tool in self-preservation. If you give in to depression, you will not have a future.

And if you are a skeptic, I will suggest that you open your mind. You may need to explore some of the odder alternative solutions available today before you find relief. Keeping an open and willing attitude will serve you well.

Preserving your life may get expensive and may take you down some interesting roads. And self-preservation isn't always pretty. Think of the wolf who is trapped in the forest. They will gnaw off their foot to free themselves from a steel trap. Because staying in the steel trap means starvation and certain death, whereas losing a foot or leg is preferable because they at least have a chance.

I think of Steve McQueen and what ridicule he took from the Hollywood community when he was dying from cancer. The conventional medical community could offer him no hope or further solutions, so he opted to try every alternative choice out there. Some were pretty wild, but if ever there was a fighter, he was.

You alone will know how far to pursue your recovery. I am simply suggesting a mindset to get you there.

*"I know the price of success: dedication, hard work, and an unremitting devotion to the things you want to see happen."*

*Frank Lloyd Wright*

# APRIL

*April 1*

## Altered Consciousness

*"It is one of the commonest of mistakes to consider that the limit of our power of perception is also the limit of all there is to perceive."*

C.W. Leadbeuter

I found that how I PERCEIVED my depression had a great affect on how I was able to function on any given day.

One way of looking at your depressive state is to see it in the perspective of an altered consciousness. Some types of altered consciousness you may be aware of are dreams, daydreaming, hypnosis, being caught up in the emotions of a movie or a piece of moving music, etc...

Just as you are able to regain your normal equilibrium by waking from a dream, you can regain your mental equilibrium by altering your chemistry to move out of your depression. This change IS "do-able". Seeing the fluidity of depressive cycles will relieve some of your pain.

Try not to see the depression as 'it will always hurt this much' or 'I will always be depressed' but, rather as a short term cycle or situation that you CAN move out of. I see the pain as just a different phase of consciousness and I can consciously make the choice to ALTER it and move back into my normal mind.

Knowing that I have the power to change - knowing I can make the pain stop - is the biggest advantage of my recovery. The depressions still come in cycles but, I have the tools to change my chemistry now. Twenty-four hours is the longest I have been in a depression in years.

Altered consciousness is usually a very pleasant state. But, we do not want to remain in the dream (or the daydream, or the movie, etc...) Say to yourself, "I am in an altered state and I am moving out of it." Even a negative state like the flu is transitory. And what is the flu but an altered state? You are not going to have the flu forever and neither will you be depressed indefinitely.

Sometimes it takes longer than other times, but knowing I am in control and that the depression does not control ME, is relief in itself.

*"The book which the reader now holds in his hands, from one end to the other,*

*as a whole and in its details... treats of the advance from evil to good...*

*from darkness to daylight ... from Hell to Heaven."*
*Victor Hugo, Les Miserables*

*April 2*

## An OUTWARD AND VISIBLE SIGN

Much as I loathe the lard that I accumulate in the depressive cycle, ironically, it serves a really important purpose, I think. It is the only visible sign that something is terribly wrong in my life.

It is as if every extra pound denotes a molecule of the anguish I am experiencing.

The fat just seems to validate what I tell people I am experiencing. I have thought it would help so much to produce a gauze head wear like head trauma victims use - something to wear when my insides are dying and I look the very same on the outside. A distinct and visible announcement to the world that my head is injured - it isn't working right.

I probably need to either create and patent something like this or maybe a sandwich-signboard that would declare that though we may LOOK fine and LOOK just like we normally do, we are terribly, desperately ill.

It would help so much if others knew to excuse our indifference and sarcasm when we are depressed. Just because we have one of the invisible illnesses, doesn't mean we are what we look like outwardly. Just like a migraine sufferer needs that little extra patience and understanding, so do we. And just like the migraine sufferer, no one knows unless we tell them.

And some days I just don't have the strength to tell. So, I'm going to keep working on this. By wearing a cross, I 'tell' others that I am Christian; a special bracelet 'tells' of critical medical data; a wedding band 'tells' of our unavailability sexually and emotionally. Surely, there ought to be a way to signal our need for understanding during our dark days.

"The depth of your misery will become your point of turning."
Stephen E. Broyles,
*The Wind That Destroys and Heals - Trusting the God of Sorrow and Joy*

## April 3

### The Journey

""There is no arriving, ever. It is all a continual becoming."
Tears fill my eyes as I recognize that she is seeing the real me."
from *A Year by the Sea: Thoughts of an Unfinished Woman* by Joan Anderson

"There is a story about a Navajo grandfather who once told his grandson, "Two wolves live in me. One is the bad wolf, full of greed and laziness, full of anger and jealousy and regret. The other is the good wolf, full of joy and compassion and willingness and a great love for the world. All the time, these wolves are fighting inside me."

"But, grandfather," the boy said, " which wolf will win?"

The grandfather answered, "The one I feed."
from *The Year of Pleasures* by Elizabeth Berg

"Recognize what is working, what is missing, and what is distorted so you can continue your journey with consistency and clarity."
Sylvia M. Sultenfuss,
www.sylviasays.com

## April 4

### Finding What Soothes Your Soul

No two of us are going to find relief or recovery in quite the same way. And I will find that while chocolate may satisfy during one cycle, it will be the crunch of Frito's or a bubble bath the next time. So, even the same individual will need different remedies at different times.

I look at these 'soul satisfiers' as medication. There is no guilt attached and no need to justify what I need to others.

If it is chocolate, it may be only a plain Hershey bar that will do. There is no point in bypassing this with anything else, as nothing else will satisfy the craving. If it is spumoni ice cream, don't think for a minute that strawberry will do.

If it is an undisturbed nap - take the phone off the hook and shut the door.

If it is a good read and you've read all the library has in your department - go buy a book and don't look at the price. Buy the book that you want.

These are 'emotional/psychological itches' that we all get - male and female, young and old alike. But, when you are in a low cycle, learn to listen to these urgings and follow your subconscious. These internal nudgings are our Higher Self telling us what it needs.

Sometimes the craving signifies an underlying chemical imbalance. My dear friend, Kathy, enlightened me that if I was craving chocolate regularly, I might try supplementing manganese - not magnesium - but, manganese. Sure enough it worked. But, the occasional urge might just need 12 oz. of Hershey's and nothing else will suffice.

If I was craving yeast doughnuts, Kathy suggested I try a good B-complex.

Bingo !! It takes a few days for you to feel the difference with the vitamin or mineral, but if it is a consistent itch, this might be a solution.

But, if it is just the agony of the bottom of the black hole, do the immediate thing. I have taken my dog and gone for peaceful strolls through cemeteries. I have watched three consecutive *SNL's* and laughed til my face hurt. I have taken long naps.

Here is the moment to be utterly self-centered. YOU need something at this moment. And no one is going to give it to you. This is something you alone can do for yourself. Delaying gratification is not a good thing here. Do what your soul needs for psychological relief and then you can move forward.

Do not discuss this with anyone. Do not ask permission from anyone. And most definitely, you will pass GO!

"Nobody holds a good opinion of a man who has a low opinion of himself."

Anthony Trollope

## April 5

## I Just Need To Swear Sometimes, Damn It !

I would like to think I had a bit of sophistication or social polish, or even good manners, when it came to vulgarity. I know that I really hate to hear foul language - from men or from women.

But, there are times when I am depressed that 'darn' just isn't going to do it. I try very hard not to be crude and there certainly are some words I won't say in any context in any situation. But, when I am frustrated, irritable and hurting, I find it quite helpful, actually, to let others know that I am 'as low as a rat's ass'. Not only does it bring a bit of levity to the moment, it gives folks a chance to visualize just how low that really is and to get a reference point of where I am at that moment. 'Feeling rotten'; 'feeling pretty low'; 'not good' - these just aren't adequate expressions.

I also find great relief in saying 'I don't give a damn', 'that is full of sh__', 'he, she or it is full of sh__', and other unladylike phrases I don't use in normal discourse.

Are you getting the picture? I sure as hell am glad.

*"Never bend your head. Hold it high. Look the world straight in the eye."*

*Helen Keller*

## April 6

## Do Not Compare Your Depression to Others'

I recently read a *Carenotes* sponsored by Abbey Press in which a rabbi was able to get up from his hospital bed where he was being treated for depression and on a dare from his wife, put on his jogging suit and go outside. He responded so positively to this, that he recommends in this booklet that others might find similar help in rearranging their furniture or hanging pictures.

My immediate, knee-jerk reaction was "yeah, well, if you had MY depressions you'd be laughing at these suggestions, too." But, that is exactly what we don't want others to do to us. A 'my depression is worse than your depression' attitude is futile and often damaging even. We can never know the depths of another's pain. It is up to us to offer empathy and understanding without judgment. Who benefits if we suffer more or less than the other guy?

Know that what you suffer is real - and so is the other persons' pain real for them. And most likely, you will never find the words to be able to share how much you hurt. I don't think the words exist for the kinds of pain we suffer in depression. I wonder if suicide is not a way that some people use to show how much they hurt?

But, falling into the comparison trap is a waste of your precious energy. Don't do it.

*"Whatever you want in life, other people are going to want it too. Believe in yourself enough to accept the idea that you have an equal right to it."*

*Diane Sawyer*

*April 7*

## There Is No "A" in Depression

This is easy. Do the best you can. No one is going to grade you on how well you have done healing your illness. "C" is a passing grade. All you have to do is graduate and it can be done on all C's.

Do what you have to do to get your life out of the ruts of depression and back on track. You - and only you - will know what it takes on any given day to succeed (pass).

And 'success' is what you define it as. If you do not make the corner office or CEO, but you make a living, you are a raving success! You may be on disability and not working at all but still a contributing member of society. Even if you are not active as a volunteer or church member or any of the other yardsticks folks would judge you by, maybe you are a great son or uncle, sister or neighbor.

Don't let others define the quality of your life.

*"Try not to become a man of success, but rather try to become a man of value."*

*Albert Einstein*

*April 8*

## Lack of Participation by Family Members

Well, I didn't think we were going to broadcast my diagnosis from the rooftops, but I was certain that those family members I had counted on all through the peaks and valleys of a normal life were going to be there - right by my side - as I learned how to deal with depression.

I was hurt and confused when this became a solo journey. It was 'ignorance is bliss' - not 'knowledge is power'.

I still have no answers as to why they are distant bystanders in my illness. I do feel that if my diagnosis had been kidney failure or cancer, their response would have been different.

Do you face this with your family? I have no easy answer here. I believe that people do the best they can generally. Especially if they love you. This may have been their way of dealing with an uncomfortable - possibly embarrassing - issue.

We don't talk about it. I find my support from others. Do what you need to do to take care of yourself and let the frustration, disappointment, anger go over their non-involvement. This is one battle you do not need to fight. Love them for who they are and not what you expect of them.

*"They say that blood is thicker than water. Maybe that's why we battle our own with more energy and gusto than we would ever expend on strangers."*

*David Assael*

*April 9*

## The Cleanest of the Dirties

You may have used this fabulous trick and never even known it! I was introduced to the practice my freshman year of college.

There were simply too many men to date, too much flirting to be done, too much socializing with my newfound friends than to be bothered with laundry on a regular basis. Doing my laundry ranked just a shade above writing to my great aunt Marie on my list of things to do.

But, there was a solution! Hallelujah! I didn't have to ever let laundry chores bother me again. Or at the very least, I could extend the deadline for a few more days.

Man! I wish I had thought of this before! Well, actually with a resident mom in the days before my freedom at college, I never worried about laundry at all until I was on my own.

But, it did seem laundry duties were part of adulthood and I sure did want all the other benefits that being independent offered. That is until I discovered another treasure - that some of the rules of adulthood were flexible; you just had to lower your standards a little.

One Friday morning at the end of a very memorable week, I was frantically trying to get ready for my 9 a.m. class. Of course, only a novice freshman would schedule classes before noon, but I was still at the beginning of my learning curve. But, lo...there was nothing clean to wear. Now what? I did know one girl who simply wore her trench coat to class every Friday. And we all knew she was absolutely stark naked underneath it. Weather not withstanding, she and the trench coat were de rigueur on Fridays.

Well, what was I to do? I didn't even own a trench coat! But, my older and wiser sophomore roommate had already passed this lifetime milestone. She knew the clothes hamper exercise of playing 'the cleanest of the dirties'. I loved this game! If life was too short to be spent in the dungeon laundry room, you simply went through the pile of accumulated dirty clothes and sniffed each piece. The least offensive was IT. You smoothed the biggest wrinkles, found two pieces - they needn't match - you weren't interested in impressing anyone else dumb enough to have a 9 a.m. class and headed out the door! Problem solved....

I can't begin to count the occasions this trick has been useful. When the dark days are upon me, laundry seems to grow exponentially. But, I revert to my younger days and let the laundry wait for a brighter day.

On the dark days, laundry is the last thing you need to expend your energy on.

*"A new beginning can start at anytime."*

## *April 10*

## And They Think This is An Emotional Problem ?

Well-replicated neurobiological findings show decreased frontal blood flow, cerebral hypometabolism, evidence of peptide dysfunction, blunted thyroid response as well as structural alterations in a depressive's brain.

The human brain has 100 billion plus nerve cells. And these cells send chemical messages or signals to thousands of other cells at the rate of approximately two hundred miles an hour.

Keep these facts in mind when anyone refers to this as anything other than a neurobiological disorder. Depression IS neuro - (rooted in the nerves) - biological (rooted in the organic body itself). I never - ever - refer to my illness as a 'mental illness' as this implies a thinking issue or capacity. Nor do I allow others to address depression as an emotional or psychological problem as this implies we have control over it.

Of all the organs in the human body, the brain is by far the most complex. Yet, when this amazing structure malfunctions, it is seen as an emotional or psychological issue. Would anyone ever consider the need for kidney dialysis an emotional problem? Why do we allow others to define the nature of a true medical condition for us?

I don't and neither should you.

*"No answer to any problem that matters is either easy or final, and the problem of suffering is the most obstinate problem of all. "*

*Stephen E. Broyles, The Wind that Destroys and Heals: Trusting the God of Sorrow and Joy*

## *April 11*

## Coma Sleep

Invariably when I told someone that I had just slept for sixteen hours, their response was one of envy - "You must feel really rested now." Be aware that the deep, deep sleep that can accompany depression is not restorative.

This sleep - regardless of duration - does not include Stage 5 or what is known as REM sleep. This phase is the one in which our bodies repair themselves. We also cleanse our emotional plane, so to speak, because of the dream patterns that are part of this phase.

The sleep I am discussing is not restorative. In fact, you arise even more tired and fatigued than before you went to bed.

I call this coma sleep because it reminds me what it feels like to wake up in the recovery room from general anesthesia. A nurse will tap the back of your hand, call your name, adjust your blankets in order to arouse you from sedation. But, the quicksand of sleep pulls you back under. You never awake from sedation refreshed. It is a contradiction in terms.

Also parallel with a coma is the blankness of memory that is a major feature of our 'depression sleeps' as well. There is no dream state - no memory no matter how vague - to this sleep. Like a bear that hibernates, there is no arousal from beginning to end - however long these depression sleeps are going to last, there are no interruptions once they begin. But, unlike the bear, we do not arise refreshed.

I discuss this just for educational purposes. I have no idea how to bypass or avert this component of some depressions. I want you to be aware not to expect benefits of normal sleep from this facet of depression.

*"Engage in a creative dance of completing the past and laying the groundwork for a more fulfilling future !"*
*Sylvia M. Sultenfuss,*
*www.sylviasays.com*

## *April 12*

## Chemical Sensitivities

Some of the oddest things can trigger a downward spiral for me. Abruptly, precipitately, deadly.

It seems the older I get, the more sensitivities I have to agents in the environment. Whether it be dyes or preservatives in food, fertilizers and insecticides in the lawn, ingredients in hair care products and make-up - even the fluoride and whiteners in toothpaste can send me in a tailspin!

I have had to spend hundreds of hours reading and researching this topic and then finding through trial and error what applies to me - what chemicals I am sensitive to and that alter my chemistry in disastrous ways. And these sensitivities change over time. It appears not to be a static condition.

Dealing with the cycles of depressions is hard enough without adding more trauma to my already overstressed body. If you feel (as I do) a sudden weariness after ingesting certain foods (anything with MSG in it just about puts me to sleep), an uncomfortable pressure behind your eyes or at the nape of your neck, increased anxiety without provocation then you might be having a negative reaction to a preservative, dye or additive.

Some of the triggers are easy to eliminate. I regretfully give up my cherished chocolate-covered cherries because the red dye (usually #5) makes me ill. Ditto for any jello as they are loaded with dyes.

I learned to live with the increasing number of wiry gray hairs as the reaction to hair coloring was so severe, that I had to use topical and internal steroids because of the welts and blisters dyes caused.

I avoid MSG and sulfites at all costs. Nutrasweet/asparatame is never in my diet.

Sometimes the reaction is that debilitating 'head fog' that is exactly like one of my depression symptoms.

In my case, a fairly large dose of Buffered Vitamin C (a 2,000 to 4,000 mg. dose per day), some calcium/magnesium/potassium supplements, acetyl-cysteine, and vitamin B-6 alone or in combination will usually reverse the reaction within a matter of one to two hours.

But, avoidance is still my chief ally.

This will be just one more tool in your battery of options in fighting depression. Monitoring your reactions and feelings of well-being is the only way to eliminate this added stress to your life.

Wouldn't it be nice if a cycle of depression could be overcome with such ease?

*"True giving comes from first having given the gift of gentle compassion to yourself."*

*Sylvia M. Sultenfuss,*
*www.sylviasays.com*

*April 13*

## Censure Your Media Input

Here is what works for me:
Although I am sure that *Schindler's List* is a remarkable film, I have not seen it nor will I ever. Once the retina is exposed to an image, that image is forever imprinted in the data bank of the brain. I simply cannot afford to log in anything more horrifying than what I am already living.

This also precludes my seeing *Private Ryan, The Titanic, Pearl Harbor.* Even though these are important historic films, they would be too disturbing for me. And for the movie lover I am, this is a pretty significant sacrifice. But, I know that I could not dismiss those shattering images and that I need to load up on chuckles and feel-good fluff to raise my optimism barometer.

I have not watched televised news in decades. No, not even September 11, 2001. I do not read a newspaper. I find that I am able to stay marginally current if I read the five or six headlines I see when I log on to the Yahoo sign-in page and I always read the headlines of newspapers in newsstands at gas stations and restaurants. If I could afford it, I would subscribe to *USA TODAY* as it provides less sensationalism and gore and more information.

I do not watch television that promotes violence or trauma either - be it *Cops, America's Most Wanted, ER* or any of the doctor/hospital-based shows. I do not read true crime books. I shy away from *Newsweek* and *Time* because of the graphic pictures.

It is not that I do not care. It is that I care too much. I will be physically ill if I absorb information about tragedies and destruction that I can do nothing about. I literally have a physical reaction that lingers. However, I can and do lead and attend and participate in support group meetings with all their suffering - BECAUSE I can do something to help in those circumstances.

Am I missing out on something? You bet I am. But, I do follow-up those Yahoo headlines when I need to and the rest I am fine without.

I just have tightened the borders of my horizon. I no longer know and no longer care where the Irish/Catholic movement is at this time; I do not know or care what the status of bloodshed is in the Middle East. This is calloused and will sound heartless. But, I am talking about preservation here. Self - preservation. And for me, this is what it takes.

The limit I use is this: no matter how bleak or hideous a situation is, if I can do something about it - however small - I will involve myself. If it is a problem outside the scope of my influence, it is an issue that 'drops off my radar'. Not that I do not remember all these other issues in my prayers - because I do.

I am just VERY selective these days in what I let into my memory bank.

*"Never stop believing in the journeys you've yet to take, the people you've yet to meet, the stars you've yet to count."*
*Kathy Tirrell*

## *April 14*

## I AM A FIGHTER

I am a fighter. I hope you are, too. Depression has always felt like a battleground to me and I want you and I to be the victors.

I have always seen my illness as an entity. Just as some folks believe in an evil power at work in the world that is to be battled at all costs, I see my illness as a force outside of myself that I must conquer. To further the battle against evil forces analogy, we are never allowed to let our guard down. Never. This is a deadly, mysterious, complex, insidious disease and we must always be vigilant. If we let our defenses down, depression can creep back into our lives and knock us off balance once more.

To me, depression has been a life and death issue. Once I was diagnosed, I clearly saw that this was a war and I would do whatever it took to subdue and overcome this illness. It would not control my life.

At times my fury in doing battle with depression spilled over into other areas of my life. Of course, it did. Depression was a shroud that covered me wherever I went during those black cycles. I alerted those around me that I was dealing with a painful illness and not to take my slings and barbs personally. Of course, this is not easily done.

This was a duel to the death. I never saw myself as just getting better. Improving. I always envisioned a return to my former robust and vigorous life. Just getting by was not an option. I was not only going to conquer this demon, I was going to thrive.

It saddens me that in my fierce tunnel vision, I have injured friends and loved ones. With my eye focused solely on the goal, I would go over, under or around anything that stood in my path. I hope to live long enough to personally apologize to any innocent bystanders that got caught in the heat of my determination. It was never intentional.

And, so inch by excruciating inch, I have reclaimed my life. I need to take more medications than most. I protect my sleep and exercise needs diligently and I have to work around stress as everyone else does. But, I am thriving and it was worth every single minute.

*"If only one could have two lives; the first in which to make one's mistakes, and the second in which to profit by them."*
*D. H. Lawrence*

*April 15*

## Laughter IS the Best Medicine

Researchers at Utah State University found that watching thirty minutes of stand-up comedy every night for thirty consecutive days reduced the symptoms of depression by up to forty-two percent.

There will be times when there seems to be nothing to watch except for crime and court dramas, the ludicrous talk shows with their focus on the warped and the wicked, or hospital re-enactment traumas. And these are NOT best for you if you are experiencing depression. Cruise your viewing selections. There will always be a rerun choice of *I Love Lucy, The Andy Griffith Show, Happy Days, Friends* or *Frasier*. Promise yourself just thirty minutes and check your mood when the program ends.

Chances are you feel lighter. It really does work.

*"I am an experiment on the part of nature, a gamble within the unknown, perhaps for a new purpose, perhaps for nothing, and my only task is to allow this game on the part of the primeval depths to take its course, to feel its will within me and make it wholly mine."*
*Herman Hesse*

*April 16*

## It Is Only Your Opinion That Matters

When it takes all your will and energy to just get through a day - literally - there is nothing left over to coddle, appease or humor others.

Rather than try at this nearly impossible time to educate or explain, keep your own counsel.

Stay home. Stay away from the phone. Don't try to be something that you are not. You may burn bridges and do damage that you cannot redeem. There is no crisis that you alone must solve. Let everything slide - anything critical will still be waiting for you when you are better able to deal with it.

Solitude is the solution at these times.

If others accuse you of 'isolating', that is THEIR opinion. They are not living in your personal hell. If friends and family determine that they know what is best for you at these times, avoid and ignore them. They mean well, but they are acting out of ignorance. Listen to your own internal voice. Do ONLY what you know is best for YOU.

*"It's only when we're relaxed that the thing way down deep in all of us – call it the subconscious mind, the spirit, what you will – has a chance to well up and tell us how we shall go."*
*Frances Perkins*

*April 17*

## Looking Back

It makes sense that if you can right a wrong or heal a relationship, then revisit the past and make amends.

Otherwise, it is futile (and excruciating) to harbor memories of negative events. No one leads a life without blunders and errors. Not one of us is infallible.

Keep your focus on the future and what is in you power to change or create. Looking forward offers hope. Looking back creates toxic guilt.

*"It is one thing to learn about the past; it is another to wallow in it."*

*Kenneth Auchincloss*

*April 18*

## Distortion

Boy, does depression shape my view of things. A casual comment by a friend or colleague can bring tears and the pain of rejection. An everyday gesture can take on ominous overtones when seen through a screen of depression. The smallest, most insignificant event can seem overwhelming and cataclysmic.

The only relief I have ever found under these circumstances is to write down what is troubling me and put the paper in a file. And by putting the paper in the file, I am putting the incident out of my mind. Once the depression has passed, I can read what the file holds. Almost always, I chuckle at the pettiness of what originally disturbed me.

What could escalate into harmful words and accusations stays safely in my possession until I can deal with it rationally.

What I do NOT do is minimize the initial discomfort or pain that I felt. The trauma of depression and what we experience while in that chemical imbalance is very real. But it need not trigger repercussions that are difficult, if not impossible, to fix.

*"Perception is a mirror, not a fact. And what I look on is my state of mind, reflected outward."*

*From A Course in Miracles*

*April 19*

## I Never Doubted You'd Get Well

One of the most powerful and healing statements I ever heard was uttered very matter-of-factly by my friend, Jordan G. On our way back from a movie one day, I was discussing the peaks and valleys of depression in my life and how many average or good days I was able to string together at that time.

I was hesitant. Uncomfortable to claim the fruit of all my effort to get better. Fearful of a sudden plunge back into the hellhole of depression.

But, Jordan was convinced. There was no shadow lurking - waiting to overtake me again.

"I never doubted you'd get well."

What a gift those words were. I kept them on a slip of paper on my mirror for years.

*"Failure is an event, never a person."*
*William D. Brown*

## *April 20*

## Putting on the Mask of Depression

How many times have you faked a normal day at work or other social circumstance while your interior monologue was a repetition of suicidal thoughts? It is not uncommon for there to be times when we are forced to face the world even if we are in the bleak grasp of a deep depression.

It never ceases to amaze me how normal we (the depressives, that is) will appear to others when, in fact, we are truly very ill.

There are two sides to the coin of 'disabled functioning'. We can - at times - be grateful that ours is one of the 'invisible illnesses'. During those times when our financial or professional future rides on a particular performance, we can reach back for that bit of strength we are surprised to learn that we have and fake our way through the meeting or conference or deadline.

This is very much to our benefit to be able to fool others at times.

But, I have often wanted to have at least one person acknowledge the severity of pain I was experiencing. Empathy - not sympathy - would have provided a modicum of relief. And, in my irrationality, not infrequently, I would be furious that I had to bear the double burden of the horror of depression and the added work of faking normality.

But, I could deal with my anger once I left the crucial performance behind and at least, my mask had allowed me to salvage myself when performance/normality counted.

There will be times you need to put on your happy face - regardless.

*"Happiness is having a large, loving, caring,*
*close-knit family in another city."*
*George Burns*

## *April 21*

## A Reflection

*'It is important to keep searching for the small joys, although they are sometimes the most elusive. Trust that these joys will appear, sometimes unexpectedly, and often in life's darkest moments...for instance, in the smile on a baby's face. "*
*Katie Gill*

I have been flabbergasted on some of the bleakest, darkest days to have one of those moments of insight and joy completely turn my heart and attitude toward the light again. There must be some collusion on your part though. Ask to be open to these moments of grace. It can make all the difference some days.

*The great Roman philosopher, Seneca, said: "There are two choices in life. You can be led by fate, or you can be dragged by it."*

## *April 22*

## Charles Grodin's Shell Game

Sometimes what I need most is to hear my situation explained in other folks' terms and words. I become so immersed in depression that I need to get an objective, looking from the outside view of where I am.

One description that really resonated with me is from one of my favorite actors - Charles Grodin. His autobiography, *How I Get Through Life - A Wise and Witty Guide*, that William Morrow and Company published in

1992, was a fun read. Very droll, like the man himself. But, when he described his bouts of depression, he really spoke for me, too.

"During this period I tried to act as though I were still my old self, except people noticed I had gotten strangely quiet, and the idea of anything more ambitious than staring off into space or eating a sandwich seemed beyond me. I still did everything I was supposed to, but it was like a shell game, and I was the shell." (pg. 41)

So, my point today is that although we may be feeling hollowed out by depression, we do not know how many others we encounter in our daily experience are in the very same dark place. And this may bring a bit of kindness into our interactions when we really feel like snarling. How do we know that the ineptness of the other person is not just an extension of depression?

I want others to do unto me with understanding. Then I will give what I want in return.

*"Assumptions are the termites of relationships."*
*Henry Winkler*
*(another of my favorite actors)*

*April 23*

## A Bit of Humor for the Really Irritable Days

"I want to thank you, Lord, for being close to me so far this day.

With your help I haven't been impatient, lost my temper, been grumpy, judgmental, or envious of anyone.

But, I will be getting out of bed in a minute and I think I will really need your help then."

Amen

*"...I mean, I want to mean something. I want it to matter that I'm here."*
*"Ah, make your mark, huh?"*
*"Don't you, I asked?"*

"I think..."she said. "I believe you make your mark inside yourself. I think we're meant to use every single thing we're given. I want to act on every impulse."

"I want more. I want someone to know I was here."

"But you still have to start with yourself, " she said. "You have to let yourself know you're here. Take things in, let things happen. Everything."

Elizabeth Berg, *Talk Before Sleep*

*April 24*

## Control

" A goal,
A love
And a dream
Give you total control over your life."

John Wayne Schlatter (adapted)

If you are in a slump today when you read this, it will not resonate. If you are on the upswing, you will feel its power.

If today is a rough one, maybe the goal for you is just to be 'feeling good'. Maybe even, just feeling better than you do at this moment. If you are in enormous pain, see the Desparate Days Checklist at the end of the book and let go of everything else.

Whether today is hideous or glorious - take CONTROL over what you have control over. Your attitude if nothing else.

Feeling better than you do at this very minute is a worthwhile goal. For everyone!

The love and dream aspects are yours alone. And they can change from time to time. What works today may not work tomorrow.

If you have a greater goal, I urge you to take the next step in reaching it.

What Schlatter gives us in such simplistic terms is workable. For everyone. This is the kind of incentive I would tape on my mirror. What a clear way to frame your life and destiny.

Really simple. Use it.

"Nobody can make you feel inferior without your consent."
Eleanor Roosevelt

## *April 25*

## Finding Hope in the Grocery Store

Because I:
1. loathe waiting
2. love to read
3. hate to spend money frivolously

I routinely pick up a magazine from the rack to skim while waiting in line at the grocery store. And one of the best short reads is *Shape* and *Weight Watchers* one page Before and After articles.

I can usually read several of these one-page summaries before it is my turn to check out and what an inspiration some stories are!

Not only are there the all-inspiring photos, but data like weight and inches lost and how each individual accomplished their goals are included in short box summaries as well.

Some of these women have overcome obstacles every bit as daunting as depression - incest, rape, drug and/or alcohol addiction, car accidents and deformities, etc... Some were discouraged and threatened by spouses and loved ones. These successes have faced what we face.

Some have succeeded after fifteen or twenty tries.

These are women and men I can relate to. They have ordinary lives and not an abundance of surplus funds. So, the personal trainers and chefs, the staff of housekeepers and retinue of assistants and secretaries that the celebrities can afford are no more available to the heroic women of *Shape* and *Weight Watchers* than to me. It slays me when I read of some of the beauty or health regimens of the wealthy. They have all the service staff and motivational guides to accomplish their dreams.

But, the real life stories I get in the grocery store line never fail to recharge my resolve. I know that if these ordinary folks can succeed against severe odds - then, I certainly have a fighting chance, too.

While losing significant amounts of weight may not seem to be as serious or life-threatening as overcoming suicidal depression, it is the power of hope and the power of will and the quality of life that accompanies their success that motivates me to try one more time - one more day.

*" Eighty percent of people eventually diagnosed with depression complain of physical pain first."*

*April 26*

## Find A Reason For Staying Here

Sometimes you have to just get through one of the black holes. You found a way to stabilize the depression and unfortunately, just too many negatives piled up at once and you slipped back into a black hole.

It is critical that you see the depression times as CYCLES. You will come out of the depression phase - just like you went into it.

But, weathering the pain is difficult.

So, I always found a reason - outside of myself - beyond the anguish of the moment - to hang on until the dark night passed. I do not have children, so I couldn't use that hook. But, I did use: my mother who would have been devastated and who had also funded much of my recovery with her hard-earned middle class dollars and I felt a moral obligation to not let her down; my two nieces whose weddings in the future I envisioned attending; there were certain doctors who had dismissed or minimized my illness and I was going to rise above this and prove them wrong; Hershey's was still producing chocolate and I needed to eat more of it!

If I quit now, I would be giving up and I wanted to beat this foe.

Your reason may be ludicrous. You may use different reasons at different times. You can use anything that works.

Put a picture of Greece on your refrigerator if your dream is to sail through those islands. I had a dog that depended on me. Find some reason for staying here. Do this on a good day and write it down so you can find it when the darkness hits.

If I could just get through one of the painful, dark days, I had won again! I always saw a good day as one that I was above ground at nightfall. I had beat the villain - depression. I was better, stronger, more worthwhile than depression. I could do this.

*Albert Camus said it best, "In the depth of winter, I finally learned that within me there lay an invincible summer."*

## *April 27*

## Letting Silence Work For You

Frances Perkins said, "It's only when we're relaxed that the thing way down deep in all of us - call it the subconscious mind, the spirit, what you will - has a chance to well up and tell us how we shall go."

If you are completely stymied, if you have no idea how to improve your health, if you feel you are at a dead end in your recovery, just sit in this state for a while.

Let go. Let completely go.

Just breathe. Let yourself just BE.

When your mind is unfettered and allowed to float and drift aimlessly, it is miraculous how so very often, this little niggling thought, a beam of light, the whisper of an idea bubbles up to the surface of our thoughts and you get this terrific insight.

But, if you are cluttering your thinking pathway with television and conversations and even reading, the process of insight is blocked.

You have nothing to lose by trying this.

Just let go and be.

*"Love yourself first and everything else falls into line. You really have to love yourself to get anything done in this world."*
*Lucille Ball*

## *April 28*

## Mind Over Matter

"The muscles of the soul are the tools we use to help dismantle and remove the roadblocks of life" says Brian Luke Seaward in *Stressed is Desserts Spelled Backward*. In this instance, Dr. Seaward is talking about how he exercised those spiritual muscles (particularly faith and humor) growing up with two alcoholic parents.

The muscles of the soul can be used against depression, too. Sometimes this is all we are going to have when we hit the utter depths. It will be your spiritual muscles that will hold you together. Keep you from tipping over the precipice. Keep your head above the turbulent water of despair.

Faith in yourself. Faith in a future. Faith that you have survived this pain before and that you can do it again. Faith that new medications and treatments are being developed daily. Faith that others have made it through this storm and you will, too.

Humor is a great spiritual muscle, but one I have to find outside of myself in the dismal days. One chuckle is all it takes to turn the tide somedays. And you are strong enough to exercise this muscle. It really is only mind over matter.

I wholeheartedly support all spiritual belief systems, but for me, prayer is a spiritual muscle that I would collapse without. And sometimes the form of that prayer is begging and screaming.

Exercise your spiritual muscles. I promise: this WILL make you stronger.

*Hunches can be angels nudging us in the right direction.*

## *April 29*

## Now I Know Why I Need To Isolate –

The lesson finally came home this morning. I was so barely here - fighting to make myself get up and take the supplements and medications that might turn this depression around and make at least a few hours of the day bearable.

I was alone except for my beloved dog, Shelby. And then on some odd impulse, I answered the phone when it rang. I usually can let that insistent ring move through me unnoticed. But, I picked it up this time.

What a mistake...

It was a brief conversation and one that required no more than small talk on my part. But, I suddenly heard myself as I hung up. You would have thought I was Pollyanna and the Chamber of Commerce all rolled into one! I have atypical depression and for brief periods of time - usually an hour or less- I can go from the bottom of despair into bubbly warmth and, of course, then, straight back to the bottom of despair.

But, it was the stomach-lurching drop that really caught me this time. I finally knew how much that brief five-minute conversation had actually cost me. All the reserve energy that was to get me through the day was sapped dry and back to bed I went.

No wonder I isolate. Even the briefest encounter can leach all my energy. As little as having to greet someone and explain what I am feeling (or not feeling) can do this.

Why not just respond from the flat affect of depression, you say? I don't know. I think the same thing to myself and then some automatic cheerful gene appears and I am a little ray of sunshine.

I heard a story once about Mike Wallace. It was reported that during his depressions he would have to be carried to his chair on the set - literally carried- so depressed he could not even walk. But, when the red 'on camera' light came on, he could give his report as he did every week. And at the end of his segment, he collapsed and would be carried back to his dressing room.

I can relate.

I have come from being nearly comatose to seeming perfectly normal to those around me in the twinkling of an eye. As long as it was a brief and absolutely critical event or call or meeting, I have learned to flip that switch. And then I would return to being vegetative the moment the 'performance' was over.

But, I know now that I isolate to protect myself. I can't seem to stay in the true state of my emotions when I come in contact with others during my depression cycles. Even with my doctor I will pull out the sunshine girl. Even when there is no need for me to pretend! I don't know why I do this, but I do know I can't seem to change this pattern.

So, when I isolate, it is not a negative response. It is actually the most appropriate way to deal with the pain - regardless of what others' opinion is. Finding quiet time with yourself has gotten a bad rap.

*"When someone tells me there is only one way to do things, it always lights a fire under my butt. My instant reaction is, 'I'm going to prove you wrong!'"*
*Picabo Street*

## *April 30*

## Keeping Your Lymph System Clean

Just like you have your radiator in your car or your AC unit in your home cleaned from time to time, you need to clean your lymph system occasionally.

The human lymph system is one of two regulating systems in the body. The other system - the heart - has a pump that moves vital fluid through the body. Although the lymph system covers as much (actually more) distance in the body, it has no motor like the heart to move the fluids of the lymph system through the body.

A healthy lymph system is critical to our recovery. (and everyone's health in general). Lymph is an almost clear fluid that lymph vessels, nodes and ducts produce and transport from tissues to the bloodstream. Essentially the lymph system clears our bodies of foreign material like cancer and bacteria and is a major component of the immune system.

Because of the possible toxicity of the multiple powerful drugs we take, the liver is not capable of flushing all the by-products completely from our bodies once they have been utilized. Therefore, new medications will not have an opportunity to work if your body is retaining the residue of previous medications. So, aiding the lymph system as it supports the liver is very important.

There are some simple, mindless exercises that can activate a sluggish lymph system. I own an inversion bed like athletes or dancers use that allows you to hang in a head-down position and boost the lymph system. However, these cost several hundred dollars.

Here are two exercises anyone can do:

1. Right where you are sitting now, take the thumb and fingers of one hand and starting at the wrist of the other arm, stroke firmly from the wrist to elbow three times; then, on the same arm, stroke firmly from the elbow to shoulder three times. Do the same on the other arm. This takes less than one minute to do both sides.

2. The other exercise is to stand comfortably with feet shoulder-width apart with your hands at your side. Bringing your hands up and over your head - inhale deeply; then sweep your arms down towards the floor (letting your fingertips touch the floor if you are able) - exhale. As you come up, inhale and bring your hands overhead again. Repeat. This is just standing upright with hands over your head sweeping your hands down to floor and back upright. This simple, fluid movement will cut down on colds and flu, too.

These are painless, brief exercises that will effectively create a clean slate for your medications to work in. I do these exercises daily; once a week would be acceptable.

When I talk about the layers of our recovery, this is one of those layers. Just taking a pill will not heal us. We must actively participate in our health on a variety of levels.

*"Stop. Be perfectly quiet.*
*Now listen, really listen to your body.*
*Sometimes it is telling you to move, to run, to dance.*
*And sometimes it is telling you it is time to be still, to feel your breath, to become aware of your senses again.*
*Dare to do nothing for a moment, and let your body fill the silence.*
*For only when you truly listen will your next step be the right one."*

*Fitness, May 2003*

MAY

*May 1*

## Foods to Avoid

If you are not responding to standard anti-depressant medications, you may have a quirky chemistry like mine. I have had to make numerous modifications in diet and learning what I had to avoid came the hard way for me. It was strictly trial and error until I found what my trigger foods were. And there were some really uncomfortable days in that learning curve.

Everyone will not need this information. Read on if you get headaches or sudden sleepiness or burning eyes or 'brain fog' after eating or drinking certain items.

Here are some of the major culprits that will help you clear out the adverse chemistry patterns that are keeping your medications from being effective:
*Aspartame/Equal
*MSG (also listed as hydrolyzed protein, autolyzed yeast, yeast or yeast extract, caseinate on labels)
*Food dyes (note that every major detergent manufacturer has made a dye and perfume-free alternative for the past decade; they would not be going to this effort if there was not a substantial portion of society who provide a significant market for these items); Jello, anything with cherries, popsicles, fruit juices
*Thimerosal in contact lens solutions
*Sulfites - any salad bar or cafeteria/buffet food

Try to eat organic foods (if you can afford these) as the fertilizers and pesticides are one more chemical burden you don't need.

Watch frozen dinners and prepackaged foods as the list of preservatives should be enough to frighten anyone.

Once I got my diet 'cleaned up', I started responding to the medications that had not been effective for me previously. The small sacrifices I had to make were nothing compared to the relief I benefitted from.

*"They say time changes things,*
*but you actually have to change them yourself."*
*Andy Warhol*

## *May 2*

## Looking at Your Life ~ Part One

Sometimes it does wonders to step back and look at your life in terms of accomplishments and goals and dreams. Take a sheet of paper (seriously, go get a piece of paper and do this) ~ and just write everything you do and have done of value. Are you a good son/daughter/wife/sister/nephew/granddaughter, neighbor, volunteer, listener, cheerleader for those who need some cheering up, follow-through person, organizer (of people or things or both), inventor, instigator of family reunions, picnics, charity participation?

Are you or have you been a trustworthy colleague ~ not only responsible, but punctual, honest? Do you bring levity and humor to a room? Are you thoughtful? Are you the one who remembers to send the birthday card, organize the party, visits friends at home or in the hospital, calls to hear the test results? Are you creative? Do you bring a novel way of seeing the world to those around you?

Ever been a Boy/Girl Scout? A leader? Choir member? Any sports in your past or present? Can you play a musical instrument? Are you handy with a hammer or saw? Do you paint? When you send a sympathy card, can you write exactly what soothes the receivers' heart?

No matter how useless today may find you feeling, you are NOT useless. Depression skews our vision and especially our self-perception. Take the time to write what your unique contribution to the world is. Stick this in your Daytimer or somewhere you can reread it from time to time. Update it on your birthday every year. It pays big dividends to actually acknowledge our growth in writing.

*"Optimism is essential to achievement and it is also the foundation of courage and true progress."*
*Nicholas Murray Butler*

## *May 3*

## Forcing Yourself Ahead

There were days when I raged. Raged at God for giving me this unbalanced chemistry. Raged at any innocent clerk who had the misfortune to cross my path that day. Raged at the unfairness of hurting so much - plus, being in debt and overweight and whatever else was wrong with me at the time. Raged and raged and raged.

I am not talking angry here. This is a white-hot furnace that blisters before you can even get near enough to make contact. This is a blaze that consumes. This is a fire that can destroy.

But, I dealt with this in one of two ways. I could not dampen this heat - it was useless to try. I knew from past experience that I had two choices:

a. I could use this heat as fuel; see it as energy to motivate me to finding my next step in healing

or

b. I could ignore it (sleep it off) until this fire burnt itself out.

You might be capable of finding another resource for rage. Or this feeling may not be one of the characteristics of your illness.

*"Let us not look back in anger or forward in fear, but around us in awareness."*

*James Thurber*

## *May 4*

## **Positive Affirmations to Change Perspective**

*"You may celebrate your journey by embracing the gifts AND the lessons, thereby generating the life of your dreams."*

*"May you claim the beauty of your gifts and talents as you design a new life of your dreams. Use your energy consciously."*

*www.sylviasays.com*

There is a benefit to having survived depressive cycles for months and years on end. The sheer 'knowing-ness' that we can do it.

Medical statistics bear this out. The longer someone survives multiple depressive cycles, the less likelihood of completed suicides. The gut-knowledge that we can do it is powerful indeed.

We can remember all too clearly the anguish of prior depressions - and we lived through those. So, there is no reason we can't survive this current phase as well.

I have found that if I take pictures or document in some fashion the happier phases - whether by journaling or a quote on my bulletin board - when in the midst of the deep pain, I can see that living was good and worth getting through this dark phase to get back to those happier times.

The two affirmations above really anchored me in what I was looking toward.

*"Never talk defeat. Use words like hope, belief, faith, victory."*
*Norman Vincent Peale*

## *May 5*

### Looking At Your Life ~ Part Two

Every single person on earth needs dreams and goals. Do you know the difference between these?

A dream is something remarkable ~ possible, but unlikely. I have dreamed of running a marathon - or even a half-marathon. Didn't even get to the training stage for that one. But, I did run a 9.3 mile race in my thirties.

A dream keeps our hopes up and our vision way out toward the horizon. We can't dream and look at our feet. We look up and ahead and visualize what could be if all conditions dovetail.

A goal is a line drawn in the sand. It can be done. Goals sound like this: I want to own my own home by the time I am thirty; I want to learn to play the piano; I want to move my parents closer to my family; I want to make exercise a habit.

Once I was told to write down my goals for six months, one and five years. Because I was in a superficial, materialistic chapter of my life - my goals were to own a condo in the country club area I was renting in, to have a winter tan, to own a Mercedes and a mink coat. (I told you I was shallow!) And every one of these goals was mine in three years. Have you tried this? I have made this type list several times and been stunned at the results when I make a real commitment to success.

What do you want? What do you need in your life that is not there today? Write it down and commit to it. Besides conquering depression ~ that is what we are doing in this year together. What else needs to color your life? Make your future brilliant ~ special. You are worth the effort.

*"A dream becomes a goal when action is taken toward its achievement."*

Bo Bennett

## May 6

## Going Down for the Third Time

Sometimes I felt as if I was going down for the third time, as they say about drowning folks. But, these little aphorisms were the life lines that kept me afloat through many a dark hour...

"When you can't go on any further, go as far as you can - when you get there you will be able to see further." Unknown

"We are supposed to forgive everyone; everyone includes ourself." Unknown

"Tough times never last, tough people do." Robert Schuller

"When you hoist the sail of faith, it is the wind, not the sail, that counts." Unknown

*"Always bear in mind that your own resolution to succeed is more important than any other one thing."*

Abraham Lincoln

## May 7

## A Description of Depression

"You're tired." ...
"I'm unhappy. It's different." ...
"It feels the same to me now...tiredness and unhappiness feel like the same thing now. I often feel as if I am tired, and of course I do work

very hard; I work and I drive myself to work harder. But, this feeling of weariness, of being beaten before I'm started, of having too much to do and no ability to do it all – this isn't real tiredness at all. I know it because I feel the same when I wake up in the morning. Even if I sleep from ten at night till ten in the morning, I still wake up feeling tired. It's not that I am tired out, it is that I am worn out. I'm not exhausted by effort, I am exhausted at the thought of effort. I don't want morning to come. I don't want the day to start. I want to sleep the rest of my life away. If I could go to sleep and never wake up at all – I would."

Phillipa Gregory from *Zelda's Cut*

I include this very accurate description of depression - not to further depress you - but, to help give expression to what you are experiencing. I never seem able to tell others how depression feels. This does a good job.

*"Hope is necessary in every condition. The miseries of poverty, sickness and captivity would, without this comfort, be insupportable."*

*Samuel Johnson*

*May 8*

## The Inner Expert

"Just knowing" or "subjective knowing" as described by Mary F. Belensky, Blythe M. Clinchy, Nancy R. Goldberger and Jill M. Tarule in an article by this name gives credence to what we already know but are afraid to claim.

"There's a part of me that I didn't even realize I had until recently - instinct, intuition, whatever. It helps me and protects me. It's perceptive and astute. I just listen to the inside of me and I know what to do."

From *Women's Ways of Knowing: The Development of Self, Voice and Mind* by these same women.

If a physician comes highly recommended but, your gut is in a knot every time you have an appointment, listen to the knot.

If you are told that having handfuls of your hair fall out is not a side effect of your medication, believe the handfuls of hair.

If you feel better after just three days on a new medication that has a typical delayed onset of four to six weeks, trust the feeling better.

Once you learn to listen to your "inner expert", no one will be able to convince you they know what is better for you than you do.

*"It is always with excitement that I wake up in the morning wondering what my intuition will toss up to me, like gifts from the sea. I work with it and rely on it. It's my partner."*
*Jonas Salk*

## *May 9*

## Do Only What Is Necessary

I hope this makes you laugh. What I consider necessary is a bit odd.

But, when I am depressed, I CAN only do what is necessary. If I am at the very depth of the black hole, using the bathroom is my only necessity. It is NOT eating, not answering the phone, not going to work, not bathing, not putting on make-up (or shaving for you men), not reading, writing, doing housework - nope. Just answering nature's call.

If the depression is not that severe, I can add in eating and bathing.

Another level up and I can begin to care about my appearance. I can make my bed.

And so on. But, when I am depressed, I do only what is necessary FOR ME. I have no interest in other folks' agenda for me. I know what I am capable of and that is all that I do.

*"The work goes on, the cause endures, the hope still lives and the dreams shall never die."*
*Edward Kennedy*

## *May 10*

## More Beach Insights

Here I am using the ocean again as my therapy.

The tide is never static. Even though this is a fact as old as eternity, I just got it on a soul level recently.

But, moreover, I REALLY got it.

The tide is always rising or falling. It is either coming in or going out. Always. In or out.

It is never just the tide - a line on the shore. And so is life and so is my depression. It is never just static. It is either coming or going.

If I can apply this simple philosophy to my cycles, I can determine where I am in it and use one of these tools I have learned to actually 'turn the tide', so to speak and move at least incrementally to a better place.

Unlike meteorologists however, there is not a table I can follow. I have to be able to assess for myself where my tide is. Learning to be attuned to how your unique chemistry works is critical in our recovery.

But, it is fluid. Depression is a cycle like the tide and is always moving. You WILL NOT stay here.

*"Time and tide wait for no man. A pompous and self-satisfied proverb, and was true for a billion years; but in our day of electric wires and water ballast, we turn it around. Man waits not for time or tide."*

*Mark Twain (suffered from depression)*

## *May 11*

## Bookstores – Free Therapy

Okay. I will confess. I am a bibliophile. And a really bad one, too. When I recently moved from Atlanta, I gave away five hundred plus books and in my most recent move, I divested myself of at least three hundred more. Now, I am down to the core two hundred that I use and refer to constantly.

I think one of the reasons I have two degrees in English was because I would get paid for doing what I love best. I would rather read than eat. That is saying a lot for me.

The quaintness, charm and unique odor of bookstores calls to me like a siren song. I can drift for hours in a bookstore. I think I could live in a Barnes and Noble store: they have clean bathrooms, coffee and sandwiches, and books - lots and lots of books. Why leave?

Do you have the same passion for music? Do music stores resonate with you like this? Are you a DIY kind of person who lives for Home Depot and Lowe's? Are nurseries with their plants of brilliant color and endless possibility a refuge for you?

If you can browse and dream and leave the wallet/purse in your car, these are havens for us. The distraction of a few enchanted hours can be strong medicine against the early stages of depression.

*"A room without books is like a body without a soul."*
*Cicero*

## *May 12*

## Feeling Like a Weenie

When the depression cycles entered my life in my mid-twenties, I also experienced a lowering of my pain threshold. I never have been terribly stoic, but my ability to withstand pain diminished.

I believe that so much of the psychic energy I use to cope with the depression is used up, there is little left over for the normal aches and pains.

I have no solution for this. But, I do give myself credit for coping with a greater pain and not necessarily becoming weaker.

Scientists are now proving this pain threshold theory with several discoveries. Substance P is being studied as well as other pain modulators.

So, if you feel pain more intensely during your depressions, you are not a weenie. There has been a chemical shift in your body.

*"Don't waste life in doubt and fears; spend yourself on the work before you, well assured that the right performance of this hour's duties will be the best preparation for the hours and ages that will follow it."*

*Ralph Waldo Emerson*

## *May 13*

### HPA Axis

Much of the latest research involves the mechanisms of the hypothalamus-pituitary- adrenal (HPA) axis of the brain. These three inter-related organs control virtually all hormone activity, energy expenditure of the body and nervous system activity.

It appears that much of the problems with depression and other neurological disorders begin with this area of the brain.

And one of the primary ways this sensitive area of brain regulation can become unbalanced is due to stress. Any stress that continues for longer than a few minutes will generate elevated cortisol levels in the body. Too much cortisol wreaks havoc on memory, sleep and concentration. Heart damage is linked to excessive levels of cortisol.

We are so fortunate in that we can remedy this issue on our own with no medical intervention.

One of the best gifts you can give yourself - and this applies to everyone - is to expose yourself to as little stress as possible. That may mean changing jobs, limiting your exposure to individuals who bring tension with them wherever they go, living a lifestyle that you cannot afford, etc...And then, exercise - even walking for fifteen minutes - is the best remedy here. Periods of just brief exercise will pull elevated cortisol levels back down into normal range.

Many of the medications and treatments in Phase Two and Three FDA development at this time focus on the HPA axis. In the meantime, by keeping your stress at a minimum and adding small bits of exercise to your daily routine, you will be able to help maintain equilibrium in this area of your brain.

*"The brain is a monstrous, beautiful mess. Its billions of nerve cells – called neurons – lie in a tangled web that displays*

*cognitive powers far exceeding any of the silicon machines we have built to mimic it."*

*William F. Allman, Apprentices of Wonder: Inside the Neural Network Revolution*

## *May 14*

## Level Two

I always mentally rate my depression on a scale of one to ten - one being near death and ten being euphoria. So, Level Two is pretty bad.

You may want to xerox this and post it on the inside of your bathroom cabinet door for those emergency days. Here is the short form for pulling yourself from the bottom of the black hole:

1. clear the slate (no work, no appointments, no meetings, no car pool, etc...)
2. change your chemistry (See January 6, August 5, August 10, August 14, December 15, December 30)
3. sleep/nap
4. do not answer the phone
5. eat any carbohydrate you crave

DO NOT -

1. defend your actions or mood
2. put others first - this is Intensive Care and YOU are the patient

This is it. Short and sweet.

*"The mind is its own place, and in itself, can make heaven of Hell, and a hell of Heaven."*
*John Milton*

*May 15*

## Ocean Therapy – Perspective and Repetition

If I can get near saltwater, I feel a lift in my mood immediately.

One day recently I was sitting with my chair half in the water. This is a new habit for me - I used to keep my chair high and dry like a responsible, good girl would. But, then a friend went with me one day and insisted we get right IN the water. What a difference!

The occasional waves cooled our feet. I'd never noticed how hypnotic the waves were sitting farther away.

I'd like to find out more about this. It felt like the waves and my heartbeat were in sync. Maybe not, but it felt as if some massive force was supporting my heart so that it need not work so hard and carry the whole responsibility of keeping me alive alone.

But, what was most apparent to me after awhile, was how the seeming sameness of the waves - was really just the repetitiveness lulling me sleepily. The rhythm and repetitiveness of many activities can creat a 'zone', if you will, of peace for us (bike riding, swimming, jumping rope, whatever,...)

What does this have to do with depression?

For me, a lot.

When anxiety overwhelms me, nothing soothes like the seashore. The waves are analogous to our illness in that when it seems the pain will crash over and drown us, there comes a lull.

Not putting restraints on myself is another lesson here. Just the difference in perspective of sitting IN the water was terrific.

Try experimenting. If you are land-locked why not take a blanket out in the back yard on a nice night and star gaze? If you are near the mountains, you can hike, picnic, climb waterfalls, horseback ride. When is the last time you rode a bike? My old coaster brake bike instantly takes me back to being twelve. I love the wind on my face and the speed at which I can see life. Treat yourself to a twenty-five cent bottle of bubbles.

Create play therapy for yourself. Childhood fun is fabulously healing. If you can't build sandcastles by the ocean, find a friend to hula hoop with or toast marshmallows and light sparklers with. Leave the adult restraints behind and love life for a minute. Everyone needs to schedule some joy into their life now and then.

*"The happiness that is genuinely satisfying is accompanied by the fullest exercise of our faculties and the fullest realization of the world in which we live."*

*Bertrand Russell*

## *May 16*

## Medical Breakthroughs

*Prevention* magazine in the October 2005 issue relates information about a new EEG device from Aspect Medical Systems that can help doctors determine if an anti-depressant is working after only 48 hours. Rather than the six to eight week period needed to tell if the medication is effective, this simple, non-invasive test shows 75% accuracy and could be available by 2007.

Instead of the agonizing four to six weeks onset of many anti-depressants, doctors would be able to bypass this long ramp up time by a simple blood test.

The November 2005 issue of *Oprah* magazine includes an article on a controversial new device to treat resistant depression. Called a VNS implant (Vagus Nerve Stimulator), this was originally approved for epilepsy in 1997. This would benefit the twenty percent (over four million) of depressives who do not respond to any protocols available today. The tiny wires of the VNS shoot electrical impulses to the vagus nerve in the neck which then leads to areas of the brain that regulate mood.

There has never been a 'better' time to have depression. The amount of money being spent on research guarantees constant innovations and better options. One of these is bound to work for YOU.

*"There are ill discoverers that think there is no land when they see nothing but sea."*

*Sir Francis Bacon*

*May 17*

## The Miracle of Touch

The skin is our largest organ. And it can play an enormous role in our recovery. Just below the surface of the outer layer of skin are the millions of touch receptors that inform us of our environment through pain, heat, cold, pressure and contact. Thirty-five years ago Dr. Ronald from McGill University announced his discovery that touch can alter the Gate Theory of pain and tension transmission by releasing those feel-good endorphins.

Here is where you can find relief: the brief scrub of a bath or shower will lift your spirits as will a massage (these can be dollars well-spent if you don't have a partner), hugs, pets to pet and sex. I used to love to hold my mother's hand ~ in church, in the car, watching a movie. This strained her Scandinavian restraint, but it made me feel better. Reach out and touch someone.

*"I tell the person I won't take a picture or sign the autograph, but I will shake their hand. That kind of personal touch is what they're really seeking."*

*Chevy Chase*

*May 18*

## Disclosing Too Soon

I like to have any new person get to know me before I disclose that I suffer from depression.

By the time an individual has gotten to know that I am warm, caring, thoughtful, generous, competent - the depression is just another aspect of me - not my identifying feature.

Beware of labeling yourself too soon. Let others get to know you. Then, in the normal course of developing your friendship, this will come out. Or not. Some people may never need to know.

Just go slow at first.

"The world is round and the place which may seen like the end may be the beginning."

Ivy Baker Priest

## May 19

# Disorders of Sleep

The journal, *Neurological Disorders,* has several articles concerning healthy and disordered sleep. It has been found that some people function well on as little as one hour of sleep while others require ten to twelve hours.

You know by your own experience that a good night's rest is one of the most effective medicines around. And the converse is true... how miserable we are when sleep-deprived.

Besides sleep apnea, there is Upper Airway Restrictive Syndrome. Sleep apnea is when a person actually stops breathing during sleep and then is wakened and goes back to sleep - this can cycle over and over again - often without ever remembering these episodes the next day. UARS is when an individual's throat or nasal passages are swollen or their tongue lies back across their airway so that oxygen is not adequately filling the lungs. Both of these are treatable and recognized by insurance companies.

If you suspect that bad sleep is exacerbating your depression, your doctor can schedule a sleep study at a hospital that has a sleep lab (most do).

Alleviating this one problem could substantially change your depression for the better. Even fixing this one factor could help you tolerate or utilize medications.

"Life is something that happens when you can't get to sleep."

Fran Lebowitz

*May 20*

## A Good Day in Hell

Okay. Here is how those bottom of the barrel days look to me.

The anguish is nearly unbearable. No wonder suicide is such a component with depressives.

There have been dozens of psychiatrists, scads of medication trials over many years and thousands - if not, hundreds of thousands - of dollars spent in search of a way out of this pain.

So, the rage and frustration are enormous. Gigantic. I feel like I am choking on them.

It is impossible to see a healthy, happy future ahead.

But, the essence of this book - the primary thought to keep above all else - is that if I can make it through today, I still have a chance. I can turn this around. I can create longer and longer distances between these black holes and I can shorten and shorten the depth I reach.

This is Scarlett O'Hara's theory in practice - "Fiddle dee dee. I won't think about that today. I will think about that tomorrow. Tomorrow is another day."

And sometimes that is the best I can do.

*"Travel has no longer any charm for me. I have seen all the foreign countries I want to except heaven and hell and I have only a vague curiosity about one of those."*
*Mark Twain*

*May 21*

## Internet Scams

In big, bold headlines it reads:

"CONQUER STRESS, DEPRESSION, ANXIETY AND PANIC QUICKLY, NATURALLY & PERMANENTLY WITHOUT TAKING DRUGS OR OTHER EXPENSIVE MEDICATIONS"

There follows the personal testimonial of the individual who has not only found the solution for these troubles, but is willing to share it with you! As you continue reading for thirteen hyperbolic pages, you will be entertained with reassurances and testimonials.

You are able to purchase this online e-book for one-time rate of $19.95 (a savings of $15) for that week only! It was surprising to me that after finding this offer on April 7, 2005, each time I check back in, that ONE WEEK ONLY !! special is still being offered.

When the agony of depression is ruining your life, it is only human to want relief however you can find it. But, it will be your wallet that is lighter - not your mood if you fall for these ridiculous promises.

If it seems too good to be true, then it is.

*"The very first law in advertising is to avoid the concrete promise and cultivate the delightfully vague."*
*Bill Cosby*

## *May* 22

## Andy Rooney Wisdom

Let these thoughts lead you where they may today:

Just one person saying to me, "You've made my day!" makes my day.

Being kind is more important than being right.

I can always pray for someone when I don't have the strength to help him or her in some other way.

No matter how serious your life requires you to be, everyone needs a friend to act goofy with.

Sometimes all a person needs is a hand to hold and heart to understand.

Life is like a roll of toilet paper. The closer it gets to the end, the faster it goes.

We should be glad God doesn't give us everything we ask for.

It's those small daily happenings that make life so spectacular.

Under everyone's hard shell is someone who wants to be appreciated and loved.

Life is tough, but I am tougher.

When you harbor bitterness, happiness will dock somewhere else.

I can't choose how I feel, but I can choose what I do about it.

Everyone wants to live on top of the mountain, but all the happiness and growth occurs while you're climbing it.

It is best to give advice in only two circumstances; when it is requested and when it is a life-threatening situation.

Andy Rooney quotes

"Life is the only real counselor; wisdom unfiltered through personal experience does not become a part of the moral tissue."
Edith Wharton

## *May 23*

## Beck's Depression Inventory

I assume too many times that because I have forced myself to learn everything I can about depression, that others have done the same. So, I assume that you are familiar with this most common of assessment tools for our illness. But, I want to include information about Beck's Depression Inventory so at least you have a way to quantify your level of depression for your own information.

There does not exist a blood test, nor an x-ray nor a lab test of any kind that can definitively diagnose depression. It is only through questioning our history that a beginning can be made.

And Beck's Depression Inventory is the yardstick most physicians and therapists use. An individual with a sixth grade reading ability can 'self-report' (i.e. answer) the twenty one questions in about ten minutes. The answers can then be added to give some kind of range of depression. This is a fairly reliable test (and I mean that in the professional statistician sense as well) that was devised in 1961 and copyrighted since 1978.

The interpretations are a great way for you to monitor your own level of current mood:

| | | |
|---|---|---|
| sadness | guilt | social withdrawal |
| pessimism | indecisiveness | |
| sense of failure | change in body image | |
| dissatisfaction | irritability | episodes of crying |
| loss of appetite | somatic preoccupation | |
| low level of energy | loss of weight | dislike of self |
| fatiguability | suicidal ideation | |

It is apparent some of these are outdated as we now know depression can be apparent through weight gain. Also, no single person will manifest all these symptoms all the time.

So, with scores ranging from zero to sixty-three, those below nineteen would be considered either normal or in mild to moderate depression; scores of 19-29 would indicate moderate to severe depression and thirty to sixty-three would mean severe depression.

Keep in mind that depression is a 'fluid' illness much like diabetes. The level will change daily and even hourly.

You might want to Google Beck's Depression Inventory and take this simple test to gauge your current mood status.

*"Mental health problems do not affect three or four out of every five persons but one out of one."*

*William Menninger*

*May 24*

## Women and Water Retention

I hate to be sexist here, but I have never heard a man complain about water retention. It appears to be a hormonal imbalance for me. But, it took me years to figure it out. I found such huge relief when I treated the water retention that accompanied the very worst of the depressions. Sometimes the sluggishness I felt from the depression was aggravated by water retention and at least I could do something about that.

Lasix is a common prescription diuretic. I fear the rebound affect of this medication, so I have found a good quality parsley supplement that does wonders for me.

It will usually take three or four of these capsules to notice the benefits. But there is NO rebound water retention from parsley.

I like the kidney cleansing help of juniper berry supplements and occasionally add some of these if I feel water logged.

I don't know that water retention is universal in depression. I have never had a single doctor inquire about it - even when I complained of feeling swollen or how bloated my face looked. Maybe this will only be effective for those who have concurrent hormonal troubles as well.

For me, I have to supplement my standard prescription medication with diuretics in the severe cycles. Maybe this will help you, too.

"I do not want the peace that passeth understanding.
I want the understanding that bringeth peace."
Helen Keller

## May 25

## Understanding Personal Growth

"...I suddenly have this gagging sensation that says I have everything I was TOLD I SHOULD WANT, but that's a far cry from what I really desire! It's hard for most women to state what they want, because they've gotten used to wanting only what's available.

At least I am beginning to see what I NO LONGER WANT: things like making life pleasant for others while forgoing my own desires..."
Joan Anderson, *A Year by the Sea: Thoughts of an Unfinished Woman*

Women have been taught to think of others first. If you are fighting depression, then you must erase this philosophy that has been hammered into your marrow. You must be resilient when others put their desires first and turn your focus back on yourself.

If you don't heal yourself, you are worthless to others anyway.

Be selfish. Now is YOUR time.

"About sacrifice and the offering of sacrifices, sacrificial animals feel quite differently from those who look on: but, they have never been allowed to have their say."

Frederich Nietzesche

## May 26

### Moving Into Your Heart

When your mind is in your heart, you are happy.

Chinese proverb

I have found when my mind is in the dark depths of depression, I can sometimes bypass that pain and move my attention to my heart. My heart is full of love and I can put all my energy into feeling that love.

If I am able, I will do something for someone in my family. I will write to my nieces or go shopping for something just for them. I will ALWAYS feel better when I get home.

Or I will sit and hold and stroke the soft fur of my beloved dog, Shelby.

I will look through boxes of old photos and the rush of joy in these memories is like the best endorphin surge in the world.

If I can move out of my mind - even if only for an hour - I can turn a bad day around. It happens everytime.

"If you have love in your life it can make up for a great many things that you lack. If you don't have it, no matter what else there is, it's not enough."

Ann Landers

## May 27

### Abandoning Yourself to the Depression

"The most difficult circumstances lead us to the edge of the void, what I refer to as the 'emptying process'; winter in the seasons of the soul....If there is a lesson to be learned through moments of loss, it is to grieve fully, and then move on."

Dr. Brian Luke Seward, *Desserts is Stressed Spelled Backward*

I hope you hear what I am about to say to you: sometimes the best remedy for depression is to fall into it headlong. With complete abandon. Wallow in it. Roll in the mud of what the depression feels like. Not only feel, but savor every painful breath. Do not censor one negative thought. Highlight and magnify every self-pitying image. Gloat over how much worse your suffering is than that of the crowded masses. Glorify your need for relief. Have at it. Full bore. Have the very best depression you can. For if 'the pain is in the resistance' as the old aphorism goes, the relief from pain is in NOT resisting.

Try this from time to time. Sometimes it may be your only way out.

"Reality leaves a lot to the imagination."
John Lennon

## May 28

## Finding Your True Center

"So much of you is waking up," she adds. "I see you bubbling all over the place - you're yeasty and I think it's grand!"

"You must have been so careful with what you did and said in your former life, so as to stifle the very essence of you. No wonder you're here and in a hurry... You are never free to do as you please when you stay with the familiar."
Joan Anderson, *A Year By the Sea: Thoughts of an Unfinished Woman*

"I desire so to conduct the affairs of this administration that if at the end, when I come to lay down the reins of power, I have lost every other friend on earth, I shall at least have one friend left, and that friend shall be down inside me."
Abraham Lincoln

Find what YOU need to do. What will make YOU feel better? What will it take for you to thrive in this life? Be utterly self-centered - now.

"Believe nothing just because a so-called wise person said it. Believe nothing just because a belief is generally held. Believe nothing just because it is said in ancient books. Believe nothing just because it is said to be of divine origin. Believe

*nothing just because someone else believes it. Believe only what you yourself test and judge to be true." (paraphrased)*
*Buddha*

## *May 29*

## A Prayer for the Tough Days

I wish I knew who to credit this poem/prayer to. What a message from the heart....

"Dear God,
I feel such pain, anxiety, and depression.
I know this is not Your will for me, and yet my mind is held in such chains by fear and paranoia
I surrender my life, right now, to You.
Take the entire mess, all of it, now too complicated to explain to anyone, but known by You in each detail.
Do what I cannot do.
Lift me up.
Give me a new chance.
Show me a new light.
Make me a new person.
Dear God,
This depression frightens me.
Dear God,
Please bring me peace.
Amen."

*"Far away there in the sunshine are my highest aspirations. I may not reach them but I can look up and see their beauty, believe in them, and try to follow them."*
*Louisa May Alcott*

## *May 30*

## Desperate For Information

Frantic might describe my approach to finding a solution to the agony that depression caused me. I have gone to some odd lengths to find relief.

Having access twice in my life to a medical school library, I would simply fake my way in and start reading abstracts. I could at least find hope that great research was being done to heal depression through the medical community and often, I would discover something that I could incorporate immediately into my life that would help (supplementing with lecithin is a good example of this).

Now, that the Internet is a tool available to all of us, I can approach the search engines with relatively vague queries and be directed to multiple sites. I particularly like Google as I have yet to fail with them. You can type in everything from anti-depressants in clinical trials to side effects of Zoloft to use of multiple anti-depressant medications.

For me, information was hope. There was always some new slant or another approach I could take to beating this illness.

I also am solution-oriented in my life in general. I wanted answers.

What I have found is that there is not ONE definitive answer - the magic bullet I longed for. But, there were many smaller pieces I could use to build a recovery. And the more I learned, the more in control I felt of this disease.

*"Science is organized knowledge. Wisdom is organized life."*
*Immanuel Kant*

## *May 31*

## Be Expectant

If you are constantly expecting better circumstances, better health, better finances, etc... you are more receptive to doors that open along your path that may lead to these resources. If you constantly expect better things in your life with ever-widening horizons, an expanding group of friends and acquaintances and ever-greater opportunities to enrich your life with monetary abundance ~ then, your vision and intent is focused on a better life in every way in whatever form that may come to you.

Be expectant. Know that the next right thing is in store for you ~ just around the corner.

"Let us be about setting high standards for life, love, creativity and wisdom. if our expectations in these area is low, we are not likely to experience wellness. Setting high standards makes every day and every decade worth looking forward to. "

Greg Anderson, The 22 Non-Negotiable Laws of Wellness

# JUNE

## *June 1*

### Avoiding Mirrors

Do you cycle fairly rapidly? I can move in and out of depression within a twelve hour period or less. And I mean an ugly, deadly level of depression.

So, it is with complete honesty that I can say that I will look totally different from one day to the next. My mother and those very close to me can spot the visual clues of depression immediately. My eyes are vacant, flat and dead. My face is pasty and bloated. I move without a shred of grace, in a loaping kind of shuffle.

It is imperative that I avoid mirrors on these days. It only serves to make me feel much worse and because it is temporary, I really don't need to be beating myself up about this.

Have you ever seen a snapshot of yourself in a depression? Do you look different? The most famous Abraham Lincoln portrait is remarkable in how visible his depression is.

Why punish yourself more on these difficult days? Just stay away from reflections until you feel like your real self again.

*"What do we call love, hate, charity, revenge, humanity, forgiveness? Different results of the master impulse, the necessity of securing one's self-approval."*
*Mark Twain*

## *June 2*

### Even Hotlines Are Not Perfect

The volunteers of all crisis hotlines are required to do many hours of awareness and sensitivity training. They may be a lifeline when you need someone at 3 o'clock in the lonely morning. But, even hotlines are fallible.

I have heard of someone getting hung up on. Do you need rejection from a stranger at a time like this? And another person told of getting all kinds of unsolicited medical advice.

It is fine to rely on hotlines for a crisis - but, they are not a long term solution. Make certain your expectations are in line with what they can provide.

Make certain that you have found support in enough areas that if you need to talk to someone, you have asked permission to call at any time of day of at least three people. That way, if a hotline counselor does not meet your needs, you are not without options.

The people who will be great for this aid are either truly good friends or folks you meet in support groups. If you assure them that this would be strictly a crisis situation and not a regular thing, most people are agreeable. In the decades I have fought depression, I have only felt this need one time. But, that one time was absolutely crucial to my survival. Create this safety net for yourself. Hopefully you will never need it.

*"Friendship is born at that moment when one person says to another: "What! You, too? I thought I was the only one."*
*C.S. Lewis*

*June 3*

## Exaggerating

I don't know that this is a tool at all. But, I want to admit that I use this. Maybe someone else will identify with it and not feel so guilty about using it. I still use it and I still feel guilty when I do. But, it has served me well a time or two and that makes it eligible for my 'toolbox'.

I will exaggerate my pain sometimes. I knowingly and purposefully do this. It's like saying I have a migraine rather than a headache. Sometimes the pain that accompanies the depression is so unbearable, I have no words to say to another person to express how severe the pain is. I think that is one of the greatest comforts I receive from attending support groups. When I talk about the 'take your breath away' kind of pain of depression, the nods of agreement around the room let me know that at least one other person knows the depth of the feeling I am trying to explain.

I was trying to tell my mother once how suicide could feel like such a reasonable alternative to me when the pain is this great. And bless her heart, she said so motherly, "Where exactly does it hurt, Connie?". It hurts EVERYWHERE when you are depressed.

So, if you are in need of telling someone what you are feeling and you cannot find the words, I tell you - exaggerate. Even then, they won't have but an inkling of how great the pain is.

*"The world is full of suffering. It is also full of overcoming it."*
*Helen Keller*

## *June 4*

## Hallelujah for Doughnuts!!!

I really hate to think of how many times I have gotten a half dozen of the biggest, fluffiest doughnuts to inhale and medicate with. Way too many for my own good. And even now, there will be that insatiable craving and I will have one or two.

But, I learned that it isn't always the doughnuts that my body wants. My very dear friend, Kathy, told me long ago, that when you crave yeast products (bread, doughnuts, etc...), your body is usually deficient in B complex vitamins.

Well, low and behold, that was the truth! It takes about three or four weeks to get your body back in balance after you start taking B complex. And it MUST be a high quality one. No drugstore or GNC-type vitamins will do. But, you will find that the cravings for yeasty foods abates. And you become calmer. About everything. This is a real anxiety killer. And once you are back in sync, maybe you only need to take this supplement two or three times a week (always take vitamins in the morning and minerals in the afternoon). But, as soon as those raised, glazed doughnuts start dominating your thoughts, give in briefly, but step up your B complex intake immediately.

A point to be noted: B complex vitamin is unique in that for B-6 to work for water retention or allergic responses or B-12 for energy or B-5 (Pantothentic acid) for digestive support - all the B complex must be ingested at the same time. In other words, take a complete spectrum B complex to get the benefits of the individual B's.

And vitamins aren't even fattening!

"Part of the secret of a success in life is to eat what you like and let the food fight it out inside."

Mark Twain

## June 5

# Find Your Funny Bone

What makes you chuckle? What makes you laugh out loud? I am not hard to entertain. I can laugh at the schtick of Groucho Marx *You Bet Your LIfe* reruns as well as the crudeness of *MAD TV*. I love the sometimes subtle puns - sometimes outrageousness of any of the decades of *SNL*. I truly *"LOVE LUCY"*. I have seen some episodes over a dozen times. And the squishing grapes or Vega-vita-veggie machine shows still make me laugh.

I found some videos through the *Wireless* catalog for old *George and Gracie* shows (actually called The George Burns Show but, he knew as well as we did that it was Gracie that was the star). I also bought their Red Skelton, Milton Berle, Three Stooges anthologies. I can watch reruns of Andy and Barnie and Opie every day.

I have seen *The Birdcage* four times and continue to howl at Gene Hackman giving a press conference hanging from an escape ladder at the side of his house.

Certain cartoons from the newspaper will get my attention.

I make a supreme effort to attend any children's performance. Whether it be the ritual Nativity scene at churchs everywhere during the Christmas season or a play or recital. The wholesome candor of children always brings a smile to my heart.

I have read every book Erma Bombeck has ever written. The early Dave Barry is hilarious. And, of course, laughing at ourselves is always so healing.

Garrison Keeler is interesting as my mother hails from South Dakota. I know so many of his characters intimately. Lake Wobegone is to the end of the twentieth century what *Our Town* was to the beginning of it.

If all else fails, go to the humor section of your bookstore and browse. Or the comedy section of the video store near you.

I care not one wit about the odd glances I get when laughing til my sides hurt at the humorous greeting card section. And this one is totally a freebie.

A good laugh clears the mind and lights up the heart.

*"Laughter is an instant vacation."*
*Milton Berle*

*June 6*

## It's All In Your Perspective

This statement can be read:

"God is nowhere!"

or

"God is now here!"

*"Like everything else in my life of any significance, the way I see it always depends on how I look at it."*
*Bernadette C. Randle*

Perspective is everything. I battle this constantly.

Every time someone is rude and aggressive in their fast driving, I think to myself, "they might have just received a phone call that their child was in an accident and they are rushing to the hospital". Now, the chances of that being true are really, really slim. But, if I think of some benevolent reason for this persons' actions, I can feel my blood pressure drop. And I know, too, then that my cortisol levels are dropping and I am not doing damage to my health.

The action or trigger remains the same, but the way I see it affects me on every level.

*"We are all inclined to judge ourselves by our ideals; others by their acts."*
*Harold Nicolson*

*June 7*

## The Split Mind

It is with wonder that I realize that sometimes having unusual or different mental wirings/capacities can be a great blessing.

I have come to realize that I am coping on two different levels when at the nadir of the depression cycle. While the despair, helplessness, hopelessness has me in a death grip, I am also functioning on another level. A very lucid, slow, reasonable thought process is going on parallel to the frantic fear thinking.

The anguish is pervasive - I feel like it owns me - body and soul - literally - in the worst part of the depression cycle. But, running alongside the obsessive "it's unbearable, I can't go on like this..." thoughts are a very clear voice objectively evaluating the reality of the moment. That voice is saying" this worry is unfounded; there is not one thing different today than twenty-four hours ago when I was feeling okay", "I have a place to live, I have no pressure to be anywhere today, I can let go and wait for this to pass", "I have always come through this in the past, I will make it through this phase too", "there are new treatments and options almost daily being made available to me, I can beat this", "this too shall pass", "I know how to do this - I know what it takes to come through on the other side of this depression cyclone", etc...

I am able to hear both internal voices equally. They are the same volume and each takes equal space. The depression voice is breathless, rapid, repetitive while the voice of reason is calm, well-paced, logical and diversified.

I use what powers of focus I am able to marshal at these times and put all the attention and energy I can into the rational messages. And then, the genuine, positive thoughts do become true for me once again.

Having a split or dual mind may only be a benefit of those who suffer from depression, but I am truly grateful that I am able to hang on to sanity when insanity beckons.

*"The test of a first-rate intelligence is to hold two opposed ideas in mind at the same time and still be able to function. One should, for example, be able to see that things are hopeless and yet be determined to make them otherwise."*

*F. Scott Fitzgerald*

*(suffered depression throughout his life)*

## *June 8*

## Fearing the Unknown

"The urge to change, to grow, to evolve, burns deep within every soul, every cell, as native to us as our hunger to learn. And yet, a part of us holds back - a part that fears the unknown."

Dan Millman, *No Ordinary Moments: A Peaceful Warrior's Guide to Daily Life*

If you are not courageous now, practice courage. Take risks. Make mistakes. Move forward.

Where you are now is not acceptable. Depression is not normal. You deserve better.

*"The golden opportunity you are seeking is in yourself; it is not in your environment; it is not in luck or chance or in the help of others; it is in yourself alone."*

*Orison Swett Marden*

## *June 9*

## Brain Pain –

Doesn't this just say it all? When folks talk about gall bladder pain, we are immediately and fully aware that they are speaking of excruciating pain and that surgery with relieve their problem.

When we have depression, it is our brain that causes our pain. And headache remedies are no solution.

Brain pain is like no other. Seek any and all relief available.
Nothing in your life will function unless you deal with your depression first. There are answers - you just have to find what fixes your unique brain pain.

"Shaped a little like a loaf of French country bread, our brain is a crowded chemistry lab, bustling with nonstop neural conversations.

Imagine the brain, that shiny mound of being, that mouse-gray parliament of cells, that dream factory, that petit tyrant inside that ball of bone, that huddle of neurons calling all the plays, that little everywhere, that fickle pleasure dome, that wrinkled wardrobe of selves stuffed into the skull like too many clothes into a gym bag."

Diane Ackerman, *An Alchemy of Mind: The Marvel and Mystery of the Brain*

## June 10

## The Menninger Clinic

The brain child of a family practitioner in Topeka, Kansas has grown from humble beginnings in 1925 to ranking first or second in their classification in *U.S. News and World Report* annual survey for seven consecutive years. This fully-accredited psychiatric hospital, that moved to Houston in 2003, excels in the treatment of all forms of neurobiological disorders.

Menningers features both day/outpatient and inpatient programs. It is also a world-renowned research facility.

If you feel you have exhausted all resources in your area and you have insurance benefits, maybe this really isn't a long shot for you. Because this is a cutting-edge group, maybe they can offer you the one piece of the puzzle you are missing to return to the life you want to be living.

At this printing, their toll free number is: 800-351-9058. If you are at the end of your rope, their creed is: "Discovering hope, one life at a time." Maybe that life is yours now.

"In positive terms, we can state that psychological maturity entails finding greater satisfaction in giving that in receiving; having a capacity to form satisfying and permanent loyalties; being primarily a creative, contributing person; having learned to profit from experience; having a freedom from fear (anxiety) with a resulting true serenity and not a pseudo absence of tension; and accepting and making the most of unchangeable reality when it confronts one."

William Claire Menninger

## *June 11*

### Having Hope

*"From the wings of a darkened night, small lights of hope are born.*
*They shine of faith and belief,*
*and in their hands are*
*The hidden seeds of new beginnings."*
*Flavia*

I ALWAYS - no matter what else happens - I ALWAYS have one or two things I haven't tried in my depression research file.

Then, no matter how bleak it gets(especially in the dark early morning hours) I can always convince myself that relief is still available to me. Just one of those new treatments may be my answer.

I have heard so many people over the years tell of long struggles before finding the remedy that worked for them. And I know as many - if not more - who found relief almost immediately. Each of us will require different answers, but keep a file of news clippings, Internet references, names of clinical trial practitioners, etc..., so that you know there are options still awaiting you.

This is how I make HOPE tangible. My depression can be so loud, that unless I have done my research during the stronger times, I will believe I have nowhere to turn. And that is a place without hope.

Always have at least one more option to try.

*"Hope is the feeling that the feeling you have isn't permanent."*
*Jean Kerr*

## *June 12*

### Lying on Applications

Well, here is another one of my controversial suggestions. This is a gray area, but when you are applying for a new job, some of the questions on the application may put you in an unfavorable light.

If you are well enough to be seeking employment, then the days of the depression owning you are in the past. You are managing your illness and moving on with life.

Now is not the time to let no longer valid information hinder your future.
The Americans with Disabilities Act (ADA) was signed into law in July 1990. This legally forbids certain questions from being asked verbally or in writing during a job interview process:
age or date of birth
sex or gender
race, birthplace or national origin
marital status, dependents, or child care arrangements
arrest record
height and weight
religion
public assistance
lawful activity (like a second job)

There are gray areas within the above categories such as height or weight being critical to job performance (ex. a lineman for a utility company).

Medically related questions that may reveal a disability are the only questions that employers are specifically prohibited from asking applicants.

Answer questions from where you are currently in your life. If you are able to avoid prolonged cycles of debilitating depression, then you are as qualified as the next person for employment.

Do not over-answer. Too much information in the work place is disastrous. These are not your friends (although some may eventually become friends), these are your colleagues. Do not bring your personal issues with you on your job.

This is good advice for anyone.

"For us there is only the trying. The rest is not our business."
T.S. Eliot

*June 13*

## Zestful Living

Even before the horror of September 11, 2001 prompted many people to examine and re-examine their lives, I believe those of us who suffer 'little deaths' on a frequent and recurring basis have already searched our lives for meaning.

I have found how precious every good moment is. I know you rejoice in the moments when you escape the prison of depression, too.

When September 11 brought us to a new awakening, it only reinforced for me that life is precious. I had determined after my breakdown in 1991 that there were certain dreams I had for life and I made each of them reality. I had control over my life and potential. The depression was a factor, but so was my determination.

Write down what three things you NEED to have happen in the next five years. Write down three things you WANT to have in your life in the next five years. Do not edit these. Write what you really want. Then make it happen.

Now, if I want to drop everything and go watch the sunset, I leave the dirty dishes and go. I go joyfully. I don't censure myself and I don't let others censure me.

If I crave a blueberry milkshake, then that is what I have. No guilt over calories. I savor every drop.

If I want to have a day completely for myself, I turn the ringer on my phone off and the answering machine on and rent four or five videos. I do not explain or defend these decisions or actions. It is my life. I am the only one living it.

My nieces learned early on not to go with me to see a comedy. I laugh whole-heartedly. I laugh with my whole body and soul. It really is pretty loud.

I 'claim ' each day in my morning meditations and make sure that no matter how I spend these twenty four hours, I will be pleased or at least satisfied with this day. I am the only one accountable. I am the only one who needs to be satisfied or dissatisfied with what I have or have not accomplished.

*"All my life I wanted to be somebody. Now I see I should have been more specific."*

*Lily Tomlin*

*June 14*

## A Way to Look at Your Recovery

I love to watch clouds. First of all, if I am doing this, it means I am at a leisurely reflective moment in my life. Those are always bonuses. So, something must be going right.

But, here is a message from the clouds for us.

There are actually two messages:
1) what one person sees as a form or shape in a cloud, another cannot see for the life of them; we are unique and our perception is shared by no other person exactly.

2) the clouds are always changing, but it is so subtle as to be indiscernible. That is precisely how we recover. In increments that are not immediately evident.

You are unique. And in the next moment you will be different.

*"We're all in this alone."*

*Lily Tomlin*

*June 15*

## A Quote by St. Francis de Sales

"The same Everlasting Father, who takes care of you today, will take care of you tomorrow and everyday. He will either shield you from suffering, or give you unfailing strength to bear it. Be at peace then, and put aside all anxious thoughts and imaginations."

This thought is really about faith. Faith in big neon, brilliantly-colored, flashing lights. Bold, graphic, tangible faith.

It IS getting better. Right this minute, you are getting better. The depression is receding. You will come out of this.

Have faith that you can be well and complete again. What is that for you? Employed, thin, vigorous, energized, married, in a relationship, financially stable? What?

See your faith as a net under you, just like the tightrope walkers use. Your faith supports and undergirds you. Rely on it. Ask your Guiding Power to strengthen your faith. To make the mustard seed of faith you feel now into a granite mountain of faith. You can rest in your faith. Ease up. Let go. God is in charge.

*"It's lack of faith that makes people afraid of meeting challenges, and I believe in myself."*
*Muhammed Ali*

## *June 16*

## Another Way to Distraction

Here is one of the few ways to pass the hours of misery when we have slept all we can sleep - yes, you guessed it. Internet lurking. No one knows if you are depressed or in your undies or unwashed. You can read chat rooms, follow a path all the way through the several hundred web sites it can lead you to, you can read a novel, and you can do all this while you stay in bed all day!

Find a humor site and laugh like a hyena. Enjoy researching areas that have always intrigued you, but that you never have time to read about.

Lose yourself in the wide world of technological information. Even research alternatives to healing depression or check out medical school abstracts that detail the research that will change our lives.

This benign form of passing time can benefit you and will harm no one else.

*"The whole Internet world seems like a distraction to me."*
*Jhumpa Lahiri*

## June 17

## Are There at Least a Dozen Components to Your Recovery Package?

This is a topic I will return to again and again. No matter how effective a pill/anti-depressant may be, there are other factors that are just as critical to our recovery that must be part of our healing.

The right medication in conjunction with the right amount of restful sleep, the right amount of movement/exercise, the right amount of healthy foods, the right amount of laughter and love and friendships and joy, the right amount of nutritional supplementation, the right amount of adjunct therapies whether what works for you is massage, chiropractic, psychotherapy, hydrotherapy, or all of the above, the right amount of indulgence - whether it be Haagen-Dazs or long, long telephone calls or equally long showers or reading till 4 a.m.; the right amount of stress - that would be the minimal daily allowance - , the right amount of caffeine, the right amount of carbohydrates, the right amount of touching and being touched, the right amount of hope, the right amount of insight and information, the right amount of solitude, etc...

It takes all of this to get our health back. Not one of these tools taken alone will do the trick, but the bag of tricks in the right combination will work. Just make sure you keep your bag full of options.

Keep searching for the proper medication. This is a critical component to recovery. But, do not forget the other factors you must have for your optimal health.

*"To fly, we have to have resistance."*
*Maya Lin*

## June 18

## Breathing Exercises

A professor once taught our class this Buddhist-type breathing exercise as a calming technique. I have used it in Atlanta traffic, to get to sleep at night and when I needed to clear my thinking during a lengthy project.

The breathing pattern shifts your focus away from the stressor or situation, but also has been shown scientifically to alter brain rhythms.

Not exaggerating the breaths, but breathing normally - just breathe in to the count of one, out is count two - repeating until you get to eleven. The next cycle of breaths, one will begin the count on the exhale. Again, repeat up to eleven. When you start the next cycle, you will be back to inhaling on one.

So, it is a simple cycle of eleven breaths alternating number one as intake or exhale.

A set of three or four of these quiet cycles will bring your blood pressure down and clear your mind. I like it when my racing mind will not let me sleep. This is a fantastic way of getting your body and mind back in sync with each other.

*"Until I feared I would lose it, I did not love to read. One does not love breathing."*

*Harper Lee*

*June 19*

## Dealing With Frustration

This is a tough one.

When we are frustrated with our lack of progress - in our healing, in our career, in our financial picture - we are justifiably frustrated. We had so many plans and dreams and depression seems to have derailed us.

But, staying in this mood will only prolong our lack of progress. Look for a different approach - a way to go at the problem from a different direction.

Life is not a smooth, constantly upward trajectory - for anyone.

Let go of your tension and look for answers. There are solutions. Work at finding them.

*"The torment of human frustration, whatever its immediate cause, is the knowledge that the self is in prison, its vital force and "mangled mind" leaking away in lonely, wasteful self-conflict."*

*Elizabeth Drew*

## *June 20*

## Apathy

My doctor gave my depression a good name yesterday. Apathy.

You betch-ya.

Not giving a damn. All of life is pale, dull gray. Ice cream sundaes taste no different that rutabagas. Saturday is no better than Monday.

This is the no-life of depression. It is existing - not living.

This is unbearable.

Try any one of my suggestions - any one. One of the amino acid supplements, a support group, a walk to the mailbox, a comedy video - any spark that will light up your life again.

That is all it takes. A tiny flame will ignite your joy in life again.

But, if you stay stuck in apathy, nothing will change.

*"I have a very strong feeling that the opposite of love is not hate – it's apathy. It's not giving a damn."*

*Leo Buscaglia*

## *June 21*

## Beach Therapy Again

So, here is what the ocean told me today: the waves are never the same two times.

Pretty simple, isn't it?

Okay, so let's apply that to healing.

No two depressive cycles are ever the same. No two pains are ever the same. No two colds are ever the same. No two days are ever the same.

Yes, there are patterns to these things. But, no two individual ones are the same.

So, use this with healing your depression, by getting a grip on what THIS depression is like. Are you having head pressure with this one? Are your eyes burning? Are the broken-record suicide thoughts going through your mind? You know how to heal each of these problems.

But, first you have to see THIS depression as unique - different at least in some small way from other depressions - and look to fix THAT problem. You won't recover from all depressions the same. Sometimes you need to start at the bottom of your list of recovery tools and start backwards.

Ask yourself the inventory questions - what am I feeling/thinking at this moment? And deal with those issues.

Next time they will be different ones.

*"Progress is impossible without change, and those who cannot change their minds cannot change anything."*
*George Bernard Shaw*

## *June 22*

## Be a Human Being and Not a Human Doing

Here I am at it again. Before my feet even hit the floor this morning the list of 'to do' was already running in my head. I should.../ I need to.../ I must....

But, about the time I got the toothbrush in my mouth, I became aware of this interior monologue and started over again. Cleared the slate in my head. Okay. Now what do I really have to do today? What appointments do I have and what deadlines are out there? Get a realistic grip and work around that.

Take a big deep breath. Again.

Okay, now pacing myself, I ease into these tasks.

And I plan to schedule in some of that 'being' time. 'Down time' as some folks say. 'Hanging out' the kids say. The richness of these unstructured moments fuel all the rest of my day.

It is imperative to remember we are human be-ings - not human do-ings.

*"Some people believe that holding on and hanging in there are signs of great strength. However, there are times when it takes much more strength to know when to let go – and then do it."*
*Ann Landers*

## *June 23*

## Getting Away From What Other People Think

I probably have carried this philosophy to an extreme. I do not own a designer anything and won't wear advertising on my person. No article of my clothing is a status symbol. Not a watch or sunglasses proclaim my ability to pay exorbitant prices.

But, most of all I do not care. What you do is okay with me - but, do not force your opinions or values my way.

So, when the depression hits, I am already in the mind-set of self-care. I can focus on what needs to get done and not get done and heal myself. I can shut out what other people demand of me and I deem unnecessary. It rolls right off me.

I am not implying you should become insensitive, cold-hearted or selfish. Although on the tough days, you will need to practice healthy selfishness. (see July 13)

What I am advocating is an interest in yourself. Give yourself the same attention and courtesy you would give a friend in need. Do for yourself what you would do for them. I found out early that you will be a chameleon if you try to please all the people all the time.

*"I prefer to be true to myself, even at the hazard of incurring the ridicule of others, rather than to be false, and to incur my own abhorrence."*
*Frederick Douglass*

*June 24*

## Keeping Your Heart Open

"There is only one door handle
on the door of your heart.

Only one bolt.

They are on the inside.
Your side.

You must listen for the angel,

throw open the lock,

And open up that door."

Dottie Walters

Now this is a tough one. When we are struggling just to survive, we shut down all but the mandatory functions. This is completely reasonable.

You have to actively choose to keep your heart open to those who are trustworthy. The warmth of their love can thaw some of our frozen places and take us just one more step closer to recovery.

Keeping your heart open really can create avenues of healing. No one has enough love in their life. No one.

"If you judge people, you have no time to love them."
Mother Teresa

*June 25*

## Hope in the Future

"Dr. John Maxwell says that if there's hope in the future there is power in the present." from *Something Else to Smile About* by Zig Ziglar

When you have the black cloud of depression filling the horizon of your life, it is nearly impossible to see even a single ray of sunshine.

Believing as I do in tangible, real tools of recovery, I will plan ahead during a strong time and write down at least two dreams to live for.

On my refrigerator, I have several postcards of the dazzling white sands of Destin, Fl and I have an ad of a gorgeous bride. When I want to let go - to give up the fight - I see these pictures and remember how much I love the clean salt air of the ocean and how much I want to participate in the weddings of my nieces.

If I can focus on this, I will take the next breath and the next and eventually - no matter what - the depression will lift.

*"The future is something which everyone reaches at sixty minutes an hour, whatever he does, whoever he is."*
*C. S. Lewis*

*June 26*

## Becoming AWARE

Has anyone ever called you 'sensitive'? Might be a good thing, if they did. I always thought of it as a weakness - a fragility or slightness. Like not being able to stand up straight during a hurricane.

But, like the little skinny trees withstand fierce winds, you too can be strong and sensitive at the same time.

Being sensitive to yourself (being overly-sensitive to others is called co-dependency) is a wonderful thing. You will catch the slide into depression early and therefore avoid huge blocks of misery. You will note the doctors who really aren't connecting with you as a hurting human being and dismiss them and find someone who treats patients warmly.

By being sensitive, you will hear the lectures before they start of those who mean well but have no knowledge of what we are experiencing and turn them away before they can damage you. You will know intuitively who to share your illness with and who to fake it with.

BE AWARE. Tune in to yourself. Hear your own heart.

*"When stressed or going through a difficult time, it is essential that you take time to relax in order to replenish your*

*mind, body and spirit. Nurture your well-being by creating an oasis of calm in your life. Getting calm allows you to get a fresh perspective and helps you cope better physically and emotionally with your troubles. Being able to control at least one aspect of your life, in this case time for yourself/to yourself, helps you to get a grip on everything else."*

*Unknown*

*June 27*

## Firing Your Psychiatrist

Did you ever think you had the option to do this? You do.

If you are seeing a psychiatrist who does not:
keep appointments without advance notification
call in refills as promised
hear your concerns
return phone calls
answer questions
take your requests seriously
take your pain seriously

..then, you are seeing the wrong doctor.

You can 'fire' them by not making any further appointments, writing a letter naming your reasons for leaving, or both of the above.

What I would not do is take the expensive time of an allotted appointment to terminate your professional relationship. With the going rate of $250 - 350 an hour, there is no point in beating a dead horse if this has been an unsatisfactory relationship. This particular doctor is unable to meet your needs. Accept that and move on. There are plenty of psychiatrists who can.

*"People are so afraid of authority figures and doctors are authority figures."*

*Martha Beck*

## *June 28*

## Everyone Who Finishes Is a Winner

The first and only time I saw this slogan was in the sixth mile of a nine mile race. A much older - and I had hoped slower - man passed me confidently. I was really struggling. Every breath burned and my calves were screaming. My feet had quit feeling anything about the fifth mile.

As the sweat blurred my eyes, I glimpsed this saying in bold letters across the back of his singlet. "Everyone who finishes is a winner."

That single thought changed everything. All I had to do was finish. That alone would put me ahead of the ninety per cent of the folks who would never even attempt a race. I didn't have to do anything but put the next foot down and then the other foot ahead of it. And again. And again. And finish.

I would have enjoyed thanking this man. In fact, someone with that attitude is someone I would have liked to have gotten to know better. And I don't imagine I was the only one who benefited from his philosophy. He passed a lot of runners those last three miles and lifted many weary hearts. I know he made the difference for me.

*"The best index to a person's character is how he treats people who can't do him any good, and how he treats people who can't fight back."*

*Abigail Van Buren*

## *June 29*

## Laugh a Little

*Do you have trouble making up your mind? Well. Yes or no?
* Never argue with a fool. People might not know the difference.
* Always remember that you are absolutely unique. Just like everyone else.
* Always borrow money from a pessimist. He will never expect it back.
* I like work. It fascinates me. I sit and look at it for hours.
* Remember that if there is a will, there are five hundred relatives.
* Someday we will look back on all this and plow into a parked car.

* I'd explain it to you, but your brain would explode.
* I love deadlines. Especially the whooshing sound they make as they go flying by.
* Children seldom misquote you. In fact, they usually repeat word for word what you shouldn't have said.
*They say hard work never hurt anyone, but why take the chance?
*If Barbie is so popular, why do you have to buy her friends?
*I couldn't repair your brakes, so I made your horn louder.

*"My second favorite household chore is ironing. My first being hitting my head on the top bunk bed until I faint."*
*Erma Bombeck*

*June 30*

## Straws to Grasp

Calvin Coolidge said:

"Press on. Nothing in the world can take the place of persistence. Talent will not; nothing is more common than unsuccessful men with talent...
Education alone will not; the world is full of educated derelicts...
Persistence and determination alone are omnipotent."

Some days, it was sheer grit that got me through. I would use childish revenge to motivate me, if that is what it took. Anger would blaze brightly when I thought of how dismissive some physicians were and I would be determined to 'show them'! Or looking at photographs of really happy times, I would vow to have that life back again.

I knew what strengths I had and what I was capable of - if only I felt like getting out of bed! And it is that fighter mentality that I urge you to use - or develop if that is not a personality trait you possess now as you go into the battle with depression. I was going to WIN - no matter what.

And as I sit here today and write these words, that is exactly what I have done. I have won - I have back my energy, a balanced life with a steadiness that I can count on, a social life, financial security, the career I want and I radiate health and vitality.

But, only you - a fellow fighter - will begin to understand the scars I carry - and you carry - from the deadly/fierce battles I have fought for so many years to get here.

But, it was the persistence - the "I will NOT give up" mentality that got me here. I possess nothing that you do not have. I am not brighter or stronger or more talented or special in any way. But, I PERSISTED. And that is all it will take for you.

*"The turning point in growing up is when you discover the core strength within you that survives all hurt."*
*Max Lerner*

# JULY

*July 1*

## An Attitude of Gratitude

I can be so low some days that I would have to look up to see the underbelly of a snake. And when I get in these slumps, I inevitably start to feel lots of self-pity.

No doubt, I am in severe pain. That is a fact. But, I have found that I can approach the day ahead from a positive place if I see it from the perspective that I am one lucky, fortunate individual.

If you are considered middle-class in the United States, you would then rank in the top one-half of one percent of people in the world. So, what is average to us is still head and shoulders above what most folks in the world have.

When I stop to mentally tick off what I have - no matter how bad I feel - I am indeed rich. I have a roof over my head, all the comforts of electricity and running water and food (usually in abundance). In fact, I have far more than these basics.

I have a decent wardrobe and shoes for every occasion. I have mementoes that I cherish, sturdy furniture, a vehicle and insurance to cover it, a host of friends, a family that I love and who loves me, an education, etc...

As soon as I focus on what I have to be thankful for, I am no longer feeling so sorry for myself. Yes, I still hurt but, I am living a life of abundance and I need to keep remembering that.

*"Abundance is not something we acquire. It is something we tune into."*

*Wayne Dyer*

*July 2*

## Primary and Secondary Cycles

One of the great mysteries of those of us who are genetically predisposed to depression is that these depression cycles appear on a regular basis according to some unfathomable calendar. Regardless of what was going on in my life, every April the descent would begin and my life lost its light and the despair crept up. I could be at a spectacular phase of my life and I would still slide helplessly into the yawning hole of depression.

And, by the same token, every August 28, 29 or 30, I would 'spike' out of the depression. I would simply wake up one day in late August and feel like the real me again.

After several years of this, it then became apparent that the month of February was in itself another cycle of depression but, much briefer and less severe.

Throughout the year, there would be what I called 'blips on my screen' - random periods of depression that seemed to have no trigger or source and varied in intensity.

But, just as the seasons of nature are inevitable, I could not stop the despair that spring and summer brought. Many suffer from SAD (Seasonal Affective Disorder) that is strongly tied to the darker months of winter. My depressions appeared to be just the opposite.

It took many years of broken promises, plans that dissolved into resentful regrets and fury that I was once again under the power of the depression that owned that part of my year, before I learned to NOT plan for the months of May, June, July and August. Being a teacher made an enormous difference in my employment history. I at least could keep my job with this pattern of cycles.

If you are not currently aware of a calendar basis to your cycles, it is going to take a while for the patterns to establish themselves. But, I found that if I kept track of my good and bad days by entering a number corresponding to my level of functioning for that day in my Daytimer, I could use this to begin to see the phases of my depression.

Just before retiring for the night, I would reflect on that day's level of productivity and sense of well-being, and assign a number to that day. Ten was utter bliss and one was death. Five was whatever 'normal' was.

Eventually, if you see a repetition of depression at certain times of the year, you can plan around those times of diminished capabilities. This is a small step that will reap enormous benefits and save you from creating deadlines and obligations that you may not be able to keep.

Another benefit from knowing your primary and secondary cycles (you may not have cycles either and that is important to know as well) is how this information may aid your physician in prescribing medication for you.

Again, knowledge is power.

*"Time is an equal opportunity employer. Each human being has exactly the same number of hours and minutes every day. Rich people can't buy more hours. Scientists can't invent new minutes. And you can't save time to spend it on another day. Even so, time is amazingly fair and forgiving. No matter how much time you've wasted in the past, you still have an entire tomorrow."*

*Denis Waitely*

## *July 3*

## Suffering Is Optional

Pain is inevitable, but suffering is optional. I have heard this aphorism often but, did not understand it until I acknowledged certain choices I was making that continually bruised and battered me. Needlessly.

In the early years, I chose to watch the news on television. Invariably, I was miserable halfway into the broadcast. I have not absorbed that negative imagery for decades now. I stay in touch with the world by reading the headlines of newspapers at newsstands, reading the headlines offered by Yahoo! when I check in to read my email and by reading *USA TODAY* when I can afford it. No, I don't know everything in current affairs, but I know enough.

Another choice I needed to make was to minimize my time around the 'pretty people'. Whether it was social gatherings and parties that made me feel inadequate and 'less than' or certain upscale malls that catered to the affluent and privileged, I needed to not compare myself to people who outwardly seemed to live lives of beautiful perfection. It only amplified my pain and I could not seem to stop comparing my life with theirs in certain trying circumstances.

The folks around me who saw the glass as half-empty were avoided.

By maneuvering my lifestyle, I could minimize some of the pain. Besides, these painkillers were free and positively habit-forming.

*"Avoid destructive thinking. Improper negative thoughts sink people. A ship can sail around the world many, many times, but just let enough water get into the ship and it will sink. Just so with the human mind. Let enough negative thoughts or improper thoughts get into the human mind and the person sinks just like the ship."*

*Alfred A. Montapert*

*July 4*

## Times to Celebrate

Today is a day of celebration. Joyous, exhilarating, focused liberation. We put down our cares and put on frivolity. We can rejoice.

I have a very special reason to light fireworks today. For me it is another year that in the midst of my primary cycle, I am functioning and feel truly connected to the rest of the world.

Today - these exact twenty-four hours - I can celebrate my freedom and `independence' from my illness. Freedom from the tyranny of depression is elation that deserves fireworks any day of the year.

So, I cherish each of these days. I do not allow others to diminish this. I see each of these days as building blocks as I lay the foundation for my long-term recovery.

*"Anyone can carry his burden, however hard, until nightfall. Anyone can do his work, however hard, until dark. Anyone can live sweetly, patiently, lovingly, purely, till the sun goes down. And this is all that life really means."*

*Robert Louis Stevenson*

*July 5*

## Disappointment

One of my strongest supporters let me down today. Because so very few friends even begin to understand what being depressed or bipolar feels like - much less what to offer in the form of support - I tend to count heavily on too few who do understand.

Everyone has their days of light and days of darkness. I need to allow others the same empathy they offer me.

What I get from days like this is that I - and only I - am responsible for my recovery. Not the pills, not the hospitals, not my psychiatrist, not my therapist, not my support groups, not my mother. I am.

I alone will find the way to get back the thriving, joyous life I have when not depressed. I can enroll others to assist me, but I am going to be the initiator in all growth.

So I accept this once again and make contact with at least one loving friend to reassure my bruised ego that I am a worthwhile person. I pray for the friend who let me down – wishing with all my heart for the same blessings for her that I want for myself and I let it go.

*"There can be no deep disappointment where there is not deep love."*

*Martin Luther King, Jr*

## *July* 6

## Working

Work is usually one of the first and most critical casualties of our illness. The days that we are unable to function at our maintenance level are days that we miss work. Some days we are a bit stronger and can put on the 'mask' and go through the motions of working. Robotic though we may be, it is a day that counts toward our employment.

There was a time that I did not work at all. I lived on disability income. And this is after working successfully for three Fortune 500 companies. When I did return to the work force, I committed to only temporary work and certainly only part-time. Many others I know begin with some volunteer work. This lessens the pressure to perform. Then some move on to part-time work, maybe take a break, even volunteer or do part-time work again and eventually a full-time career can be resumed.

The course of your illness dictates this schedule. I learned not to set deadlines around working full speed, full time again. The stress this created always moved me away from, not toward, my goal.

Let your body - your internal sense of your wellness - tell you when and how much work is right for you.

*"I never did a day's work in my whole life. It was all fun."*
*Thomas A. Edison*

## *July 7*

## Bright Days of Sunshine

April through August is my primary cycle. I would see the brilliant cloudless skies out my windows and know that there were people all around me experiencing the radiance and light-heartedness this day had to offer.

The darkness of my depression completely overshadowed any sunshine for me. As I shuffled from my bed to the bath, I would catch a glimpse of this summer light. It never failed to stop me in my tracks. The contrast between what the majority of the world was experiencing and my dreadful reality was painful. My heart ached and I could not do one thing to bridge the gap.

My darkness was so pervasive, it was difficult to comprehend that other existence. But, my determination to have what others had was rekindled. I used my rage at the injustice of living in darkness when others lived in the brilliant light of these summer days to keep me focused on my goal. I vowed that I, too, would live again in the sunshine.

*"Summer afternoon – summer afternoon; to me those have always been the two most beautiful words in the English language."*
*Henry James*

## *July 8*

## Breathing

There were days when BREATHING was all I could do. I counted my breaths and focused on that.

That was literally all I was capable of.

Again, my coping method of distraction saved me for another twenty-four hours. It may be my most desperate form, but it works.

I focus on breathing in. I focus on breathing out.

Considering how active I am most of my life, this sounds ridiculous. Well, it sounds ridiculous period.

But, there were days that this was my best.

And if that's what it took to get through the day, then counting my breaths was acceptable. I had no energy to distract myself from the pain any other way.

*"It is my experience that natural breathing is in itself a powerful form of self-healing."*
*Master Mantak Chia from The Tao of Natural Breathing: For Health, Well-Being and Growth*

## *July 9*

## Getting Through the Day

Be patient.

Use the 'twenty-four hours at a time' theory of Alcoholics Anonymous to cope. Maybe look at just getting through the morning, or the next hour, or the next minute, or the next breath.

Any step of recovery is not a LEAP back into normality, but small steps of progress that needs periods of rest before more steps of progress are attempted.

Too much too soon is a sure prescription for relapse.

Focus on right now and then the next moment. It's all any of us have.

*"How poor are they that have no patience!*
*What wound did ever heal but by degrees?"*
*William Shakespeare, Othello* **(1604)**

## *July 10*

## Dual Diagnosis

Dual diagnosis is a relatively new term for some of us. The two diagnoses usually are depression and alcoholism. Sometimes one of the diagnoses is bulimia, schizophrenia, hormonal imbalances, obsessive-compulsive disorder; but, it basically comes down to some form of mood disorder and substance abuse.

Not everyone experiences two simultaneous illnesses. Current research is showing more evidence that the genetic vulnerability of these illnesses are linked. Better than seventy per cent of manic-depressives are alcoholic. The overlap is too striking to ignore.

One theory is that manics or hypomanics use alcohol subconsciously to depress their mood closer to a normal emotional range and to slow their racing mind enough to sleep. Another theory is that depressives prefer the oblivion of an alcoholic blur to the pain of depression. Or it may just be that both illnesses exist in the same person concurrently.

A common, though controversial, approach now is to make treatment for depression (or the less frequent mania) primary. It is thought that by alleviating the mood imbalance, the drive for a panacea is reduced and the chances of a recovery from alcoholism is enhanced. This theory is an innovative one and an anachronism to twelve-step dogma. There is no denial of both problems. The quandary is in which illness needs to be addressed first.

Frequently, however, an individual will get sober and maintain this only to find that they are miserable. The addition of appropriate medication and therapy is necessary to assure balance. To just quit drinking does not alleviate the depression.

But, I believe for each of us, it is our own 'soul-knowledge' that will tell us which path to seek first. You will intuitively know the process for your recovery. Trust that.

*"The value of identity of course is that so often with it comes purpose."*

*Richard Grant*

*July 11*

## Taking Breaks

Pacing and spacing.

Pacing and spacing.

Pacing and spacing.

Pace yourself and space out your tasks. I cannot stress how critical this is to ongoing health and recovery from depression. On our better days, it is easy to feel that we have to make up for the lost time our illness costs us. To rush around and frantically try to catch up is counter-productive. Long-term recovery requires a measured pace to our day.

Pacing - the speed at which we proceed through our day and spacing - the sequence in which events follow each other are the foundation of balance.

It may be necessary to use "pacing and spacing" as a silent litany to remind yourself.

If long-term recovery is our goal, we must acknowledge that we cannot hurry it. Healing will come. But, we must be available for it.

Pace your tasks and obligations and spread them out over time. Do not try to push the river. Go with the flow.

*"All rising to a great place is by a winding stair."*
*John Quincy Adams*

*July 12*

## Psychic Pain

Whenever I try to tell someone what I am experiencing, the painfulness of the illness always comes up. But, as I explain the excruciating pain that accompanies this chemical imbalance in the brain, I am often misunderstood. Most people think that I am referring to a headache. Psychic pain is amorphous. It does not have distinct borders; it is not clear-cut; it doesn't have a color; it doesn't have a texture; it doesn't have a definite beginning or ending; it doesn't come in sizes - it only comes in extra-extra-large; it doesn't have a time-frame; it destroys my very soul.

For me, psychic pain is the hardest part of my illness to deal with. It seems to own me. I feel completely impotent in the face of this vague terror.

So, I relent to it temporarily and do what ever it is that I need to do to survive. I save my energy for what I need to do to get by. I do not tell myself that I am weak or I have given in by doing this. I choose to say to myself that I made a reasonable decision and that I am wise to know my limits.

There is no pill for psychic pain.

*"Pain is no evil unless it conquers us."*

*George Eliot*

# *July 13*

## Healthy Selfishness

This is the greatest concept. Everyone should practice this.

What it doesn't mean is egocentricity, or abrasiveness, or thoughtlessness. It isn't about 'me' only and 'you' never. It can be overdone. But, in balance, it is one of the strongest tools at our disposal.

What it does give us is permission to take care of ourselves. For me that means saying 'no' when I know I have reached my limit of activity for that day; it means calling to cancel after I've said 'yes'; I can let my answering machine take all my calls, I don't feel obligated to answer letters, answer the door or to answer 'why not?'; I have permission to sleep for twelve straight hours if that is what I need; I have permission to eat carbohydrates and sugar; I am gentle and tender to me.

The emphasis is on HEALTH and SELF. These are our greatest responsibilities.

*"Selfish, adj. Devoid of consideration for the selfishness of others."*

*Ambrose Bierce*

*July 14*

## Abandoned by God

It feels like screaming into a void. The tree falling to earth in the forest and no one to hear. It is desperate. It is infuriating. It hurts.

"It" is depression.

I have felt that these silent screams reverberated unbearably loud inside my head.

Eventually I looked at this as therapy. Someone once asked me, "how big is your God?". I believe in a God greater than I am able to comprehend. So, I use this omnificent Being to be the therapist I need when no one is available.

I am able to say/scream/cry the vulgar words that describe my fear and pain. I rage at the helplessness I feel. I cry for the life that gets put aside whenever my illness appears. I hold nothing back.

When I am done, I feel spent. Clean.

Temporarily there is relief. And I never doubt that my Higher Power understands. I need to feel that spiritual connection to see beyond my pain.

So, if I feel adrift from this anchor, I get attached again before anything else happens. This is my priority.

*"God is our refuge and strength, a very present help in trouble."*
*Bible; Psalms 46 vs. 1*

*July 15*

## Finding and Using a Good Pharmacist

I believe I could do without a good psychiatrist or a good therapist before I'd give up my pharmacist. It takes a bit of effort to find a good one. Ask others. Call different pharmacies at different times to ask your questions and see what response you get. Don't eliminate a particular pharmacy on one pharmacist's ignorance or indifference. Call during another shift.

I have found some incredibly compassionate, patient, informed professionals who can answer my concerns. Medications for brain chemistry imbalances are complex and powerful drugs that can cause powerful and complex reactions or interactions.

Two other medication tools I find indispensable are Dr. Jack Gorman's *The Essential Guide to Psychiatric Drugs* (a current, comprehensive, readable guide) and the insert sent by every pharmaceutical company with their medications. Although these inserts are written in 'medicalese', you will be able to understand the side effects and drug interactions sections. But, don't rely on the printout most pharmacies give you with your medication. Ask for the physicians insert. You can skip much of the chemistry section, but you will find a complete, thorough listing of all side effects and contraindications in the fine print.

By utilizing the pharmacist, the book and/or the inserts, you will be able to deal with medication adjustments and hopefully, hasten your healing.

One extra suggestion that I want to share is the comfort of a twenty-hour pharmacy. Because I live in a large metropolitan area, this is available to me and many is the time that I have called at 4 a.m.. Although I may not get the answer to my current symptoms (most times I do), there is something reassuring just to 'connect' with another human at that bleak hour. If this is available to you, it can be another tool.

*"None of us have gotten to where we are solely by pulling ourselves up from our own bootstraps. We got here because someone bent down and helped us."*

*Thurgood Marshall*

## *July 16*

## Personal Hygiene

Not many people would think about this. But, it has always been a barometer of the depth of my depression. How I groom myself is an outward and visible sign of the condition of my insides.

I normally am very particular about cleanliness and tidiness, both in my home and in my person. But, as the 'I don't cares' begin, so does my lack of interest in appearances.

I know I am near the bottom when I do not do simple functions like brushing my teeth, bathing or even brushing my hair. I just can't seem to muster the energy these activities would take.

Because I know from past cycles about how long this phase will last, I let go and cruise these days. I understand that I am not practicing my normal habits here and they will resume in time. I usually am not in contact with people when I reach this point - except by phone - so, I'm the only one to offend.

Try to save this energy for reading, journaling, watching television when you are about tapped out. Use all your resources for healing. This is not a negative behavior. It is a coping strategy.

"Soap and education are not as sudden as a massacre, but they are more deadly in the long run."
Mark Twain

## July 17

### The Necessity of Laughter

I discovered Norman Cousin's *Anatomy of an Illness as Perceived by the Patient: Reflections on Healing and Regeneration* (and the video of the same name) early in my illness. This widely-known writer and editor determined that being an active participant was critical to his recovery from his life-threatening collagen disorder and realized that laughter contributed therapeutically to his regimen. By viewing two or three movies - usually classics of the Laurel and Hardy genre - daily, he improved his activity threshold greatly. He also survived far beyond his doctor's prognosis: sixteen years from the onset of his collagen illness and ten years after his heart attack. (You may want to read his other book: *The Healing Heart: Antidotes to Panic and Helplessness).*

It certainly did not bother me to go to the nearest video store (if I was at the point where I still felt able to drive) in a coat or raincoat over my nightgown. I didn't feel obligated to look 'presentable' and I could be in and out in minutes. An added bonus was they usually sold popcorn and candy, so I could really indulge.

Occasionally, I felt comfortable asking a friend or neighbor to pick up a few videos for me.

There was never a time - not once - that I found myself not able to laugh. No matter how bleak my outlook was, chuckles bubbled up from somewhere and at times I actually howled laughing.

And the other benefit that I never failed to receive was a rapid escalation in my mood. Not that I was euphoric, but I was definitely better. By the end of those few hours, I felt like putting on clothes and I stayed out of bed for the rest of that day.

Not everyone's sense of comedy is the same - but, that section - Comedy - in video stores is one of the largest. Obviously, humor is a powerful resource for many. Take several - go frequently - watch the stand-up comedian specials - Bob Hope and Lucy are timeless - stretch your humor in new directions.

This is one of those "I promise you's". It is one of the best medications you will ever take.

*"I am thankful for laughter, except when milk comes out my nose."*

*Woody Allen*

## *July 18*

### Abraham Lincoln Eyes

Have you ever seen a picture of President Lincoln smiling? Even the thought is difficult, isn't it? His suffering is painfully visible.

I used Lincoln in two ways. One way is that I taught people close to me to look carefully at my eyes. When I was depressed a glaze replaced the light and life-force normally there. I would acknowledge this lightly by saying, "I've got Abraham Lincoln eyes again". And this was about the only visible clue to those closest to me that I was in a depression cycle.

And the second extremely powerful tool I utilized when alone in my darkest moments, I would remember that Lincoln did not die of his illness. Not only did he survive painful, debilitating years of depressions, he held the most prominent and dynamic office during America's most divisive time and he had no medication available or even the promise of any. The fortitude and resilience this took always moved me. And, "if he can do it, I can do it" was motivation enough for making it one more day.

*"Always bear in mind that your own resolution to succeed is more important than any one other thing."*
*Abraham Lincoln*

# *July 19*

## Doing Unto Others

"Getting out of yourself" is a highly effective method of dealing with suffering or self-pity. By taking the focus off of yourself and putting it on someone else, you move from needing help to giving help.

I have found this to work. I would call someone and 'act as if'. I pretended 'happy' - I said little about me and showed interest in their life and problems and joys.

This takes less than ten minutes and can be magical.

My perspective would shift before the conversation ended. I was able to help two people this way.

*"Dare to reach your hand out into the darkness, to pull another hand into the light."*
*Norman B. Rice*

# *July 20*

## Men

I think men have it rougher with depression. Repeated studies have shown that women will seek help whereas men tend to keep their illness to themselves as much as possible and try to gut their way through. Women will talk to friends and share their problems whereas male conversation is dominated by facts and not feelings.

I encourage the male sufferers to use whatever means to find an emotional outlet. A spouse may be a source or you may want to utilize your partner for other needs. I've often seen where a female friend is less threatening than a buddy. Therapists make a career out of doing this. Pastors will do it for free. Have at least one person there to listen. Pride is not an issue here - surviving and healing are.

Even the smallest towns have community agencies that offer help.

Someone can hear you. Find that person.

*"The most important thing in communication is to hear what isn't being said."*

*Peter Drucker*

## *July 21*

### Awareness

The person you can count on being most accurate with what is going on with your balance or imbalance is you. The body is a divine, perfect mechanism that seeks balance at all times. Our bodies are miraculous. There is a voice that is constantly in communication with us if we can only develop the ability to tune in to it. It is always there and all of us have access to it. That still small voice that is your Higher Self - your personal feedback system built right in!

Many of you learned about self-knowledge early on. It is easy to adopt and listening to the part of us that always knows best works for other areas of our life as well.

Even as early as age two, one hemisphere will dominate an individual's decision-making process. The left hemisphere analyzes rational thought (knowledge, definitions, science, technology, etc...) while the right hemisphere is responsible for our creativity, emotions, sensitivity, etc... However, everyone can access and utilize this intuitive self from our right brain.

Getting on this path requires little time and little effort. The next time you are hungry, close your eyes and silenty ask your mind what would most satisfy you at this time? The answer that immediately comes to your mind is THE answer. Do not rationalize and try to convince your left brain of something different - your intuitive self, your right brain, told you correctly.

What we fight sometimes is the rationale of the response. The first time I got 'creme-filled doughnuts', I was sure it was a mistake. So, sure enough, I ate all the reasonable things I knew to be healthy and 'right' for me during the day and still wasn't satisfied at bedtime. So, after eating a full day's amount of food, I needed to eat the creme-filled doughnuts to satisfy some chemical imbalance in my body.

I could have saved myself lots of frustration - and lots of calories! - if only I had not censured that voice that told me what I needed in the first place.

Trust this voice - this Higher Self - about what you need at that moment. Your solution will always come.

Let this voice guide you in your healing. This is our Higher Self's voice speaking personally to each of us.

I will intuitively know that I need a nap; or more protein; or sunlight and exercise; or solitude; or companionship and support, etc... I will intuitively know that my doctor is not taking my worries about side effects seriously. I will know that I am taking on too many projects and tasks and the pressure of deadlines is causing my chemistry to run amuck again.

We always KNOW. If we will only listen.

*"Let me listen to me and not to them."*
*Gertrude Stein*

## *July 22*

## Lying

In my home, being called a liar was the ultimate degradation. So, complete honesty was the standard to live by.

However, I've come to believe that it is unnecessary to be brutally truthful all the time.

If I have no strength to explain how much pain I am in and how little energy I am able to muster, I will sometimes say that I have a migraine. Everyone relates to that. If a friend or colleague tells us they are experiencing a migraine, we immediately understand that they will be in great pain; this migraine might last a few hours or a few days; all their normal activities will be delayed until they are better; they will not function at home or at work until the migraine ends; they can do nothing but wait for this to pass.

Everyone will 'get it' about a migraine, but few will understand that the very same adjustments apply to clinical depression.

If I screen my calls, I don't make elaborate explanations or apologies. I allow the other person to assume I was not home.

I hate lying, but will use the white lie of migraine pain to abbreviate the necessity of explaining my temporary forfeiture of responsibility.

Who I do not lie to is my psychiatrist, my therapist, myself.

I realize this is justification. I am still lying - even if it is a justifiable white lie. But, until our society grasps the nature of our illness, I prefer to call it self-preservation.

*"Truth is beautiful, no doubt; but, so are lies."*
*Ralph Waldo Emerson*

## *July 23*

## Can You Laugh at Yourself?

Well, I know for sure that my wires were crossed in my brain this morning. I knew my faithful coffee pot was long overdue for a vinegar rinse to clean out the lime build-up. So, I went through the routine - one pot of half vinegar and half water - to run the whole cycle.

But, I got a real good laugh at myself when I went to check on the progress a few minutes later. I had forgotten to remove the old coffee grounds first!

Can you laugh at yourself when you fumble in life? Can you turn an irritating mistake into a good laugh?

This works for the whole world. Not just us.

A great psychology joke:

New Answering Service Installed at Mental Health Institute:
"Hello, and welcome to the mental health hotline.

If you are obsessive-compulsive, press one repeatedly.

If you are co-dependent, ask someone to press two for you.

If you have multiple personalities, press three, four, five and six.

If you are paranoid, we know who you are and what you want. Stay on the line so we can trace your call.

If you are delusional, press seven and your call will be transferred to the mother ship.

If you are schizophrenic, listen carefully and a small voice will tell you which number to press.

If you are dyslexic, press 696969696.

If you have amnesia, press eight and state your name, address, phone number, date of birth, social security number, and your mother's maiden name.

If you have bipolar disorder, please leave a message after the beep, or before the beep, or after the beep. Please wait for the beep.

If you have short-term memory loss, please press nine. If you have short-term memory loss, please press nine. If you have short-term memory loss, please press nine.

If you have low self esteem, please hang up. All of our operators are too busy to talk to you.

*"Anyone who takes himself too seriously always runs the risk of looking ridiculous; anyone who can consistently laugh at himself does not."*

*Vaclav Havel – Czech playwright and President*

## *July 24*

## Support Groups

Finding a support group may be one of the tougher parts of dealing with this illness. It is acknowledging, often to total strangers, that we are dealing with one of the invisible illnesses. It is effort when we don't have the motivation to take a shower. But, it is personal education that we cannot afford to ignore.

Use the phone directory to look for these contacts: a local university or psychiatric hospital might sponsor such a program; in the government section there will be a variety of social agencies listed that at the very least can refer you to who you need; maybe the suicide hot-line knows of groups. Ask your psychiatrist or therapist. Call the local psychiatric association.

If you feel able, maybe starting an informal group on your own may be the answer.

The relief that comes from being understood is invaluable. Hearing others' stories of recovery is hopeful. Learning of new treatments can shift our therapy into a better arena.

This is not an illness to handle by yourself. Others need you as much as you need them.

*"Although the world is full of suffering, it is also full of the overcoming of it."*

*Helen Keller*

## *July* 25

### Hope

This is a tough one. The quandary of hoping when feeling hopeless is difficult.

When I can see no light from the bottom of the black hole I'm in, I focus on hopeful things. I read inspirational literature. I will listen to motivational tapes. I read a lot of 'success' stories of others.

And I remember the survivors of the Nazi gas chambers and the prisoners of war who returned to us. Under overwhelming odds, these individuals made it through. Just knowing this will make me feel better.

But, in all medical theories, mystical guidelines and spiritual texts it is acknowledged that hope is the one essential factor in healing (in survival even). Time and again, an individual with a minor illness will die and another person with a terminal illness will not only live but, thrive. And it is that one component - hope - or lack of it that makes the difference.

Optimism and hope are united. The power of these emotions we have control over can not be underestimated.

"Hope is that thing with feathers that perches in the soul and sings the tune without the words and never stops...at all."
Emily Dickinson

# July 26

## Research

I love libraries and books and reading. So, it was completely natural for me to find my way to the nearest library on a frequent basis.

I also am a 'need to know' type of person.

Now that the Internet is available to everyone and is even free through your local library, it is so easy to find out anything you want to know. I always start with *Google* or *Refdesk.com* and follow those links.

Although you may not characterize yourself as curious, I encourage you to educate yourself as much as possible about your illness. You will understand how long it might take before your antidepressant might begin to work; how to take your medicine (with meals, between meals, single dose, in the morning); side effects to expect; understanding why you suffer from this brain illness; how others have dealt with it, etc...

Knowledge IS power.

Support groups are excellent for information as well. Invariably, I knew about new medications and their uses six months before my pharmacist or psychiatrist did from those in the support group I attended.

Publications from the national organizations for depression and bipolar are specific and understandable. See the Depression and Bipolar Support Alliance (dbsalliance.org), National Association for Research on Schizophrenia and Depression (narsad.org), Moodswing.org, National Alliance for the Mentally Ill (nami.org) or the Society for Light Treatment and Biological Rhythms (sltbr.org) for starters.

Biographies and autobiographies can be used to comprehend what is happening to you. The courage of Patty Duke to publicize her trauma with and subsequent remission of bipolar disorder is fabulous (*A Brilliant Madness: Living with Manic-Depressive Illness). Darkness Visible: A Memoir of Madness* by the Pulitzer Prize-winning William Styron or any of Dr. Kay Jamison Redfield's books: *An Unquiet Mind: A Memoir of Moods and Madness, Touched with Fire: Manic-Depressive Illness and the Artistic Temperament* can provide hope.*In the Jaws of the Black Dogs: A Memoir of Depression* by John Bentley Mays or *The Noonday Demon: An Atlas of Depression* by Andrew Solomon are instructive.

It was difficult for my mother to understand why I would read about depression when I was depressed. I felt validated emotionally for one thing. And I was always seeking hope. These were people from every walk of life who had faced the depths of depression and come back out the other side into the sunshine.

Anything I could learn was another brick in the foundation of my recovery that I was building.

And it worked. Here I am writing to you from halcyon days and a solid, fulfilling life.

"We have a hunger of the mind which asks for knowledge of all around us, and the more we gain, the more is our desire; the more we see, the more we are capable of seeing."
Maria Mitchell

## *July 27*

## Utilizing Endocrinology

Endocrinology is the medical field that specializes in non-surgical treatment of the endocrine system of the body (the thyroid, pituitary, adrenal, ovary, testes, and part of the pancreas). We know that the thyroid controls metabolism or how fast our cells utiltize energy. The pituitary controls growth and the pineal gland controls sleep. The adrenals are our adrenalin factory. The pancreas secretes digestive enzymes and insulin hormone. And, of course, the ovary and testes are our reproductive organs.

Anyone who has ever suffered depression is aware that energy, weight loss and gain, sleep, sex drive and stomach problems are massively impacted by depression. I owe an enormous part of my turning a decade and a half of unemployment and chronic depression back into full time work and a thriving life to the endocrinologist I saw who worked patiently with me. Because each of the endocrine systems are interrelated and extremely fragile, this is a tedious process. But, it can be essential to have a qualified endocrinologist as part of your recovery team.

There are not many women who have not experienced the ghoulish days of menstrual and premenstrual distress. The desperation for carbohydrates, irritability, mood swings, weight gain, bloating and poor concentration are what plague us during these uncomfortable days.

But, which of these symptoms do we not associate with depression as well?

The difference between hormonal imbalance and true clinical depression is 1) duration and 2) intensity.

An imbalance of the neurotransmitters in our brain lasts weeks or months - not days. And I never felt suicidal when I suffered from menstrual cycle problems.

There are several simple blood tests that are relatively inexpensive to diagnose estrogen/progesterone complications. See August 14 concerning thyroid tests and their interpretations. Having each panel of endocrine tests that applies to your symptoms is critical. Each possibility of an endocrine imbalance should be eliminated before antidepressants are introduced.

You may still need antidepressant medication, but antidepressants will not make your thyroid work or your gender hormones or insulin balanced. It is imperative that you eliminate all endocrine problems before beginning trials with antidepressants.

Antidepressants can minimize or exacerbate the medications used for sex hormones, thyroid, etc... So, having an able endocrinologist who will work with your overall medical needs is worth any extra effort you might need to go through. You may be able to even preclude using antidepressants at all.

*"In the hands of the discoverer, medicine becomes a heroic art...*
*wherever life is dear, medicine becomes a demi-god."*
*Ralph Waldo Emerson*

## *July 28*

### Willingness

Be open.

Try.

Try harder.

Be willing to go to any length.

If you are closed to any recommendation, any option, any new remedy however odd, you will stay exactly where you are now.

*"What we call the secret of happiness is no more a secret than our willingness to choose life."*
*Leo Buscaglia*

## *July 29*

### Compliance

Boy, I hate this word. It means that I have to do what someone else wants me to do.

*Merriam-Webster Dictionary* defines compliance as: the act or process of complying with a desire, demand or proposal or coercion; conformity in fulfilling official requirements or a disposition to yield to others.

In other words, in this instance, it means following your doctors' orders and taking your medications as prescribed.

Many of us are repeatedly hospitalized under 'noncompliance'. Being compliant means taking your medication long after you are back on your feet.

Being compliant means if we are taking medication, that we take it regularly and on schedule and in the proper doses. Even if the side effects are debilitating at the moment.

Being compliant means keeping appointments with the professionals we have enrolled in our care.

Being compliant means being mature and responsible for ourselves.

*"I know the power obedience has of making things easy which seem impossible."*

*Saint Teresa of Avila*

## *July 30*

## Making Up for 'Lost' Time

I used to keep a mental ledger of all my down time. Time I was not productive in the usual sense of the word. Time missed from work. Time spent in bed. Holidays and special occasions missed. Time I had nothing to show for.

I don't do this anymore.

This habit was making me live in yesterday and I have no access to then. I do have access to today. I focus my energy on here and now and give up stumbling through the present because I'm looking back over my shoulder.

These twenty-four hours are what I have and you have. I can't make up for yesterday and it is futile to try.

Wasting energy on what I have left undone prevents me from getting anything done today.

*"Wasted time means wasted lives."*

*R. Shannon*

## *July 31*

## Creativity as Part of the Illness

Now it seems to me that if I had to carry the misery of this brain illness, at least I could reap the benefits of that special genius that is so often part of the disorder. Those who suffer the blight of depression (and, in particular, bipolar disorder) are often gifted creatively. Just look at Vincent Van Gogh, Sylvia Plath, Ernest Hemingway, Vivien Leigh, Beethoven, Edgar Allen Poe and Winston Churchill as examples.

Unfortunately, I got the first and not the latter.

But, there are those of you who have magic available to you. You enter thought realms not accessible to others. You make new things by reshaping ordinary things.

Depression will rob you of this talent temporarily. But, it is only a temporary interruption. You did not lose the gift. It will always be waiting for you.

*"Creativity is the power to connect the seemingly unconnected."*
*William Plomer*

# AUGUST

*August 1*

## Being With Others

I was having lunch with a very good friend one day (she has no brain imbalance) and it occurred to me I was becoming more uncomfortable by the moment. Not only did I lose my appetite, but my stomach was in spasms by the end of the hour.

Now I realize what went wrong. It had nothing to do with her and it actually had nothing to do with me either. What was wrong was what was between us.

She is naturally gorgeous. Nor had she even bothered to put on make-up that day and still was captivating. She is slim to the point of almost being underweight. And she was bubbling with news about an old love, a new love and a current love.

I, on the other hand, was beginning the quicksand approach to a dark depression. My complexion was pasty, my eyes were dull and my hair was uncombed. I was bloated, forty-five pounds overweight and had barely enough energy to keep my job, much less date. In fact, I hadn't dated for a year.

It was a mistake to expose myself to the contrast between us that day. We are still great friends, but I shield myself now from reality that is harsher than I can deal with.

When I am in the trough of depression, I must limit my exposure to folks who - at least on the surface - have perfection at their fingertips. In my misery, I compare myself to them and it only deepens my pain.

I would like to say I am above comparing myself to others, but who would I be kidding? I can no more stop that behavior than I can squelch a sneeze.

Now I just make plans when I know I will not leave the engagement feeling worse about myself.

*"We... tend to evaluate others on the basis of physical, outward appearance: their "good looks", their social status, their family pedigrees, their degrees or their economic situations. The Lord, however, has a different standard by which he measures a person. When it came time to choose a king to replace King Saul, the Lord gave this criteria to his prophet Samuel: "Look*

*not upon his countenance or the height of his stature;... for the Lord seeth not as man seeth; for the man looketh on the outward appearance but, the Lord looketh on the heart."*

*Marvin J. Ashton*

## *August 2*

## "This Too Shall Pass"

I did not believe it for a minute, but I said it anyway. I said it hundreds of times a day.

I'd been told that the mind does not know if what it is told is the truth or a lie, but that it works according to the information given it.

I was hoping by repeating this aphorism frequently enough, I would make it a reality.

There are days when I say "this too shall pass" from dawn until dusk. And because I have seen the pattern of returning to my normal, exuberant self after every cycle of depression - no matter how bleak and terrifying - I know this aphorism to be true.

So, the more I mutter "this too shall pass" to myself, the more I know it to be true. It has NEVER failed me and that is the hope that I hang on to.

*"Time ripens all things. No man is born wise."*

*Unknown*

## *August 3*

## Chocolate Again!

Chocolate is one of the cheapest, most accessible drugs that I know of that is still legal. And no matter what extreme I carry my indulgence to, I never feel that I have overdosed or that I build up a tolerance to it!

I love the texture of chocolate. I love the aroma of chocolate. I love the way it melts on my tongue.

I know now the chemicals contained in chocolate that make my endorphins zing, but fundamentally it is the pure, delicious pleasure of chocolate that gives me such exquisite joy.

For less than $2.00, I can feel better every single time! Nowhere else on earth can you get guaranteed relief - and in under thirty minutes!

"Life is like a box of chocolates. You never know what you are going to get."

Forrest Gump (Tom Hanks)

"All I really need is love, but a little chocolate now and then doesn't hurt."

Lucy Van Pelt (from *Peanuts* by Charles M. Schulz)

"Chemically speaking, chocolate really is the world's perfect food."

Michael Levin,
Nutrition Researcher

"Don't wreck a sublime chocolate experience by feeling guilty. Chocolate isn't like premarital sex. It will not make you pregnant. And it always feels good."

Lora Brody,
*Growing up on the Chocolate Diet*

"Chocolate causes certain endocrine glands to secrete hormones that affect your feelings and behavior by making you happy. Therefore, it counteracts depression, in turn reducing the stress of depression. Your stress-free life helps you maintain a youthful disposition both physically and mentally. So, eat lots of chocolate!"

Elaine Sherman,
*Book of Divine Indulgences*

"It's not that chocolates are a substitute for love. Love is a substitute for chocolate. Chocolate is, let's face it, far more reliable than a man."

Miranda Ingram

"There are four basic food groups: milk chocolate, dark chocolate, white chocolate and chocolate truffles."

Unknown

*"Strength is the capacity to break a chocolate bar into four pieces with your bare hands – and then eat just one of the pieces."*
*Judith Viorst*

*"Save the Earth! It's the only planet with chocolate!"*
*Unknown*

*"Chocolate. It's not just for breakfast anymore."*
*Unknown*

## *August 4*

## 'Signs' That Someone Is Protecting You...

Maybe it is because I am so stubborn or hard-headed, as my mother would say. Can you relate to this? Maybe because it's better for us humans to see before we can believe/accept. But, it never ceases to thrill me and send shivers chasing up and down my spine, when I get one of these 'signs'.

Let me give you an example of what I am talking about. And no doubt you will begin to remember many of these occasions in your life - each unique to you and your circumstances. After I had become stabilized for just a short while, my medication seemed to begin to lose its effectiveness and I seemed to be lapsing back into depression. I could not - would not - believe that this was really happening. After all the years of waiting to get to this point - to feel like the 'real Connie' again - to only be back to normal just a few months before sliding backward and downward again seemed just too cruel to be true! The very thought of losing what I had gained depressed me.

A few weeks into the dark hole again, on an average Wednesday just at dusk, I was rounding a corner behind a small truck. This was a heavily trafficked area, under construction, with lots of temporary directions. So, driving was difficult here under the best of circumstances. Just as I rounded the corner, a stainless steel case about the size of a chair dropped in the road immediately in front of my car. Because this was not a straight section of the highway, only the car directly behind me could see that I was braking. All other cars were accelerating to make the light. Not knowing whether I would take the oil pan off the bottom of my car or do real structural damage, I knew that to sit there would mean a multi-vehicle pile up - no doubt about it. I feared being hit from behind and driven into the new concrete retainer wall less than two feet from me.

In these frantic seconds I was forced to make a critical decision that would affect me and others as well. So, I actually drove on pushing the case in front of me with my bumper into a slight opening where one of the orange and white construction barrels had been moved by some other motorist.

I was able to wedge this heavy metal case and my car into this tiny opening and get out of traffic.

Now, this is a long story to make the point that I believe with every part of my soul that this had nothing to do with a potential roadway accident, but rather God was talking to me in the extreme, explicit way that seems the only way to get my attention. I was feeling abandoned and bereft because my miracle medicine had only been effective for a sickeningly short six months. I certainly wasn't receptive to trusting God/Someone just to be crushed and disappointed again.

Now, are you relating to this?

So, despite the poor visibility of that time of day, in construction on a curve less than thirty-six inches from the impassable concrete wall, I found myself within five or six inches of the one opening in that section of highway - of all the miles of construction, this one barrel had been moved. Also, the driver behind me was alert and I was able to push the heavy object rather than run over it.

I am telling you, I felt God very clearly and distinctly saying to me, "You see, Connie, I am always protecting you and watching over you. Even now I know what's happening to you. I am reminding you that I am always here and that you can trust me."

I could tell you of dozens of these experiences throughout my life. And doubtless, you could tell of as many in your life.

It is sad that I need such dramatic intervention for my heart to grasp the message that although my current circumstances may stink, I am still under the care of Someone who is guiding me ALL the time.

Yes, I was still in a depressive cycle and things did not immediately improve in my health. But, I felt so much better. I did not feel abandoned and alone in my struggle. And that was enough to keep me going until I did turn the corner again.

*"We should always pray for help, but we should always listen for inspiration and impressions to proceed in ways different from those we may have thought of."*

*John Groberg*

*August 5*

## Checking Out Your Medicine Cabinet

Maybe help is as near as your bathroom medicine cabinet. Some medications that you are already taking may be your trigger for depression.

Are you aware that beta-blockers, estrogen and acne medications can cause serious depression just as a side effect? This is the easiest of depressions to treat as you and your physician will just need to find an alternative medication that does not destabilize your mood. Not that you need to eliminate this medicine, but that you and your doctor could possibly make a substitution.

Every step toward joy and light and away from the darkness is important to our recovery. Can you help yourself here?

Below is a list of medications that are reported to cause depression:
(from *Psychiatric Times*)

Acyclovir (Zovirax)
Amphetamines
Anticonvulsants
Asparaginase (Elspar)
Baclofen (Lioresal)
Barbituates
Benzodiazepines
Beta-adrenergic blockers
Bromocriptime (Parlodel)
Calcium-channel blockers
Corticosteroids
Cycloserine (Seromycin)
Dapsone
Disopyramide (Norpace)
Disulfiram (Antabuse)
Estrogens
Fluoroquinolone antibiotics
Histamine H2-receptor antagonists
HMG-CoA reductase inhibitors (statins)
Interferon alfa (Roferon-A)
Isotretinoin (Accutane)
Levodopa (Dopar)
Mefloquine (Lariam)
Methyldopa (Aldomet)
Metoclopramide (Reglan)
Metrizamide (Amipaque)

Metronidazole (Flaglyl)
Narcotics
Pergolide (Permax)
Phenylpropanaolamine (Dexatrim)
Progestins, implanted (Norplant)
Sulfonamides
Thiazide diuretics
(Adapted with permission from The Medical Letter, Inc. "Some Drugs That Cause Psychiatric Symptoms." *The Medical Letter on Drugs and Therapeutics:* Feb 13, 1998 Vol. 40 (Issue 1020) pp. 21-24.)

This list is by no means complete but, a good place to begin. ALWAYS ask your doctor AND your pharmacist about possible side effects and interactions of your medications.

*"In the sick room, ten cents' worth of human understanding equals ten dollars' worth of medical science."*
*Martin H. Fischer*

## *August* 6

## Confusing symptoms

Look at this list of predominant depression symptoms:

irritability
mood swings
changes in appetite
changes in sleep
changes in weight
lack of interest in formerly pleasant pasttimes

physical aches and pains

inability to concentrate
feelings of hopelessness/worthlessness

This list is virtually synonymous with PMS symptoms.

This is why a good endocrinologist is necessary for your recovery. If you are, in fact, suffering from a hormonal imbalance, all the anti-depressants in the world will not make you feel better.

As I have recommended before, please have a reputable endocrinologist or your family physician screen for thyroid levels and hormone levels.

Once these are in balance, some people never need depression medication at all.

A PMS GUIDE for MEN:
Dangerous: "What's for dinner?"
Safer: "Can I help you with dinner?"
Safest: "Where would you like to go for dinner?"

Dangerous: "Are you wearing THAT?"
Safer: "Gee, you look good in brown."
Safest: "Wow! Look at you!"

Dangerous: "What are you so worked up about?"
Safer: "Could we be overreacting?"
Safest: "Here's fifty dollars."

Dangerous: "Should you be eating that?"
Safer: "You know, there are a lot of apples left."
Safest: "Can I get you a glass of wine with that?"

Dangerous: "What did you DO all day?"
Safer: "I hope you didn't overdo today."
Safest: "I've always loved you in that robe."

## *August 7*

## "Inner Strength"

If you can start the day without caffeine or pep pills,

If you can be cheerful, ignoring aches and pains,
If you can resist complaining and boring people with your troubles,
If you can eat the same food everyday and be grateful for it,

If you can understand when loved ones are too busy to give you time,
If you can overlook when people take things out on you when, through no fault of yours, something goes wrong,

If you can take criticism and blame without resentment,
If you can face the world without lies and deceit,
If you can conquer tension without medical help,
If you can relax without liquor,

If you can sleep without the aid of drugs,

If you can do all these things,

Then, you are probably the family dog.
Unknown

Isn't it refreshing to know that the whole world faces these conflicts every day and that we are not alone? I love the perspective I get from this comic piece.

Everyone struggles. Everyone has a cross to bear. We are not the only people facing a tough battle.

But, we can overcome our depression. Some folks aren't that lucky.

*"When a man sits with a pretty girl for an hour, it seems like a minute. But, let him sit on a hot stove for a minute – and it's longer than any hour. That's relativity."*
*Albert Einstein*

*August 8*

## Lecithin – A Natural Healer

Lecithin is a natural emulsifier called a phospholipid. It is hard to get enough in our diets as it is primarily found in egg yolks, soybeans and some animal brains. Do not fear though! The supplements are all derived from soybeans and soybeans only.

This miracle nutrient is essential to every cell in the body and is a key building block of cell membranes (maintaining permeability). Lecithin protects all cells from oxidation and is abundant in the protective sheaths surrounding the brain. It supports the circulatory system and is a fat emulsifier. It prevents arterial congestion, helps distribute bodyweight, increases immunity to virus infections, cleans the liver and purifies the kidneys.

You may be asking yourself why you haven't heard of this amazing supplement before now. I asked myself the same thing. The reason may be that it is natural and cannot be patented nor is it expensive.
But, besides all of the fabulous benefits I have already mentioned, I have found lecithin to boost my mood and give me strong energy when depressed.

And this makes great sense considering that lecithin is primarily composed of B vitamins, phosphoric acid, choline, linoleic acid and inositol. Choline is a lipotropic substance which functions as an aid in the digestion of fats and can lower blood cholesterol as well as improve memory.

Lecithin can be purchased most anywhere - even groceries carry it in their vitamin section. It is available in capsules or granules. I recommend - as always - that you purchase the highest quality supplement that you can afford. There IS a difference in brands and price is often a reflection of this.

Lecithin is even cheap! I have never found a downside with the possible exception that if taken late in the day, it can delay sleep.

I would recommend taking four to six capsules a day if you are depressed. As with any change in your medications, start slowly and see how your individual chemistry reacts with lecithin. You may want to take one or two capsules on a regular basis and boost that amount during a dark phase.

There are a number of medical studies that support the use of lecithin as an adjunct to depression relief. Use the Internet to research this further if you are concerned. I studied this at length when my mother suffered from Alzheimer's disease and found that we were able to keep her in Stage One during the last four years of her life by giving her lecithin and L-Carnitine (an amino acid) daily.

This is a very benign supplement and one that may be hugely beneficial to your recovery. What have you got to lose?

*"The ...patient should be made to understand that*
*he or she must take charge of his or her own life.*
*Don't take your body to the doctor as if he were a repair shop."*
*Quentin Regestein*

## *August 9*

## Some General Medical Guidelines

Keep in mind that prescription drugs often begin to work within forty-eight hours while natural remedies will take days or weeks to become effective.

Some alternative remedies and supplements can cause side effects just like drugs can. Your unique chemistry will dictate how you respond.

Never underestimate the power of your daily intake of food. All the supplements in the world will not compensate for a sloppy diet. Everyone knows that green leafy vegetables, lean proteins and complex carbohydrates are the backbone of a healthy individuals' daily intake.

If your physician says "that stuff doesn't work", he or she may actually be saying "I know very little about it." Do your own research and experiment with what you are comfortable with.

Be aware also that what works one time may not be effective in subsequent depressions. Or that quantities may need titration or even brands need to be changed.

There is a massive library of information available on the Internet about supplements and alternative medicines. You alone are responsible for your health and you need to spend at least as much time researching options for depression relief as you do in researching your next automobile!

*"I think you might dispense with half your doctors*
*if you only would consult Dr. Sun more."*
*Henry Ward Beecher*

## *August 10*

## What Tyrosine Can Do For You

In some of my darker days with no new anti-depressant medications on the horizon, I really searched for relief anywhere I could find it. One path led me to two very helpful amino acids. One - DL-Phenylalanine - is the precursor to the other - Tyrosine.

Amino acids come to us through our diet in the form of proteins like beef, fish and chicken. I don't eat much meat so I learned the great benefits of supplementing with tyrosine. Researchers at the U.S. Army Research Institute of Environmental Medicine found that tyrosine prevents stress-induced declines in mood and mental performance and stimulates the nervous system thereby reducing fatigue. Tyrosine also produces norepinephrine which is a neurotransmitter that boosts alertness and metabolism.

Tyrosine must be purchased from a reputable supplier. I use Thorne Research out of Sand Pointe, Idaho because their supplements have no fillers or binders and are of the highest quality. You don't want to take DLPA and tyrosine in the same day as one is the precursor to the other.

Also, do not take either DLPA or tyrosine late in the evening as it could delay sleep onset. I do not know of any side effects from tyrosine but YOUR body is your laboratory so you may react differently. During a depression, a typical dose would be four to six capsules of 500 milligrams. I did not find a need to supplement with tyrosine during my well cycles.

This may be a great factor in your recovery. As with all changes, start slow and monitor yourself carefully for side effects.

*"Red meat is not bad for you. Now, blue-green meat, that's bad for you!"*

*Tommy Smothers*

## *August 11*

## Hope on the Horizon

If ever we were to have a brain illness, this is the time to be ill. I try to stay current on new treatments as they become available and it never ceases to warm my heart to see the millions of dollars being spent on research and the unusual and multi-pronged approaches to relief from depression that are being sought.

Here are just three novel approaches:

The American Journal of Psychiatry reports (May 2004) that as many as seventy-seven percent of patients who received an MRI-like brain scan had an immediate boost in mood. It appears that the electric fields produced by the scan alter the function of the neurons in the brain, correcting the imbalances that cause depression. Although this non-invasive treatment currently costs approximately two thousand dollars per treatment, ways of creating the same affect less expensively are being researched.

The controversial abortion pill, mifepristone - also known as RU 486 - has been shown to be affective for psychotic depression when nothing else seems to work. By blocking the effects of both powerful and fragile hormones, progesterone and cortisol, mifepristone appears to balance that part of the chemistry that has gone awry.

"...Modafinil (Provigil) is the first nonpsychomotor stimulant medication that has been approved for the treatment of narcolepsy (may be beneficial) to patients with residual bipolar depression and fatigue ... or unipolar depression."

Bipolar Network News: Vol. 9, Issue 1

There are a multitude of new approaches to our age-old problem. One of them will be effective for you.

*"Hope awakens courage. He who can implant courage in the human soul is the best physician."*

*Karl Ludwig van Knebel*

## *August 12*

## Practice Being a Turnip

My very wise friend, Linda, told me once that some of her best days were spent practicing to be a turnip. It took me years to get my mind around this concept and embrace it.

Turnips do nothing. They lie around and grow.

There are days in everyone's life that are best spent practicing to be a turnip. We are able to actually accomplish great things by letting ourselves be still and grow.

We don't always have to have some document or product or accomplishment to show for a successful day.

Healing takes place on deep and hidden layers. We need to 'vegetate' to allow that growth to take place.

*"Growth is a spiral process, doubling back on itself, reassessing and regrouping."*

*Julia Margaret Cameron*

## *August 13*

# Professionals Who Don't Have a Clue

Just because someone's title begins with "doctor" or they wear a white coat or are in a position of authority does NOT mean they know more than you do.

Keep in mind that half of all physicians graduated in the bottom half of their class. And some very learned people bring personal biases to their practices. There are therapists who believe that all problems facing folks are mother-created. There are physicians who believe that depression is just anger turned inward and if you can only get to what you are angry about and deal with that suppressed emotion then your depression will go away.

Do not believe everything at face value that any professional tells you. If something does not sit right with you, do some research on the advice. Get a second opinion.

Psychologists, therapists and physicians are human and we need to allow room for error. They can no more be perfect than we can.

*"All my life I had been looking for something, and everywhere I turned someone tried to tell me what it was. I accepted their answers too, even though they were often in contradiction and even self-contradictory. I was naïve. I was looking for myself and asking everyone except myself questions which I, and only I, could answer."*

*Ralph Ellison*

## *August 14*

# Subclinical Thyroid Disease

"People with mild thyroid failure have traditionally been thought to be asymptomatic. A detailed history and physical examination, however, will reveal several symptoms and signs, such as fatigue, depression, loss of energy, muscle weakness, dry skin, and sleep disturbances.

...Many other conditions are believed to be related to mild thyroid failure, including increased risk for depression - which is more difficult to treat with standard antidepressant therapy if it is not supplemented with levothyroxine - and decreases in cognitive functions, such as memory. ...Nevertheless, even in the absence of apparent symptomatic improvement, there are sufficient data supporting the salutary effects of therapy on lipid profiles, propensity to athero-genesis, and cardiac function to warrant early intervention."

*Women Health Orthopedic Edition* 2003; 6(2):57-63

Getting an accurate thyroid profile is absolutely necessary in treating depression. "Until 2002, doctor's had relied on a TSH (thyroid stimulating hormone) level ranging from 0.5 to 5.0 to diagnose and treat patients with a thyroid disorder ... Now the American Association of Clinical Endocrinologists (AACE) encourages doctors to consider treatment for patients who test outside the boundaries of a narrower margin based on a target TSH level of 0.3 to 3.04. The AACE believes the new range will result in proper diagnosis for millions of Americans who suffer from a mild thyroid disorder, but have gone untreated until now."

www.thyroidpower.com

Levothyroxine is Synthroid - an inexpensive, low side effect medication. Adding even a tiny amount of thyroid replacement to your regimen may reap enormous benefits. Renewed energy and weight loss are two factors in corrected thyroid problems.

*"What I dream of is an art of balance."*
*Henri Matisse*

## *August 15*

## Typical Vs. Atypical Depression

Do not be dismayed if what you experience in depression is the complete opposite of what others say they are feeling. I really thought I was crazy when even my symptoms weren't normal. In fact, atypical depression has the exact opposite symptom profile of the major four indicators for 'normal' depression: appetite which is lowered in regular depression is elevated in atypical depression; body weight which is lowered in regular depression is elevated in atypical depression; sleep needs which is lowered in regular depression is elevated in atypical depression; slowed movement and speech is normal in regular depression but the symptom is heightened movement and speech in atypical depression.

So, if you - like me - cannot get enough sleep and gain weight in a depression, you just have a different DMS-IV diagnosis and will need different medications to alleviate your illness.

The best thing you can do for yourself (and to aid your physician in treating you and getting you back on your feet) is to monitor your moods and symptoms. For years I kept a system in my Daytimer of rating my mood - giving each day a number - and logging my symptoms. This was invaluable in helping my physicians medicate and treat me.

Becoming an authority on your unique chemistry is THE first step in recovering your health and vitality.

*"Uncertainty will always be a part of the taking charge process."*

*Harold Geneen,*
*founder, MCI Communications*

## *August 16*

## No Wonder We Are Depressed!

Dr. Nancy Andreason in her landmark book, *The Broken Brain*, discusses many of the newest findings in brain research. One that really feels right to me and maybe it will to you, too, is the new tomographic studies of Regional Cerebral Blood Flow (RCBF). Although there are very few centers with the imaging capability to study RCBF, it is highly promising in understanding depression.

If it can be proven that depressives actually do have restricted blood flow in critical areas of the brain (cerebellum, temporal lobes, lower frontal lobes, etc...), then it is no wonder that we can't concentrate or work at our normal levels.

Andreason states..."pictures of this type suggest that patients suffering from depression may have a decreased metabolic rate in their brains, which may either be a cause or a symptom."

*"The nuclear generator of brain sludge is television."*

*Dave Barry*

*August 17*

## What "FDA Approved" Really Means

Until recently I naively thought that FDA approval of medications meant that some non-biased, thoroughly objective government agency ran the years of medical trials that go into approving a new pharmaceutical for public consumption. That once we saw "FDA Approved", we were assured of the efficacy and safety of what we were going to ingest.

How wrong I was.

In the June 16, 2004 issue of *USA TODAY*, Robert Davis states that "drug companies and other for-profit firms, which fund more than 80% of the USA's medical research, hide bad news."

So, not only are the drug companies disclosing their own findings on research that they will profit from, but now it appears that "studies with positive findings are more likely to be published than studies with negative or null results. We are concerned that this pattern...distorts the medical literature." (Joseph Heyman, trustee for the American Medical Association from same *USA TODAY* article).

The article goes on to say: "New York's attorney general has charged that London-based Glaxo-SmithKline failed to disclose findings that suggested its anti-depressant Paxil didn't work well on kids and could potentially trigger suicidal thoughts."

The same word of caution applies here as everywhere else. Use your own judgment - every single time - to make decisions that impact you and your loved ones. Doing your own research (and with the Internet now there is no excuse for not digging pretty deep on some of these issues) is critical.

*"Many people say that government is necessary because some men cannot be trusted to look after themselves, but anarchists say that government is harmful because no men can be trusted to look after anyone else."*

Nicolas Walter

*August 18*

## Suicide Less Likely in Later Stages of Illness

Statistics prove that the longer one lives with severe depression, the less likely is suicide.

I think I understand why that is.

Not only have I developed better tools for dealing with the bottom of despair, but I am living proof that you can come out the other side.

I keep pictures of great moments - I am always laughing with friends in these - around my home, so that when the black hole hits, I remember that there are periods of happiness if I can survive the current agonizing misery.

It is impossible to feel this - to feel that there will ever be another happy time with friends - that I will have fun again - when I am in the dark cesspool of depression. But, I know when the pictures were taken - the gaiety is real - and I can hang on to the picture as proof - even if every fiber in my being doesn't believe it is possible.

*"If I had no sense of humor, I would have long ago committed suicide."*

*Mohandas Gandhi*

*August 19*

## The Power of Self-Permission

Some of you may need to just skip this section. You may be empowered already to give yourself the time and funds and energy to accomplish whatever it takes to find or maintain wellness and balance in your health. I give time and funds and energy so readily to others, but must be pushed to my very limit before I will accord myself a fraction of what I give to family, friends, neighbors and colleagues.

So, giving myself permission to turn away from those who usually count on me and focus on myself comes at a great emotional cost for me. And those who are the usual recipients of this help aren't too crazy about the change either!

But, I have found that if I do not give what I need to myself, no one is going to show up and do it for me. So, one way I mentally justify this 'selfishness', is that if I don't take the necessary action and put my attention on my health and recovery, then who will be there to help these friends and loved ones later?

Sounds kind of weak, I know, but, it is difficult for me to take time (don't think you will FIND time after you help everyone else) and put me first. Whatever justification works for you, use it.

*"Where self-interest is suppressed, it is replaced by a burdensome system of bureaucratic control that dries up the well-spring of initiative and creativity."*

*Pope John Paul 11*

*August 20*

## Exercise Is NOT Optional

You have probably found out this vital information through your own experience. I would like to underline the importance of moving - whether that be slamming tennis balls into the back wall of your garage, walking your dog, doing ten jumping jacks when you get up in the morning, riding your bike.

Adrenaline creates more adrenaline. Even moving a little bit helps oxygenate your blood and improve mood.

If you are still a non-believer, read this:

"In 1999 researchers at Duke University published the results of a study in which they divided depressed patients ages 50 to 77 into three groups. The first did thirty minutes of jogging or brisk walking thirty minutes three times a week; the second took the antidepressant Zoloft; the third did both. After four months, patients in all three groups were doing equally well, the medication offering no particular advantage over the regular practice of working out, except in relieving the symptoms a little faster. When the researchers followed up six months later, however, they found a major difference between the types of treatment. About a third of the patients who initially improved on Zoloft (alone and with exercise) had relapsed, whereas 92 percent of those benefiting from just the aerobic exercise program were still doing well. Most of the joggers and walkers had decided on their own initiative to keep exercising even after the study had ended."

Dr. David Servan-Schreiber, "Shortcut to Bliss", *OPRAH*, January 2005.

*"Few people know how to take a walk, The qualifications are endurance, plain clothes, old shoes, an eye for nature, good humor, a vast curiosity, good speech, good silence and nothing too much."*

*Ralph Waldo Emerson*

*August 21*

## When Your Soul Is Sick

Plato said, "The greatest mistake in the treatment of diseases is that there are physicians for the body and physicians for the soul, although the two cannot be separated."

Depression and the other neurobiological illnesses (anxiety disorder, schizophrenia, etc...) are the only diseases of a biological nature that seem to so profoundly affect our soul.

I feel like my soul is throbbing in pain when depression strikes. People with kidney ailments never feel this. Migraine sufferers do not feel soul sick. Heart patients do not feel shriveled in their core.

But, if you are depressed, some aspect of your soul is afflicted as well. Physicians do not address this issue and often we are even embarrassed to mention it. But, this center of ourselves/core/soul is definitely a component of the mind. We usually say brain for mind - as surgeons can operate on a brain, but they cannot locate our minds.

The only tactic that I know of to use when your soul hurts is to know that the self-loathing, the suffocated spirit, the crushed self-esteem will disappear when the depression lifts.

But, no amount of affirmations spoken to the mirror or upbeat thoughts will fix this elusive pain. This is just one of the mystery components of our illness. I have found no remedy for soul sickness except for time to heal the depression.

*"I simply believe that some part of the human Self or Soul is not subject to the laws of space and time."*

*Carl Jung*

## *August 22*

## Stepping into the Void

John Greenleaf Whittier said:

"The steps of faith fall on the seeming void

And find the rock beneath."

How many times have you heard - "you have to step out in faith"? That is exactly how many of the trials felt like during the healing from this deadly grip of depression. I would have nothing to go on - maybe one person's success, maybe an article I had run across - but, I would step out into the void with faith and pray for the best. And some of what I trusted did not work and some helped just a little bit. But, I kept taking that next step - often into empty air, it felt like - and hoped to find solid ground beneath me.

But, what I did have is a rock solid faith that this misery was not what I was destined to live with. I knew there was more for me than this daily agony. I kept hearing that old refrain - 'the longest journey begins with a single step'. So, I saw my duty as only needing to keep putting one foot in front of the other. No great leaps - no giant strides. Just tiny, incremental steps in the right direction would get me to the top. (And it has).

*"Faith is like radar that sees through the fog."*
*Corrie Ten Boom*

## *August 23*

## Shutting Down a Social Life

For the entire year of 1989, I made not one single commitment socially. I was so ashamed of feeling as if I was abusing my friends for incessantly calling to break a date for something we had planned to do together. I would plan some normal activity while I was feeling good and too often when the time came, I was unable to go.

The pain of constantly backing out on my friends overcame the need to see new faces or have fun. If you are married, the situation is only slightly different. You are still going to be caught in the spiral of making plans and then canceling out at the last minute. It can really wear on even the best of relationships.

Making plans to even attend church - a simple activity that only minimally engages us - can be too much in some phases of depression. Whereas a spouse can still attend and make our excuses, if you are living an independent lifestyle, all the responsibility falls to you.

And to make the situation worse, I was too ill to explain what was wrong when I needed to cancel out and if I said I was 'depressed', innocently the other party would insist that it would be best for me to get out with others, blah, blah, blah.... I was usually in no state to handle this and so, I compounded the guilt by lying. It was accepted and understood if I just begged off with 'a migraine'.

But, I loathe deception - even when I felt it was necessary - and so, it became far easier to just decline all invitations at the inception.

Hopefully, you will never go through a protracted period of a year, but, only you can be the director of your recovery and there are times when you need to focus one hundred percent on yourself. When a person is in medical school, we automatically excuse them and understand their tunnel vision. It is unthinkable to ask a woman in labor to do anything other than give her entire attention to a healthy delivery. If someone is preparing for a funeral, do we expect anything other than that from them? Absolutely not! So, my mental concentration needs to be at the same peak to get myself well - or sometimes even just to survive the current black hole of depression.

And I give myself permission every single time. Be kind to yourself. Treat you like you treat others.

*"The most beautiful discovery true friends can make is that they can grow separately without growing apart."*
*Elisabeth Foley*

## *August 24*

## Where I Stand

I have my incoming freshman at the university write an assessment of their values in a "Where I Stand" essay. And this assignment evolved from the work I had to do when depression decimated my life in my mid-30's.

I had to step back and re-evaluate every facet of my life. And taking a look at where I stood was essential. I had to rethink my goals, my hopes, my free time, my work - or actually lack of work, my financial priorities, my beliefs, my NEEDS.

I shifted virtually every single aspect of my world during this time.

When I was able to return to a relatively normal life fifteen years later, I had to go back and reassess 'where I stood' all over again.

Give yourself time and permission to rethink your positions. I especially had to look long and hard at: 1. trust and 2. my faith in spiritual powers.

There will be areas of your life that you will need to make changes to in order to compensate for depression.

No change has to be permanent. That is your choice.

*"He who rejects change is the architect of decay. The only human institution which rejects progress is the cemetery."*
*Harold Wilson*

## *August 25*

## Shakespearean Wisdom

This thought kept me going during some of the bleakest depressions:

*"Many strokes though with a little axe,*
*Hews down and fells the hardest timbered oak."*
*William Shakespeare*

I can't recall the *Bible* verse that is a corollary of this, but this philosophy made sense to me on several levels. I knew that something as trivial as the Japanese torture of constant drips of water on a prisoner's forehead was all it took to destroy a man. In ordinary circumstances, a drop of water is meaningless. But, it is the constancy that creates the ultimate damage.

So, I would envision my recovery as tiny little steps of progress that would eventually lead me to the completely renewed me that I saw in my mind's eye. I could rebuild Humpty-Dumpty by gluing one small fragment back in place at a time. I did not look for one big element to pull me out - no magic pill, no perfect doctor, etc... I saw my healing in little, manageable units - little strokes of the axe - that would fell the burden of depression cycles.

And when my thinking was clear, I made sure that I kept a record of incremental steps in my healing. Even if it was one step forward and two back - as it felt so many days - the overall pattern was an upward one of progress. I no longer had blocks of coma sleep for seventy-two hours. I no longer avoided making plans. I had lost ten pounds - not the fifty I wanted to lose, but I rationalized that I had gained the weight one pound at a time, so I would lose it one pound at a time. No one loses ten pounds in a day - it is always in increments. (Although I must admit that some weeks it seemed like I lost in ounces!)

So, this image of chopping down the tree - and my depression seemed to be of Sequoian proportions - was never accomplished by one blow and my recovery wasn't going to be either. As long as I kept chopping, it was going to come down. And that is a fact.

*"Those who expect moments of change to be comfortable and free of conflict have not learned their history."*
*Joan Wallach Scott*

## *August 26*

## Random Helpers

On a sluggish day, use caffeine to keep your motor running and take more than one shower to benefit from the negative ion healing power.

Create your own Intensive Care unit and check yourself in.

Splurge on bouquets of luscious flowers.

If all else fails, use the Ostrich Approach - stick your head in the sand and your butt in the air until the problem or issue passes.

And let humor soften all rough spots.

*"Surviving a downturn is a bit like going over Niagara Falls in a barrel; when you hit bottom, you're either dead or happily bobbing in calmer waters."*
*Ted Pile*

*August 27*

## The Four Cures

My basic premise is that depression is due to altered, imbalanced chemistry.

But, if that mode of recovery is eluding you at this time- i.e. medication that will rebalance you - here are the four no-fail options:

Sleep
Reading
Moving (as in exercising)
Distraction

Use whatever combination of the above to get you through the valleys. They WILL work - I promise - until you can find the chemical harmony to keep you stable.

*"A good laugh and a long sleep are the best cures in the doctor's book."*

*Irish proverb*

*August 28*

## Here Is What You Don't Need

Do not obsess over money. The guilt you punish yourself with is unnecessary. Medicine and doctors cost dearly. If you had cancer, the funds would be provided for your recovery. Your brain is sick and needs medical attention and that costs money. Let this worry go as worrying will not solve this issue.

Do not practice doom and gloom thinking. "I will never get out of this, I will lose my job/husband or wife/ sanity/etc......" The brain is capable of embracing only one thought at a time. So, if you are thinking, "I wish that idiot knew how to drive", you cannot simultaneously be thinking, "I am an exceptionally good neighbor." If a negative thought intrudes, interrupt it and replace it with a benevolent thought.

People in your life who are judgmental, bigoted, selfish, cold-hearted, unreasonable need to be avoided at all costs.

Avoid unnecessary stress. Choose your battles.

Recovering from depression is all that you need to focus on. Let everything else go (for now).

*"Worry never robs tomorrow of its sorrow, it only saps today of its joys."*

*Leo Buscaglia*

*August 29*

## This is a Gift

Alright. Now you know I must be kidding. Right?

No, I am not.

I can get to an objective place from time to time and see that because of the depth of suffering the pain and misery of depression creates in my life, I am far more sensitive to what others are facing and experiencing in life. My ability to empathize with and understand the suffering of others is heightened. I am a more caring friend, a more thoughtful colleague or neighbor. I can lend what I want others to offer me. I may know the right word to say that will make someone's situation a little more bearable.

There is no book that teaches like experience.

*"It's all about helping, and anytime that you can help someone, go out and do it because it makes you feel better. It makes you a better person."*

*Kim Perrot*

*August 30*

## Using Your Circadian Rhythm to Heal You

Humans are known to have a circadian rhythm - a biologically set schedule of wake and sleep cycles - and knowing your best hours for productivity helps. If you are a morning person, do not sign up for night classes or sales in a retail environment as malls are open until late evening. If you are a nocturnal producer, do not schedule appointments or commitments before noon. We have become such a 24/7 society that it is actually very easy to accommodate widely varying lifestyles to best fit your chemistry.

There have been so many scientific studies to prove that this natural rhythm is imprinted in our genes. One particular study that I keep in mind is one from the mid- 70's. The population studied were those who could give up a pretty big block of their time (weeks) - prisoners, students, housewives even gave of their time. And the biggest factor was their environment. The participants had to all stay in rooms that had no windows or access whatever to visibility of the outside world. They had no clocks, watches, radios, televisions (computers weren't commonplace then), no newspapers, nothing that would give them any clue as to time.

Another feature of this study is that meals were varied. Lunch would precede breakfast or there would be two breakfasts in a row. And the staff who brought meals in to each participant in their individual "apartments" were never the same. So, no one was able to guess that it was "morning" because a certain staff member was bringing their meal to them.

And just as the study directors had predicted, within one week, all the participants who had stated on their intake documents that they were "morning" people were awakening in the morning hours. And these people were naturally going to sleep in the mid-evening. Just like they said they usually did.

And the "night" people were still active and awake until the wee morning hours and naturally awoke closer to noon. Just as they said they did in their normal lives in the world outside of the study walls.

But, the participants were responding to their biological circadian rhythm only. Because they never saw daylight or night or could count on meals to regulate their sense of time, their genes naturally found the cycle they lived and worked best under.

Think of how powerful this imprinted code is on all of us. You will further unbalance your chemistry if you try to fight against your natural sleep/wake cycle.

You may have to change your employment (as I did) to fit this unalterable factor. I was able to be ultra-active between 5 and 10 a.m. in my early thirties. But, as I aged and my chemistry shifted due to the depression cycles that began in my mid-thirties, I could not get any rest until 2 or 3 a.m. and was most productive between 7 and 10 p.m. It only further aggravated my already unbalanced chemistry to try to make my mind and body work at 8 a.m.

Although this may cause a change in lifestyle and finances, it behooves you to find a way to create your life (and income) around what your body dictates.

*"If you can't sleep, then get up and do something instead of lying there worrying. It's the worry that gets you, not the lack of sleep."*

*Dale Carnegie*

## *August 31*

### Blame

When depression creeps in and steals your life, it is only human to want to lay the blame somewhere. Was it that rotten boss who never was happy? Was it living with your in-laws the first two years of your marriage? Was the inability to conceive and have a family at fault? Has it been years of not being able to keep your head above water financially?

Parents are often sick with guilt when they think that it was their gene pool that may have caused you all this pain.

Just like a car accident, nothing changes in the present circumstances - no matter who or what is to blame.

Dismiss all thoughts of blame. Do not allow yourself to waste energy you could be using toward recovery and do not allow conversations to continue if blame is the topic.

Blame has no place in your healing.

*"I pay no attention whatever to anybody's praise or blame. I simply follow my own feelings."*

*Wolfgang Amadeus Mozart*

# SEPTEMBER

## *September 1*

### Staying at a 'Safe House'

Once, in the early days of my diagnosis, a really great friend, and fellow sufferer, offered me her spare bedroom. I lived alone at that time, so I didn't need the privacy. What I needed was a place to go, if the hospital was not an option, where I knew my suicidal urges would be quieted.

After being taken aback, I saw the simple need for this. I would have a key, it was understood that I would only have to call and tell her I was coming, I would not have to have any contact or conversation with her at all. This wasn't about support in the usual sense. I just needed the shelter of her home to get me through.

She was available if I needed her, but that was secondary.

Having a safe house set up is a fabulous idea. It can't be just anywhere. This must be a non-invasive, non-co-dependent friend. All arrangements need to be made during a good phase. Maybe you need to have a fall back house as well.

Just knowing that my friend's house was available was enormous comfort during many a dark and bleak period. Ironically, I never needed to use it. Maybe just the security of knowing I had a haven to go to was all I needed.

This may not be a tool you need, but it never hurts to be prepared.

*"He who cannot rest cannot work; he who cannot let go cannot hold on..."*

*Harry Emerson Fosdick*

## *September 2*

### Solving Chocolate Cravings

I discuss chocolate as a highly effective treatment tool for depression several times throughout this book. See August 3 for other references.

But today's tool is about handling a chocolate crisis. Here are my minimal calories/most satisfying solutions:
* a glass of reduced fat milk with Hershey's syrup (very filling with the added calcium benefits)
* Cool Whip with chocolate pudding stirred in
* RediWhip makes a delicious chocolate whipped cream in the aerosol can
* low fat version: Cool Whip with added plain, non-fat yogurt and several tablespoons of Nestle's Quik mixed together
* Chocolate Teddy's Grahams (even a binge of the entire box would only be 1,110 +/- calories and 45 grams of fat)
* I keep a can of the best quality canned chocolate frosting in my refrigerator so that a tablespoon or two can quiet the chocolate cravings
* Ditto - keeping a chocolate Wendy's Frosty in your freezer helps; even two or three tablespoons can put you back on track
* I have even been known to eat a few tablespoons of Nestle's Quik dry - just by itself - in a pinch (maybe fifty calories total)

What I do NOT keep in my house:
* M & M's; I just don't have the willpower
* Hershey's chocolate of any kind

The thinking that I can overcome chocolate cravings with willpower has long gone the way of hula-hoops. It isn't going to happen. When I crave chocolate, butterscotch or vanilla or any other substitute is NOT going to work. So eat the chocolate and get it over with!

*"Foods like ... chocolate can be physically addictive. People blame themselves and imagine that they lack willpower, but food cravings are due to a physical property of the foods themselves. These foods trigger opiates in the brain that cause a feel-good effect."*

*Neal Barnard, M.D.*
*in Breaking the Food Seduction.*

## *September 3*

## What a Difference a Day Makes

I have been flabbergasted how very near the edge I am one day, thinking there is NO HOPE and the very next day, there are blue skies and life is good again.

I do not know how or why this radical shift can take place in so brief a time period, but I am living proof that it can.

I will use this phrase - "what a difference a day makes" - repetitively on a bad day. I will think of all the aspects of my life that are exactly the same today when I am hurting and sick at heart, that were the very same yesterday when life looked bearable, changeable - when I had options and hope and plans and dreams.

I use this phrase to think of the many times in my life that one day has brought either a great insight, new information, a new person or contact that radically changed the landscape of my life. Suddenly, the world is a different place. Something that wasn't even a remote thought on the horizon, has popped up and made itself (or themselves) available and that quickly, everything is different. Everything has shifted.

So, I use the tools I have learned to get through these twenty four hours, and depend on these little miracles to make themselves known to me.

Tomorrow is a new beginning.

*"Life is a train of moods like a string of beads; and as we pass through them they prove to be many colored lenses, which paint the world their own hue, and each shows us only what lies in its own focus."*

*Ralph Waldo Emerson*

## *September 4*

## Using Black Humor

A dear friend who suffers from Bipolar Disorder and many other illnesses - including a narrow miss with cancer- has a laugh that is impossible not to join in with. You need not even know what she is laughing at, her chuckle/belly laugh is so contagious.

But, unless you know her, it is easy to be offended. Her humor is a 'gallows' humor if I ever knew one. She has said she would laugh at her firing squad and I can believe it.

Yet she lightens every group she is a part of. Her ability to laugh at herself and some of the absurdities of this illness and life in general are awesome. Considering what she has to deal with on a day-to-day basis, I truly feel it is her humor that keeps her alive to fight again another day.

If you can see some aspect of your illness in a humorous light - yuck it up. Some folks are easy to laugh with and I have learned who to cut up with. With these friends, we have often taken the absurdities of our behavior or doctors or whatever and nearly cried laughing. I remember howling with a friend when I confessed that I had to set the alarm for noon so I could make a 1 p.m. appointment. She joined in with similar stories of her own.

It is not that this woman cannot hear the pain or discuss the terror with me, because she does. But, I do not remember a single conversation with her over the years that did not contain a cleansing laugh.

Scientists have proven that laughter creates endorphins. This is a freebie. Use it!

*"A keen sense of humor helps us overlook the unbecoming, understand the unconventional, tolerate the unpleasant, overcome the unexpected, and outlast the unbearable."*
*Billy Graham*

## *September 5*

## Some Lifestyle Suggestions

You might consider living in an apartment or condominium rather than a house. This eliminates worries about maintenance and upkeep, a yard to maintain, shrubs to trim. You can container garden if digging in the dirt is one of your loves. The proximity of others and the likelihood of meeting folks also comes with apartment or condo living. When I was single and living in a house - even though I was in a subdivision - once the garage door was down, I was really isolated.

You might consider limiting your visits back to your parental home. Is this place a haven or are you expected to 'perform' and appease while you are there? Some friends make it a point to visit home only three times a year and no visit is longer than three hours.

You might consider preparing yourself for working in a different environment. The training to be a medical transcriptionist might be extra work now, but would allow you to make a fair wage on your schedule/around your illness, in your bathrobe if need be.

Or you might do as I do, and teach college (a full time position requires only 15 contact hours a week- I can grade papers at home in bed). This requires having a Masters' degree at minimum, but we are thinking long-range here.

Or you might look into telecommuting. Again, a bathrobe is acceptable office attire. As of this writing, both J.C. Penney and UPS pay benefits for part-time workers. Use Richard Bolles' best seller, *What Color Is Your Parachute?* for further brainstorming.

Other changes I made were: disconnecting my doorbell - sleep was too precious for unnecessary intrusions; using my answering machine religiously - having and using the screening capabilities in case it was someone I did need to speak to; never getting below four days of medication before I refilled my prescriptions; not making plans to be away from my home/doctors during my primary cycles.

Look at your lifestyle realistically. Are there some modifications that might ease some tension for you? I thought about having someone clean once in a while but it was better to live in the clutter than to have someone in my home when I was at my worst. Can you change to a pharmacy that will deliver?

Pick up take-out menus each time you visit a restaurant and keep a file in case you need food delivered.

Keep an open mind here.

*"When choosing between two evils, I always like to try the one I've never tried before."*

*Mae West*

## *September 6*

## Self-image

I have a piece of paper on my desk with the words "Our expectations create our reality". This is the Pygmalion effect of transforming ourselves into the person we choose to be. Our brain does not know the difference between a lie and the truth. If we say to ourselves, "I am really happy; I am having a great time; I am well and healthy", we can imprint on our minds that perception even if it is not reality. If you say these affirmations regularly, it is as if you are applying fresh coats of paint to a dingy wall. After a few layers, the wall looks pretty terrific and the darker underside is not visible.

This is a form of mind control. The Hindu's have practiced mind control for centuries and can use it to block pain. They have been able to maintain a physical posture until that position becomes frozen and they actually transform their physical structure.

It is hard to imagine this working when our minds aren't functioning normally. Fake this one anyway. You may not feel euphoric, but you will definitely feel better.

This tool has been scientifically proven to work. And it does.

"I can beat this. I AM doing better. I can thrive. I have so much to live for."

*"What we call the secret of happiness is no more a secret than our willingness to choose life."*
*Leo Buscaglia*

## *September 7*

### Memory Loss

We may experience memory loss in two ways. Depression itself can block parts of our information data banks and occasionally, medications have a mild effect on memory as well.

It will help if you remember that nothing has removed what you know. All the information is still stored in your brain. There's just a curtain pulled over that area for now. You will lift the curtain in time.

All you have ever learned is kept safely in the vault of your brain. Just because you can't access some of that information from time to time does not minimize its existence.

If you have noticed a major shift in your short term memory after a medication change, ask your physician about a possible change in dosage or even a change in the time you take your medication. Often a simple alteration can ameliorate the negative symptoms.

I have felt terror on occasion when going through a dark cycle, I would blank on a name or fact. I learned that I was merely experiencing the 'brain fog' of depression and it was only a matter of time before my mind was working normally again.

Do not be afraid if this happens to you. It is only temporary.

*"If you think you can, you can. If you think you can't, you're right."*

*Henry Ford*
*(also attributed to Mary Kay Ash)*

## *September 8*

## Laugh Out Loud

Today is a great day  to get your endorphins in full swing. See if this helps:

Some novel ideas -
Save the whales. Collect the whole set.
99 percent of lawyers give the rest a bad name.
Honk if you love peace and quiet.
On the other hand, you have different fingers.
I drive way too fast to worry about cholesterol.
Bills travel through the mail twice as fast as checks.
You never really learn to swear until you learn to drive.
The problem with the gene pool is that there is no lifeguard.
Get a new car for your spouse - it will be a great trade!
If at first you don't succeed, then sky-diving isn't for you.

See, you feel a bit better already, don't you?

*"The human race has but one effective weapon and that is laughter."*

*Mark Twain*

*September 9*

## Available Job Paths

The career you have chosen in the life you led before your illness became active may need to be greatly altered. If your sleep patterns are not congruent with your work schedule or the stress of your current position constantly hampers your ability to function, then it is time to think about a career/job change.

I have found that I could stay in the same career - teaching - but, in a different arena. The five day a week, 7:30 a.m. to 3:30 p.m. schedule demanded of a high school teacher was not one I could maintain. Now, I teach an afternoon/evening schedule three days a week at a university. I get less pay, but I still qualify for benefits and am considered full time.

To provide income for yourself and your family, you may have to reconsider your options. The three areas that must be addressed are: stress, flexibility and minimum functioning level (what you are able to do on your worst days).

Being a manager of a large department, a fireman, a physician, a truck driver, a stockbroker, a pilot or a delivery person may no longer be an option for you. A career shift to a support person (aide, secretary, technician, staff) within your field might alleviate stress to the point that your medications are able to function adequately and you can keep your benefit status.

Working in sales allows an individual to work their own schedule for the most part although there may be the pressure of a quota. Many firms will now consider flex hours for proven employees and telecommuting offers even greater flexibility.

Teachers work an abbreviated day and a nine-month work year with frequent vacations. Some jobs like landscaping, clerking, warehouse work, or maintenance work can keep your body going while your mind is not functioning at peak power.

I am not implying for a moment that any work is not meaningful and productive. But, what you would choose to do and what you are capable of doing may not be the same thing.

And a change may only be temporary. But, being in the work force in any capacity gives you contact with others, a reason to get up in the morning and a sense of accomplishment. Most of us need the coverage of medical expenses through a strong benefits package almost as much as we need the salary.

So, you may need to shift your work day to compensate for depression. The current environment creates enormous opportunities to work with whatever changes you need to make. Make your health a priority and then fit the work around what climate you function in best. I find Richard Bolles' *What Color is Your Parachute?: A Manual for Job-Hunters and Career-Changers* or his JobHuntersBible.com website to be the easiest, most realistic sources available. The *Parachute* book has been in print for thirty years and twenty thousand people a month still purchase it!

I looked at what expenses I could change (my car payment, my rent or mortgage, etc...) and got to the lowest monthly minimum I could afford and still LIKE my life. I drive a fabulous Jeep now that is fifteen years old, but paid for. When I moved from Atlanta to this small university community, my living expenses dropped by three-fourths. I do not know IF you need to make changes, but if you do, think long and hard about what you need to be happy and then create that.

If you are living a treadmill life of stress and pressure, you will NOT heal. Only YOU can evaluate your needs and circumstances.

*"To accomplish great things, we must not only act, but also dream; not only plan, but also believe."*
*Anatole France*

## *September 10*

## Insurance

If you are fortunate enough to have medical coverage, even though the limits are often fairly narrow on what is covered under mental health, you are in good shape. Some of the major corporations like UPS or JC Penney will offer benefits to employees who work twenty hours a week. Having some form of medical coverage is important to everyone today - especially those suffering from a chronic illness like depression.

Unfortunately, some insurance companies regard depression and other brain illnesses as psychological/emotional illness rather than biological illness. Therefore, your coverage of medical expenses becomes clouded due to your diagnosis or your doctors' documentation of what he/she does for you.

These are some ways of dealing with this frustrating issue however:
psychotherapists can often be reimbursed if a medical doctor will co-sign your insurance forms;
some therapists and doctors will work on a sliding scale;
public health services are usually adequate if not excellent;
you can always get insured if you are employed by a large enough company - you will be part of the limited risk group included in big corporations;
HMO's might be an option;
generic prescriptions are significantly cheaper than their name brand counterparts, however, generics are either toxic or not effective for many and if that is true for you, you will not have saved any money in the long run;
if you can be considered 'indigent', some of the hospitals will fill any prescription for a flat fee (usually in the two dollar range) or you can find the toll-free phone number of any pharmaceutical company at http://www.edhayes.com/indigent.html and how to apply for their free medication programs programs or try Partnership for Prescription Assistance at www.paparx.org or 1-888-4PPA-NOW.

Having insurance is pretty important and one of the biggest determinants in career decisions. If you find your coverage is lacking when it comes to covering depression, find ways to work within the guidelines of your insurer. There are numerous alternatives to being denied.

*"I'm a great believer in luck and I find the harder I work, the more I have of it."*

*Thomas Jefferson*

## *September 11*

## Keeping Track of Your Mood

If you are not a person who keeps their life in order with a tool like the Daytimer, you might want to use one of the calendars available through the Internet or one that companies give for gifts at Christmas. But, to manage your recovery, you do need to keep some kind of monitor on the ebb and flow of your depression.

Being able to see clear and distinct patterns to your lulls and highs can help your doctor in knowing what to treat you for.

I use a simple one to ten scale. One being the very bottom and ten being euphoria. Use any scale that works for you.

Just take a moment at some point in your day to step back and look at where you are mood-wise and log that. I find that how I feel first thing in the morning is not how I will feel after I have taken my supplements and medications for that day. So, a truer picture of my well-being would be about two hours after I have started my day.

The other area besides treatment and diagnosis that tracking will benefit you, is to look back and see how far you have come. I love to see how much fuller my calendar is currently compared to the low numbers and low energy days of several years ago.

You know your chemistry. Just make it a habit to track your patterns.

*"You can never plan the future by the past."*
*Edmund Burke*

## *September 12*

## Acupressure and acupuncture

Although some of the more controversial forms of treating depression, these two ancient healing arts can be extremely beneficial. Acupuncture uses many different size tiny needles to painlessly clear blocked nerve bundles or energy sources. Acupressure addresses the same blocked areas, but by soft and brief pressure rather than needles.

The one area of concern that must be addressed for both modalities is the knowledge and expertise of the practitioner. Many states legalize acupuncture only for pain relief (primarily back pain) and for smoking cessation. However, occasionally some of these practitioners will assure you that they treat depression effectively as well. You must research licensing regulations for your state and ask those friends or others you trust for referrals. A call to the research department of your library should answer most of these questions. Do not - in your need for relief - allow yourself to be treated by someone who is not adequately trained.

The acupressure specialist who gave me immediate, long-term relief is also a chiropractor. This is a natural combination as both fields practice healing as simply putting the body back in balance. Their theory being that disease comes from imbalances and that the body is miraculous and constantly seeking health and balance, therefore invasive measures are not necessary.

I found acupressure to be one of the biggest additions to my prescription medications that completely turned the path of my illness around. I continue to see the acupressure specialist on a maintenance basis and will continue to do so.

Hopefully, one or both of these alternative treatments will be a useful tool in your recovery. They tend to be relatively inexpensive but, are not usually covered by any insurance programs.

*"Good thoughts are no better than good dreams, unless they be executed."*

*Ralph Waldo Emerson*

## *September 13*

## Disability Income

Disability income is strictly for covering a portion of what you earn if you become unable to work. There are two types of disability policies. Private policies are those you pay a premium for through your employer as a part of your benefits package. Because you are part of a large group, the premiums are usually very low and are deducted from your pay each pay period. You can sometimes purchase disability income through an insurance agent on your own but your premiums will be significantly higher. However, even a higher premium is a small price to pay if you lose the ability to work for long periods of time.

Private policies are purchased prior to your inability to work. So, like all insurance you purchase, you are protecting yourself from possible problems in the future. I sleep better if I have insurance and then pray that all the premiums I have paid have been unnecessary in the long run.

There is a waiting period before your disability income would begin (after you are unable to work for a consecutive length of time that varies from weeks to months).

The other type of disability income is available to everyone who has worked and paid into Social Security. The government is your insurer in this situation. Due to the complications of the government forms and documentation, there are various companies that can be found through the Internet that specialize in doing all the paperwork and follow-through for you.

You can receive both incomes under certain circumstances.

Both private and Social Security disability income have a two-tier structure. There is a short term income that begins under much less stringent qualifications and is exactly that - short term. If your inability to work (i.e. there are definitions that need to be met here; not being able to work in the position you most recently filled does not mean you are unable to work at all in some other situation, etc...) lasts longer than the short term coverage, you will need to move into long term disability status.

If at the end of a specified period of consecutive disability (often two years) you are unable to work and you meet further criteria, your coverage is extended until you are able to return to work or until you reach age 65.

If this sounds daunting and complicated, it can be. Especially when you feel so ill. However, there are community resources, etc... to help you through this process and if it keeps food on the table and a roof over your head while you focus on your recovery, then it is worth every aggravation. You usually are paid approximately sixty percent of the average of your income for the prior three years. Depending on who paid what part of the premiums, the entire amount you receive monthly can be tax-free.

But, the opportunity to cover your day to day needs is really a blessing. I strongly recommend paying the insignificant premium if this is available to you in hopes that you will never need to utilize it. Having monthly income can be the lifesaver you need most when you enter a long depression. And we never know how long a cycle will be until we come out of it.

*"To live for results would be to sentence myself to continuous frustration. My only sure reward is in my actions and not from them."*

Hugh Prather

*September 14*

## The Quiet Approach of Depression

Sometimes going into a depressive cycle feels like a fog silently descending upon you. There are no distinct edges and there's nothing solid to fight against.

But, it surrounds and covers.

Awareness is the key to dealing with this. During one of your strong times, list three or four of the identifying symptoms for you. Keep this list handy - maybe taped on your bathroom mirror. As soon as two or more symptoms are evident, begin to use your tools for healing defensively.

If possible when the cycle starts: increase your exercise, your intake of carbohydrates, your dose of DL- phenylalanine, get a lot more rest, and slow down your schedule.

Even though depression creeps up on us silently, we can do a great deal to alleviate the severity of the pain if we can catch a downward cycle in its earliest stages.

*"Action may not always bring happiness, but there is no happiness without action."*
*Benjamin Disraeli*

*September 15*

## Dr. Jekyll and Mr. Hyde

I always referred to my healthier days as living as the 'real Connie' and the rough days as living as the 'alien'. It was almost a physical reality that there were two separate identities inhabiting my body. The two personalities couldn't have been more different.

I wanted desperately to not be the critical, irritable, angry person I was when in the grip of depression. I knew my real self was the loving, supportive, gregarious me of my sunny days. But, Mr. Hyde of Robert Louis Stevenson fame was only seen after dark and my ugly self could only be seen in my dark days, too.

I wanted the responsible, trusted Dr. Jekyll persona to be the only side of me that others saw.

Do the best you can to alert others to give you a wide berth during the tough days and keep reminding yourself this ugly side is merely a visitor who will soon be leaving.

*"Man cannot remake himself without suffering, for he is both the marble and the sculptor."*

*Dr. Alexis Carrel*

## *September 16*

## Allergies

Surprisingly, food or environmental allergies or sensitivities can cause serious depression. These indications and theories are new enough to not be common knowledge yet, but if you suspect you are troubled by certain chemicals, try to educate yourself in this area.

Also, because these theories tend to be outside normal parameters of traditional medicine they are often overlooked or dismissed.

I find that even the smallest amount of Nutrasweet (asparatame) will not only give me an excruciating headache, but can throw my mood into a severe funk. I find the same to be true, but to lesser extents, of anything with: food coloring (especially the red dyes) like that found in Jello, maraschino cherries, or cranberry juice; monosodium glutamate (MSG), - so common in Oriental food; the sulfites and other chemicals used in commercial salads and salad bars to keep food from turning brown - etc...

If you feel chemical sensitivities or allergies are hampering your depression cycles, find a specialist to work with you. If the appropriate person is treating you, it is common to discover allergies to such common staples as wheat or dairy products or environmental chemicals that include pest control sprays or perfumes.

Exactly what mechanisms create mood changes because of exposure to these elements is not known. So, for now, avoidance is the only remedy if you are tormented with chemical triggers.

*"Everyone thinks of changing the world, but no one thinks of changing himself."*

*Leo Tolstoy*

## *September 17*

## The Suicide Tape

When my brain shifted silently from that lucid and bright place to the clouded and ugly place of depression, certain things shifted with it. For one, my attitude. I have been nicknamed Pollyanna at several phases in my life and I am a strident optimist. But, during my shifted cycle, I have a far different tape playing in my mind. I literally feel that the normal/real tape has been completely removed (as if my brain's thought activities played themselves out on a tape deck in my mind) and another tape has been dropped into the broadcast area. This tape is much shorter and tends to repeat the same half-dozen messages incessantly. One of the loudest of these messages is "I can't stand this anymore". During these times, I would fantasize about suicide and the relief from my pain.

This is one of the toughest areas to deal with for me. I have come to believe that among the myriad of powerful wires and switching systems in the human brain, there is a section that if intersecting improperly, activates self-destructive thoughts. Just as I believe areas of improperly working brains activate depression and suicidal thinking, I believe there are areas that activate violence, schizophrenia, psychopathic behaviors and migraines to name a few others.

The image I have of my brain is of a complex sphere made up of fine, hair-like wires interwoven in a dense, complicated circuitry. Some brains were misassembled and built with a faulty part or not aligned properly at birth. With the intricate, infinite functions the brain carries out even in a second - the real quandary is why there aren't a great deal more folks with flawed brains.

I use this electronic circuitry image to visualize myself pushing the stop button on my mental tape deck and physically removing the suicide cassette and replacing my normal tape and pushing the play button. Some days I need to do this exercise twenty times. But, every time I use this imagery to shift my perspective, I am in control and my illness is not.

This alone makes an improvement on my outlook.

I cannot allow the repetition of suicidal thoughts to play endlessly in my mind. And in some of the deep depressions this tape wants to take up permanent residency. So I change my channels. It is up to me to change my thinking and therefore, my reality.

*"We don't see things as they are, we see them as we are."*
*Anais Nin*

## *September 18*

## Believing Everything You Read

When in a rough phase, we often are desperate for relief. Any new treatment or medication we read or hear about is like a shot of adrenalin. Hope is our great weapon.

I absolutely believe that educating yourself about your illness is necessary for your recovery to a full and active life of stability. However, as in every field or endeavor, there are incorrect reports and analyses and you need to absorb these with a grain of salt.

How do you know which are the incorrect reports? The more you read and study, the easier it will be to see through quackery and false promises. Actually, I have found very little misinformation concerning bipolar disorder or depression, but that doesn't mean it doesn't exist. Stick to your instinct if something is not true for you.

There is no authority greater than you. Once while I was a participant in an FDA approval study of a new drug, the doctor in charge of the program kept insisting that my hair couldn't possibly be falling out as that wasn't a side-effect. If this was a study to determine WHAT the side effects of this proposed medication was, then how could she be so convinced? No matter what you read in pharmaceutical inserts - if it's a side-effect for you - it is - period.

If you read that depression is anger turned inward and that's not your reality, dismiss that.

So, while I am a strong advocate of learning all you can about depression, I also advocate not believing everything you read.

There is NO authority greater than you. You are the only person living in your laboratory.

"There are two ways to slide easily through life; to believe everything or to doubt everything; both ways save us from thinking."

Alfred Korzybski

## *September 19*

### Walking, the Telephone and Intimacy

This may strike you as an odd topic at first. But, experience has taught me that a casual conversation struck up on a walk or a normal telephone call may be the bridge to conversations that may not otherwise be shared. It is really hard for me to express how bleak life looks to me or how desperate I am - how much I am hurting - if I have to look the other person in the eye. I fidget and hedge and hesitate and stumble all over my thoughts.

So, sometimes the medium in which a conversation takes place is the criteria for how much of what is REALLY going on with me I will share with the other person.

Not only is walking one of my favorite things to do, but it also activates adrenalin and lessens depression, too. It just seems so much easier to say the difficult things in this non-threatening style of walking side by side with someone.

The telephone helps too as I am somewhat removed from the other person and for me this creates a safety zone in which to expose my true self when I am hurting. There may be other ways to create avenues for dialogue. Let yourself discover what is best for you.

Just don't quit talking about what you need to share.

"Liberty, taking the word in its concrete sense, consists in the ability to choose."

Simone Weil

*September 20*

## Determination

You may not have been born with a fighting spirit, but you can develop the tactics that fighters use to win.

If you can keep a determined attitude to beat this illness and not lose this fight, you have taken yourself more than fifty-percent of the way to good health. In every book, article or pamphlet I have read or television docudrama I've seen, the common thread is always **attitude** for those trying to beat a serious ailment or problem. Every single one of those profiled sees themselves as victorious and do not entertain any other thoughts.

These folks meet each setback and obstacle with unflinching determination. Winners use every emotional and mental resource to focus on success and nothing will deter them from this position.

You've heard or read about these folks, too. They may not have been fighting - spirited or deeply committed to things before their illness or crisis, but they have learned to fight and win.

Be absolutely determined to beat this illness. As those in training for the Olympics do, see yourself going over the bar, crossing the finish line first, accepting your medal - living a complete and fulfilling life. It is true that the mind can't distinguish between a lie and the truth and it is also true that the mind is capable of handling only one thought at a time. So fill as many of those thought slots as possible with winner messages.

Be sure that your allotment of thoughts for any given day are a higher ratio of positive statements and you will have been a winner - for one more day.

*"First say to yourself what you would be; and then do what you have to do."*

*Epictetus*

## *September 21*

## Using Imagery

We all have a projection screen in our mind. And we are the one running the projector. I feel it is more than just imagination. It is a step beyond that.

The mind can hold only one thought at a time. Period. So, if you are seeing on your mental screen a vibrant, thriving you - it is impossible to also be seeing a disgusted, frustrated you. It is your movie. You can choose to keep the mental picture bright and successful.

The other great thing about the mind is that it does not know the difference between reality and fiction. So, if you visualize yourself living in financial abundance, gloriously alive and attractive -the mind holds that image as truth. And it seeks that reality for itself.

If the depression has pulled you too far into the darkness, take a sheet of paper and paste pictures on it of what you want to be your reality. Tape these images to your mirror, the refrigerator, your dashboard, your computer. Hide these pictures in with your credit cards, so that every time you reach for one, you have to look at this healthy you. Your mind will record this snapshot of well-being in the vault of your mind and the bigger your file of success and good health, the more it dominates the sick, unmotivated you.

It is mental gymnastics at its finest.

*"The most pathetic person in the world is someone who has sight, but has no vision."*

*Helen Keller*

## *September 22*

## Labels

It hurts to be in a group when someone tells a joke that refers to 'psychos'; when an individual is called a 'loony'. Other denigrating names are 'nut case', 'mental', 'crazy', 'weirdo' and you can probably add others.

Immediately upon hearing one of these ugly names, whether it is directed at you or in reference to another person, visually erase the word from the movie screen of your mind and substitute, "brain illness". What we suffer from is a disease of a primary organ of the body. It is no different from heart disease, liver damage, diabetes. And no one calls someone with these problems a derogatory name.

Do not ever accept one of these labels.

You are not your illness.

*"If you are distressed by anything external, the pain is not due to the thing itself, but to your estimate of it; and this you have the power to revoke at any moment."*
*Marcus Aurelius*

## *September 23*

### Paranoia

You know this feeling. The questions in your mind that reflect paranoia are:
How good an actor or actress are you during the down phases? How convincing are you that all is definitely well in your world? Are you terrified about those blanks in your job history because you were sick and could not work? Will a new person in your life guess this dark secret before you trust them enough to tell them about your depression cycles? How much honesty can you afford? What if, what if, what if?

I know this underlying feeling. It is certainly persistent.

But, keep uppermost in your mind that depression comes in cycles. Every single person has shadows in their life that they do not want the stark light of exposure focused on. You have periods of illness and so do other folks. They get the flu or food poisoning or migraines or car wrecks or ....so, minimize your illness. The REAL you is the one they see. You give other folks understanding due to their circumstances - why would you not deserve the same treatment?

But, you are to 'fake it til you make it'. Fake it. All the time it is necessary to preserve your mask. You are fine. You don't have a problem. Be the best con artist you can be. If you are fearful, it will show and if you are confident that will be evident, too.

I've never felt God was the least bit upset by my charade. Sometimes telling white lies is not a bad idea.

*"No person is your friend who demands your silence, or denies your right to grow."*

*Alice Walker*

## *September 24*

## What 'Well' Is

"How are you today?"

"Very well, thanks."

"Hope this finds you feeling well."

"Get well soon!"

Well, what is 'well' actually?

Now, this is one of those areas that we tend to have a distorted concept of. Because of the permeating effect our illness has on virtually every part of our life, we tend to egocentrically believe that we are sick and others are well. It is not that clearly delineated.

We obviously can acknowledge that there are many thousands of folks who are suffering from asthma, cancer, kidney failure, heart ailments etc... What we also need to acknowledge is that everyone suffers in some way. I had a tough time getting this. Some people just looked too good and their life seemed to be so right, I couldn't conceive that they had skeletons in their closets or rain on their parade. Trust me. It may be a child who cannot get off street drugs; it could be IRS legalities; it can be any one of a myriad of sordid problems. Some may be health-related and some may not.

So, who is 'well'? And what is 'well'?

No one has a clean slate. Every person is flawed, crippled in some way, hurting about something. So, they are not well - either physically or mentally.

Even if a mental illness is not your only ailment - and for many of us it isn't - you can still be relatively well. To see this clearly, make a list of all the things you do not have. "I do not have: diabetes, high cholesterol, kidney problems, anything wrong with my skin, all my limbs are intact and functioning, cerebral palsy, Huntington's chorea, poor teeth, migraines, etc...". Brainstorm. This list might well have several hundred entries.

Now, start again. "I do not have: any relatives in jail, any problems relating to my parents, any problems with my neighbors, any trouble with my spiritual beliefs, anything wrong with my singing/writing/drawing ability, any problem with my sense of humor, any problem relating to elderly people, etc...".

Keep this list. Make it easy to find. Read it often. Make additions. You're as 'well' as anyone else.

*"The greatest part of our happiness depends on our dispositions, not our circumstances."*
*Martha Washington*

## *September 25*

### Breaking Down

Sometimes the stress of our illness is too much at one time and our circuits overload. This may manifest itself in some brief psychotic behavior, a loss of time, or whatever a "nervous breakdown" is.

This can actually be a new beginning. By getting to our very bottom, we are forced to adjust our schedules, our work, and our relationships to accommodate the illness that we deal with.

Sometimes it is an opportunity to 'come out of the closet' about our health. If the health crisis has been significant enough, we may no longer be able to hide our illness from the world. There is the chance for great relief here.

We may be forced to come to terms with our situation and options may open up that were blocked before.

Rather than 'breaking down', we could describe the experience as 'turning the corner'.

*"He who refuses to embrace a unique opportunity loses the prize as surely as if he had tried and failed."*
*William James*

## *September 26*

### Hypoglycemia

If you have not already ruled low blood sugar out as a possibility for your mood swings, find a competent endocrinologist to run several tests on blood sugar levels for you. Hypoglycemia is often difficult to diagnose and yet is a major source of emotional upheavals.

Eliminate this as a cause for your illness. If not the only factor in your illness, it may be contributing substantially.

Hypoglycemia used to be dismissed as just a trend illness, but it is real. The body does not regulate insulin properly and can cause lightheadedness, irritability, short-term memory loss, weight gain and mood swings.

And to cure this imbalance is so simple. Small dietary changes usually fix much of the problem.

Having a good endocrinologist is essential to finding solutions to depression. So, your next check-up have this test run. What a difference it can make.

*"Life is a process of becoming, a combination of states we have to go through. Where people fail is that they wish to elect a state and remain in it.*
*This is a kind of death."*
*Anais Nin*

## *September 27*

### How Is Your Attitude Today?

Even if today is one of deep depression, your attitude still must be that this pain is temporary. Under no circumstances can you ever allow the thought to enter your consciousness that depression is bigger than you are.

This is a CYCLE. It WILL go away.

You have tools to move yourself out of this misery.

Depression will not be your future. It is not your life.

On all days - even the really difficult ones - you are unshakable in your belief in your recovery. This is not wishful thinking. Your recovery is a fact.

*"Our attitudes control our lives. Attitudes are a secret power working twenty-four hours a day, for good or for bad. It is of paramount importance that we know how to harness and control this great force."*

*Tom Blandi*

## *September 28*

### Waking Up

It seems pretty prevalent that mornings are rougher than evenings for folks who suffer with depression. Getting out of bed, much less facing the day's tasks is a struggle for many.

Work with yourself on this. Be gentle here. I try not to think about my sluggishness or berate myself for not bounding out of bed. It seems that if I can focus on something pleasant ahead of me - some part of the day ahead that will be enjoyable - that catalyst alone is enough to get my feet on the floor. This could be banana pancakes for breakfast, lunch with a good friend, the fact that it's Friday, whatever awaits you.

Do not rush. Set the alarm to allow for an extra fifteen minutes or so to ease into the day. This will also set the pace for your day in general. Go slower. The fact that you're up and moving is accomplishment enough.

Keep in mind that adrenaline creates more adrenaline so that you will feel better as the day progresses. And movement alone creates adrenaline. So, just by simply getting out of bed, you have begun to turn your day around.

*Anticipation is a magnificent motivator.*

*September 29*

## How Big is Your God?

Time and again I hear, "if it weren't for my faith, I wouldn't have made it this far". A spiritual life seems to be a very constant denominator in those who have put depression into remission in their lives. The manner of worship or membership has no bearing. A belief in a Power greater than ourselves appears to be a great tool in dealing with the dark cycles.

My belief in God has been critical to my recovery. But, how big is that Source someone once asked me? Could I be mad at my God - furious - disappointed - disillusioned - rageful? Could I have a God, in other words, that I had an honest/real relationship with? Not just the pretty stuff to share, but the whole of what your life is about?

The more I could envision this truly omnipresent form - that He/She truly was everywhere simultaneously and that's pretty big - the more I felt comfortable leaning on Him.

I screamed, I yelled my ugliest thoughts, I begged, I tested. Sometimes I would adopt the behavior of a two year old and not pray or do anything that even remotely resembled spirituality - just pout, because I was so furious and disgusted with the life depression forced me into.

If this was going to be a substantial, valid relationship, then it had to weather the valleys with the mountaintops.

And I needed a force so huge and so powerful as to be indestructible.

How big is your God?

*"One needs something to believe in, something for which one can have whole-hearted enthusiasm. One needs to feel that one's life has meaning, that one is needed in the world."*
*Hannah Sennesh*

*September 30*

## Fear of Depression

It took me a long time to figure out how terrified I was of this illness. Waking up with some symptoms of an approaching onslaught would be so fearful, that I would exacerbate the problem.

I have discovered not only a way to alleviate this problem, but also to use it to my advantage.

Depression creeps up on me. It does not appear full-blown one morning. So, now I monitor my symptom checklist daily.

Here is what I check for:
• head 'fog' - can be a feeling of pressure; slow, 'clogged' thinking, or a sense that my head feels swollen - too heavy to sit on my shoulders
• a heavy spirit; regardless of what the day holds, I do not anticipate it
• fighting for wakefulness; the overwhelming desire to just close my eyes and sleep longer
• hearing the mental response "I don't care" like a broken record in my head
• craving carbohydrates; let nothing come between me and cake!
• I hate all my clothes
• I hate the face that looks back at me in the mirror
• I have that glazed look in my eyes
• I experience extreme anxiety - usually about a family member who is experiencing difficulties - or money
• I avoid answering the phone
• I avoid people and social occasions
• I am irritable; not one other person on the highway is driving correctly, all salesclerks are inept and rude, being put on hold when calling a business is infuriating
• I want to be left alone - by everyone
• I am 'spaced out' while driving

This list is not inclusive, but if even two of these are true for that day; almost ninety per cent of the time, I can add some supplements or change my medications and completely abort a depression. The other ten per cent of the time, I can squelch the depression to a more moderate/bearable cycle.

At least I do not feel powerless and this alone conquers the fear.

"You gain strength, courage, and confidence by every experience in which you really stop to look fear in the face. You must do the thing which you think you cannot do."

Eleanor Roosevelt

# OCTOBER

*October 1*

## Everyone Starts Healing at a Different Place

Where are you in the recovery process at this exact moment? Stop. Just take a minute and assess your present health. On a scale of one to ten, one being dead and ten being euphoria (making 'normal' whatever that is ??), how would you rate your well-being at this moment?

Some of you will be feeling 'okay'. The money coming in this month will cover your expenses, you have not had a really 'out of it' day in a while, you are getting along pretty well with family, friends, neighbors and colleagues. Some of you may be just coming out of a depressive cycle. You feel better than you did a week ago, but certainly nowhere near 'functional' yet.

Some of you may be wretched. The misery of depression envelops you.

Regardless of where you are at this moment, you can begin to heal. Even if that means just getting through today. That may be all you need to do - or all you can do - for now.

Do not compare your recovery to someone elses'. This is your life - your unique path - your individual chemistry.

You can start healing from here. Wherever you are at this time. This is as good a place as any.

PRAYER

"I do not ask to walk smooth paths
Nor bear an easy load.
I pray for strength and fortitude
To climb the rock-strewn road.

Give me such courage I can scale
The hardest peaks alone
And transform every stumbling block
Into a stepping stone."

Gail Brook Burket

*October 2*

## Inching Ahead

It was vitally important that I make progress in my recovery. I felt that if I let my defenses down - even momentarily - I would slide backward into the quicksand of my depression. Of course, it is unreasonable and impossible to always make headway. But, my attitude was that I needed to be succeeding. I had to see my victory at all times.

Sometimes just not relapsing or taking a step back was progress. I kept the aphorism "every great journey begins with a single step" on my desk and took it as my personal mantra.

One step added to a second step to another step created a path. And all paths lead somewhere.

I knew exactly where mine was headed.

I was going to be active, healthy, productive, thriving; so help me, God.

THE POWER OF THOUGHT

*"As you think, you travel; and as you love, you attract. You are today where your thoughts take you. You cannot escape the results of your thoughts, but you can endure and learn; can accept and be glad.*

*You will realize the goal (not the idle wish) of your heart; be it base or beautiful, or a mixture of both, for you will always gravitate toward that which you most secretly love.*

*Into your hands will be placed the exact results of your thoughts; you will receive that which you earn – no more, or less.*

*Whatever your present environment may be, you will fail, remain, or rise with your thoughts, your vision, your ideal.*

*You will become as small as your controlling desire; as great as your dominant aspiration."*

James Allen, *As A Man Thinketh*

## *October 3*

### Beyond Our Sight

*"The stars are there, however dark the night,*
*Although we catch no least glimpse of their light*
*Here in our world where we run in and out*
*From dreary faith to faith and doubt to doubt;*

*The stars are there, and they are burning bright!...."*
*James Dillet Freeman*

When I am in the dark pit of depression, I need all the encouragement I can get that this misery is not permanent. I will use the above poem or the common refrain, "the sun is always shining someplace", etc...

My sight may be limited at this point. I need to grasp that I am not able to see potential, options and hope but they are there regardless. At these times, I trust others' view more than my own to show me - even peripherally - the radiance the world holds.

*"Far away there in the sunshine are my highest aspirations.*
*I may not reach them, but I can look up and see their beauty,*
*believe in them, and try to follow where they lead."*
*Louisa May Alcott*

## *October 4*

### More Ocean Tide Philosophy

Every paper - even the throwaways and neighborhood weeklies - near either coast of the United States carries large tide schedules. Very meticulous. Very precise and detailed. Fishermen make their living using this tool. But, what does it have to do with the rest of us?

We know now that the tides are part of the pull of the lunar system. The moon controls the biggest part of the cover of our planet - water. Hard to believe. We also know that our bodies are 85% water, so we are strongly influenced by water bodies and therefore, the tides.

But, what this information says to me - in what I like to think of 'God-speak' (the spiritual whispered enlightenments I receive when I let myself listen)- is that no matter what - even the highest tide will recede. It is a matter of time. Historically, it has NEVER failed.

So, this is the guiding message for me. No matter how critical the depression - it WILL recede. Historically, it has never failed.

Some days, I just need to keep reminding myself of this.

*"Faith is the bird that feels the light when the dawn is still dark."*

*Rabindranath Tagore*

## *October 5*

## "It's only a Rough Patch in the Long Road of Life" Unknown

This concept - repeated as a mantra - may be one of the tools that gets you through a dark period. Say it to yourself. Say it out loud. Say this again and again and again.

Because it is true.

This depression will pass. Always. The miracle of the human body is that it is always seeking balance. Your chemistry will normalize again no matter what.

That is how Abraham Lincoln and other depressives who lived without our current options survived. They just waited the cycle out.

This unhealthy detour is just a pothole in your path. Get around, under, through or across it. And keep going. The next curve in the road might just offer what you need to repair your problem.

*"I deserve to be happy and I know how – whether I'm using the knowledge or not."*

*Unknown*

*October 6*

## Begin New Medications Separately

When you are desperate for relief, you want to use every option available to you. ANYTHING to lighten up this load of anguish that is your life right now.

I have been there. And I made the mistake of trying all (usually two) available resources as soon as they were prescribed for me. I knew it was imperative to introduce new medications or supplements one at a time. But, in my eagerness for relief, I would take whatever options were available - even if it meant adding two or three new meds at once.

Inevitably, this backfired. Every single time.

I believe we have altered chemistries. So, depressives and bipolars do not assimilate chemicals/pharmaceuticals like the general population. It is also my experience that we have exquisitely fragile chemistries. Ingesting even a small amount of what would be a normal dose for other folks, can bring dramatic results for us.

So, either it was that one of the new medications/supplements triggered side effects that were unacceptable or the synergy of the two chemicals together created a bad reaction. Often, when I have given my system a rest and tried one of the new options again in the smallest dose possible, I did find it helpful and bearable.

I will not use that heinous phrase - "you need to be patient". I was livid when that trite nonsense was preached to me. I HAD been patient for twelve plus years! And if they needed to understand that in terms of suffering, then I was talking about 4,380 days of being patient. And when I was REALLY suffering, I let the 'authority' who was telling me to 'be patient' know that what I was really talking about was 105,120 hours of being patient ( or even worse, 6,307,200 minutes of being patient)! It was unbearable to think of how sometimes it was one second at a time I would suffer through.

Can you think of a woman who could survive 105,120 hours of labor? Of course not. Would someone tell this poor woman to be patient? NO!

So, I will not.

Besides, if you are to try two medications/supplements at once and have a negative reaction, it is very likely that one alone might be beneficial and you will unknowingly discard a possible source of relief.

Believe me when I tell you that I know how it feels to be utterly desperate for relief. But, if you can pace yourself and try just one new option/one new medication at a time, you will see your return to health be much quicker. I promise.

"You can get through dark situations. Go as far as you can see.
By the time you can get there, you'll be able to see further."
Unknown

## October 7

### Making the Effort to Find a Support Group

"Fear, even in its worst form - evil - can be dealt with and reconciled over time. We must take the first step toward decreasing the toxic effects of distilled fear. And there is strength in numbers, for there are always those who can help us."
from *Stressed is Desserts Spelled Backwards* by Brian Luke Seaward, Ph. D.

The first support group I attended was in Tampa, Florida. I did not know at the time that this is an exceptional group and that this chapter has been recognized as the outstanding chapter in the United States for NDMDA (National Depressive and Manic Depressive Association). There would be several hundred hurting souls there on any given night.

But, what I got from these people is that you get there no matter what. Even - as one man used to do - if you wore a trench coat over your pajamas! I really have used that self-permission many times in my recovery. He never apologized - in fact, he never talked - his depression was too profound. But, I watched his eyes focus on whomever was sharing. He was benefitting from being there.

Once I saw a taxi drop someone off. I saw one man driven by a relative to every meeting. I saw one elderly man come for his wife when she couldn't be there herself.

But, the energy of the group was healing. I never - NEVER - failed to hear something that I could use. It might be about side effects or a referral to a great psychiatrist. It really does pay to call NDMDA (now known as the DEPRESSION AND BIPOLAR SUPPORT ALLIANCE 1- 800-826-3632 -or http://www.dbsalliance.org) to find a group near you.

*"Each time we sense the possibility of a new direction in our lives, we are being given a chance to grow."*
*Unknown*

## October 8

## Medicating with Television

Money is always an issue with our illness. Not only is the brain and its dysfunctions not considered a 'medical illness' by the insurance companies (I wonder how they justify this policy biologically?), so that our medications and treatment are not covered, but the loss of employment and the necessity of therapy concurrently add to the financial abyss.

But, the one luxury that I convince myself is a must is television. Where I live, you must have a cable provider and in my area there is no choice of providers. You pay what the provider demands or you suffer with rabbit ears from Radio Shack.

I am not crazy about television. In the normal scheme of things, watching the boob tube is way down on my list of things I like to do. But, I will medicate with the *Comedy Channel* for hours and days when I am down. It may be the distraction of *The Learning Channel* or *Arts and Entertainment* that gets me through.

But, even if it means doing without a regular phone line into my home (in my area these monthly expenses are roughly equal) then, I do without a telephone land line and have my cell phone as my sole telecommunication. (An added bonus here is that I have never received a solicitation call on my cell phone!) But, I consider television as vital as my meds in the deeper phases of depression and I justify it that way.

When I am at my very low points, reading is not even an option. Watching television is one step above sleeping. But, it gets me through and that's all that counts.

Medicating with television may not be an option for you. But, I urge you to find some mindless activity to get you through the dark passages.

*"When dreams become goals, they have a way of calling us forth. Goals organize our lives, so that we may reach them."*
*Unknown*

## *October 9*

## **Life is Difficult**

The famous book, *The Road Less Traveled* by Dr. Scott Peck begins with this simple and very profound statement. Life is difficult. For everyone. Everyone - no exceptions.

We want to believe the fables and fallacies that movies and best sellers project. But, there are NO princes on white steeds, no lottery jackpots that will solve all our problems, no pots of gold at the end of the rainbow. Life is difficult.

If depression is a part of your life, then you know pain already.

But, it does not have to win. This a battle. This is life or death. You can recover. You can be happy again.

Winston Churchill - a fellow depression sufferer - gave one of his most quoted speeches in 1941 at the Harrow School in England. Although it is misquoted, he is said to have stood and stated: "Never, ever, ever, ever, ever, ever, ever, give up. Never give up. Never give up. Never give up." Then, he sat down. (In truth this is only a part of the speech he gave.) The audience waited expectantly for the famous orator to complete his speech. But, that was his message. Never give up.

It is that simple. You WILL win - you will beat this depression - if you NEVER GIVE UP.

*"Our evolution is not without purpose and design; therefore, we need not concern ourselves with the future. It will educate and comfort us as it becomes the present."*
*Unknown*

## *October 10*

# Pet Therapy

I am owned by an eighteen-pound Humane Society-breed, Benji-looking dog. Growing up with small dogs was good, and I have owned a cat - but, Shelby is unique. This small gray dog with a heart the size of Wyoming is a big part of what gets me through the bleak days.

Here is how:
I have to walk her,
The neighbors need not see the pathetic nightshirt I sleep in, therefore, I must get dressed.

I have to make sure she has food and water. So, I have to get out of bed whether I feel like it or not. She motivates me when nothing else will.

Shelby is lap-size and a lover, so I will spend hours holding and petting her. This skin contact and loving warmth chemically shifts me somehow.

I will talk to Shelby without fear of judgment or repercussion. I will tell her how desperate I am, I will curse God, I will moan and whine without reservation.

The little puppy kisses I get help enormously. Cat kisses with their little sandpaper tongue can add dermatological benefits, too, I'm sure.

I do not feel the ache of loneliness. When I can't be around other folks due to the severity of the depression, I don't feel deprivation as long as I have Shelby.

The variety of pets is huge. Maybe adding this special therapy to your lifestyle is a good step to take now if a pet doesn't already own you. The cost is so minimal and the benefits so magnificent.

*"Outside of a dog, a man's best friend is a book; inside of a dog, it's very dark."*

*Groucho Marx*

*October 11*

## Between A Rock And A Hard Place

*Between A Rock And A Hard Place* is the name of a very small book that a friend gave me one Christmas. Just the title alone gave me comfort as I realized it perfectly described how I felt some days.

But, the quotes found in this little jewel were sometimes the only thoughts I had (or needed) some days other than the repetitious thoughts of suicide.

I always kept these thoughts near - there were times when I just needed one bit of hope to get me through that particular twenty-four hours.

Use what you can from these:
"When you get in a tight place and it seems, you can't go on...
Hold on. For that's just the place and the time when the tide will turn."
Harriet Beecher Stowe

"The lowest ebb is the turn of the tide." Unknown

"Our greatest glory is not in never failing, but in rising up every time we fall." Confucius

"The force of the waves is in their persistence." Gila Guri

*"You have to leave the city of your comfort and go into the wilderness of your intuition. What you'll discover will be wonderful. What you'll discover will be yourself."*
*Alan Alda*

*October 12*

## Getting Rid Of Tear Congestion

There are times when I don't feel too good - not real bad, but not really good either. Just kind of a heaviness. A sluggishness of spirit. Like there is a bag of sand I am having to drag with every step I take. A slowness and dullness of thought.

Sometimes, it goes so far as having a low-key headache. Not enough to run for the Tylenol, but enough that I know it lurks there behind my eyes.

And it so happens that I had one of those terrific Friday nights of self-indulgence when in one such funk. It was just me, my dog, Shelby, and a ten-hanky video after a lovely, soothing bubble bath. And thirty minutes of therapeutic sobbing later, I was cured!

I think we can build up tear congestion. There are enough accumulated small hurts, trivial disappointments, stinging words to create a blockade in our brain. I find I need a trigger, such as a chick flick, to get that logjam moving. The relief reminds me of how tough and uncomfortable it is to throw up, and how light and clean I feel after.

Those tears just need to get out. Clean those residual slights out. Make way for brighter thoughts, new ideas and a fresh outlook.

*"To affect the quality of the day, that is the highest of arts."*
*Henry David Thoreau*

## *October 13*

## Reliable No More

I had a most painful illumination last week. A Vocational Rehabilitation Specialist commented that I wasn't reliable at that point.

After an initial outraged response of pain and denial, I let the fact that 'the truth hurts' sink in. Having been an ultra-responsible person my entire life - and priding myself on this attribute for decades - I realized that I can't be counted on much of the time now. This is not a character defect or personality problem. I need not be ashamed. My illness incapacitates me at times. And therefore, I am unable to be counted on during those periods.

To put it in perspective another way: if a friend of yours was sick with a migraine, would you expect her to be there for your birthday dinner as she had been for years? Would you expect her to remember to call you about the results of your big work evaluation? Would you expect her to meet the deadline on the project you were working on? No - you wouldn't. Then give yourself the same kindness of spirit.

No, when we are ill we are not as reliable as we would like to be. NO ONE IS!

So, learn to forgive yourself for the blunders and mistakes that are part of feeling lousy and leave that blame behind you.

*"Arrange whatever pieces come your way."*
*Virginia Woolf*

## October 14

### Guilt

Feelings of intense guilt are one of the ten or so identifiers of depression. It can be elusive. An on again - off again kind of thing. It can be present only fifteen minutes of a ninety day cycle and be excruciatingly intense or it can linger weakly during every day of the depression. Guilt can be different every single cycle.

Guilt is one of the most irrational aspects of our illness. I would often ask myself what I was feeling so guilty about. My work-ethic conscience would feel bad about missing work. My financial conscience would dread the thought of how exorbitant this cycles' medication and doctor's visits were going to be. My social conscience would hate letting my friends down. But, it eventually came down to the fact that what I really felt guilty for was my illness.

Because the guilt is so misplaced and unjustifiable (no matter how you feel), it must come from one of those crossed - wire areas of our brain. It is just a fluke of circuitry that plays the 'you don't deserve it' tape.

It seemed so clear during my good days that every one of those thoughts were utterly unfounded. Yet, within the depression, guilt was a universal truth.

The most effective way for me to override this problem was to actualize it. I gave it a form - an identity. I would mentally rebuke every guilt statement with the truth.

This actually had a positive outcome. My anger had a place to dissipate. And the endorphins generated by my fury at this injustice actually lifted my mood! The other method that seemed to work was to make a 'worthwhile' list during my good times. To write down the contributions I had made in my life so far, the people who counted on me, the talents that I possessed. Reading through this relentlessly during bouts of guilt was irrefutable data that I had so much good in my life and it gave the realistic pride a chance to offset the pain.

*"The worst guilt it to accept an unearned guilt."*
*Ayn Rand*

*October 15*

## Skin Hunger

This New Age therapy term struck a real nerve for me the first time I heard it. No one had to amplify or explain. I absolutely knew the meaning.

Have you ever felt it? I hope not. But, if you have you will know why:

people have pets

women have sex when they only want affection
old people die early without their mates.

I have learned now that the itch I feel emotionally can be scratched. I need only hug a friend, hold my dog, cuddle an infant. But, in our isolation during depression, we neglect this most fundamental of human needs.

The infamous post-World War II study of infants in orphanages gives us scientific proof of this phenomenon. Because these children were not held or touched, but cared for in every other way (adequate food, etc...) and yet, they not only failed to thrive, but more than a dozen died before the study was halted, is literal proof of our innate need for human contact.

Just knowledge of this need and keeping your awareness in tune with what your body is telling you at any given time will add another component to your recovery package.

*"Treat yourself the same way you treat strangers: with kindness and respect."*

*Unknown*

## October 16

## "The Ego Reacts, the Soul Responds"

"The ego reacts, the soul responds. Allow yourself permission to respond rather than react so that you may be guided by spirit always."

from *Stressed is Desserts Spelled Backwards* by Brian Luke Seaward, Ph.D.

I understand now - after lots of therapy - what that means to act and not react and how to invoke it into action in my life. But, too often I fall back into the knee-jerk, unhealthy response that gets me nowhere (except deeper into the heat of the argument). Then, I have that much farther to dig myself out to reach a resolution.

The trick is to learn to 1) acknowledge the clenching of your teeth, the spasm in your stomach or the flush on your face as a stringent reaction to someone or something 2) take a deep breath 3) envision the outcome you most want in this scenario 4) 'respond' from that perspective.

This takes practice. It's worth it.

The instance that most frequently challenges me and where I most need to practice this 'respond, don't react' is when someone is giving me unsolicited advice about how to handle my depression cycles. The hair stands up on the back of my neck instantly. And, honestly, ninety percent of the time, these individuals mean to help. I need to remember that when I take that deep breath.

The point of this information is to give you another tool to use when in an irritable, miserable depression. It is just a damage control technique. Use the extra moment a deep breath gives you to stop the knee-jerk reaction and clear your head enough to be able to respond from a genuine, benevolent posture.

There will be so much less wreckage in your path if you do this.

*"We make a living by what we get, but we make a life by what we give."*

Norman MacEwan

## *October 17*

### Whimsy

Okay, whimsy is just the ten cent word for silliness. But, silliness is a tool no one can live without. It doesn't take depression to make goofiness a necessity.

I love whimsy. I was great at this as a kid. I was a leader in my field when it came to shedding sophistication and doing the next most ridiculous thing. I have read those tomes on manners and good breeding and do know which fork to use at a formal dinner party.

But, heaven forbid that I should abide by those stuffy rules for the better part of my days! And I do mean, the better part. The great memories I have are not of the stiff and often pretentious moments of my past, but rather those of foolishness.

There aren't many better experiences than to deflate an overly serious person; to grab solemnity by the throat and choke it with delight.

I even have a friend who lost it at a funeral. In her earnestness to lay her rose at exactly the perfect spot on the coffin, she stepped into the newly turned earth and sunk up to her knee. The contortions and struggle that ensued as she fought to crawl out of the grave were priceless. Not minimizing the pain of the grieving one whit, this was a mere reminder of our shared human-ness .

There are times to go fly a kite, sing off key at the top of your lungs, be truly silly. You won't regret a moment of it.

Funny Words of Wisdom

1. I can please only one person per day. Today is not your day. Tomorrow isn't looking good, either.
2. I love deadlines. I especially like the whooshing sound they make as they go flying be.
3. I'd explain it to you, but your brain would explode.
4. Someday we'll look back on all this and plow into a parked car.
5. There are very few personal problems that cannot be solved by a suitable application of high explosives.
6. Tell me what you need and I'll tell you how to get along without it.
7. Accept that some days you're the pigeon and some days you're the statue.
8. Last night, I lay in bed looking at the stars in the sky and thought to myself, "Where the heck is the ceiling?"
9. I don't suffer from stress. I'm a carrier.
10. Always forgive your enemies. Nothing annoys them so much.
11. I used to have an open mind but my brains kept falling out.
12. I couldn't repair your brakes, so I made your horn louder.
13. Do you have trouble making up your mind? Well, yes or no?
14. Death is hereditary.
15. Everyone makes mistakes. The trick is to make mistakes when no one is looking.
16. They say hard work never hurts anybody, but why take the chance?
17. Always remember that you are absolutely unique. Just like everyone else.
18. Always borrow money from a pessimist. He won't expect it back."

http://www.indianchild.com

*October 18*

## Using Rage to Heal

I certainly have never seen this theory condoned in any accredited form. But, I do know that I have successfully turned the power of my fury into action and used it to fuel the next step in my recovery.

I did not have good role models for anger growing up. My strong, intelligent mother would freeze and let the crisis blow right over her. My dad was a gale force that could not be contained. I must have been thirty before I heard anger acknowledged as just another emotion. Just one in the whole range of emotions that all ordinary folks are expected to feel everyday!

Wow! I had never thought of anger like that.

Looking at it in that perspective actually gave me permission to feel that hot undercurrent that lived within me.

But, when I am in a depression, it is not anger I feel. No, it is huge. Enormous. A tidal wave of blinding red force. I am enraged.

Most of the time, it is at the injustice of this illness. Or the brutal indifference of the insurance companies. Or a doctor who won't return my call. All justifiably anger-inducing. But, sometimes I think I am going to choke on this rage, it overwhelms me so.

So, I have learned to 1) be attuned to myself enough to recognize the emotional state I am in 2) visualize myself taking this impotent hurt and fury and turning it into a generator of massive strength and use it to....

Well, what can I do with that? Sometimes, I have used it to get me moving. Literally. If I have been frozen with depression, I will get out and walk. Or I will pound the life out of a tennis ball against a bare wall.

The endorphins that grow from these activities flood me with a euphoric sense of well-being.

Or I will write a scathing letter to the person, corporation, whatever that created this anger. I will blister the keyboard with my ire. And sometimes these letters are so articulate and sound that I mail them. And some of them have actually accomplished what I wanted in the first place.

Or I will clean a closet, scrub a floor, mow the grass.

What I will NOT do is drive a car, make a phone call or stuff myself with calories to stuff that pain back down into oblivion again. These all have negative consequences and I don't want to step back. I want to use this force to hurl myself forward just as far as I can.

I like to think of this impotent anger as fuel in the gas tank of my recovery.

*"Whenever anger arises, think of the consequences."*
*Confucius*

## *October 19*

### Relaxing Is Hard Work

If you push yourself to get through every day, you will experience this same effort in trying to slow down and rest. The enormous determination that gets most of us through the worst days of fatigue and misery, drains all the reserves we have in our energy bank.

So now that unwinding becomes as difficult as work is.

When do you fully relax? What erases all the knots in your stomach?

Some folks like bubble baths, some a long, no-destination bike ride, some an uninterrupted Sunday morning leisurely reading the newspaper.

Make a habit of relaxation. You work so hard at everything else. Work hard at finding time to unwind.

*"To make a stressed life more memorable, you need enough of the 'good', perception-sharpening stress ... and enough sustained breaks to give yourself a vacation from brain-sapping long-term stress."*
*McGaugh*

## *October 20*

# Quasi-functioning

There are days - and just parts of days sometimes - that I can function on a modified level. I call it 'quasi-functioning.' I am not at full-strength, but I am not idle either.

I would never undertake paying bills in this state. It would take weeks and months to undo the mess I would make and it just is not worth it. I would never try to give a party or speech or presentation - no matter if it was NBC that had to be told that I had to cancel at the last moment. I would never prepare a meal for others or write a business letter or start a project on these minimally functioning days.

I would, however, read the paper, wash a load of clothes, watch television, walk my dog, or sit in the sun. I am capable of calling a friend, fixing something to eat and other menial tasks.

There are few rules I give myself about this illness. The cardinal rule is to listen to my body and go at the speed I am capable of. Judgments - whether my own or others' - go unheeded.

Know your limits. What are your steadfast rules? What guidelines must you set for yourself for your safety and the safety of others?

Remember, this state is only temporary - but, the consequences could be forever.

So, if 'quasi-functioning' is the best you can do today, that is enough.

*"Tough times never last. Tough people do."*
*Robert Schuller*

## *October 21*

# Over the Counter Options

In recent years, we have seen SAMe and St. John's Wort become touted as popular anti-depressant options. These may very well benefit someone suffering from mild depression, but neither should ever be used concurrently with prescription anti-depressant medication and most definitely not by someone with moderate to severe depression.

SAMe (S-Adenosyl-L-Methionine) usually comes in 400 mg. tablets and is an amino acid derivative naturally found in the brain and that is said to boost the effects of dopamine and serotonin.

St. John's Wort (Hypericum perforatum) was reported in the February 2000 *Lancet* this way :

St. John's Wort appears to be an inducer of an important metabolic pathway, cytochrome P450. As many prescription drugs used to treat conditions such as heart disease, depression, seizures, certain cancers or to prevent...transplant rejections or pregnancy (oral contraceptives) are metabolized via this pathway, health care providers should alert patients about these potential drug interactions....

In short, you must judge for yourself whether these - or any other over the counter medication - helps you or is potentially harmful to you.

"I believe we are solely responsible for our choices, and we have to accept the consequences of every deed, word and thought throughout our lifetime."

Elisabeth Kubler-Ross

## *October 22*

## Carbohydrates are Great Medicine

Don't let the high protein diets currently in vogue convince you to give up carbohydrates. You will have a severe rebound effect and possibly a depression cycle followed with a binge. Our bodies need carbohydrates. Period. Not only need them, but we need carbs more than the average person.

Drs. Judith and Richard Wurtman of MIT and Harvard (Judith Wurtman, Ph. D. is a Research Scientist at MIT and founder and director of Harvard University's TRIAD Weight Management Center and her husband, Richard Wurtman, M.D. is Director of MIT's Clinical Research Center and a professor in the Harvard-MIT Program in Health Sciences and Technology and MIT's Department of Brain and Cognitive Sciences) have researched the transformation of carbohydrates into serotonin in the body. We literally are medicating ourselves when that craving for bread, potato chips, cake and cookies, pasta overcomes us.

Most assuredly it is best to use whole grains and complex carbohydrates to put the missing serotonin back into our chemistries. But, I have learned to listen to these messages from my body. I don't need to overdo and binge if I am listening carefully on a steady/regular basis. I can pick up on the message from my body at an early stage and eat moderate amounts of carbs at frequent intervals. And I do feel better. I have more energy and I am more optimistic.

I read once that thirty-five percent of the sugar from carrots is absorbed through our gums even before we swallow! This is precisely what will replace the serotonin our bodies crave when medications aren't working.

I follow my tastebuds and do not think of weight loss or diet at these times. If I have a loaded baked potato on my mind, that is exactly what I will go to great lengths to eat. I used to eat what I had planned to eat, what others were eating, what was 'good' for me to eat, a balanced meal, etc... And after eating whatever I was supposed to eat, I was still craving that loaded baked potato. So, I would end up overeating.

If I ate the loaded baked potato - with the whole works - bacon bits, sour cream, cheese, butter and chives - if that is what I really wanted - then, I was satisfied. And I do not let the 'head chatter' of what I 'should' do interfere.

It could be a double cheese pizza that is uppermost in your unconscious. I have craved wedding cake - that gooey sweet frosting and moist cake - at times. Whatever it is, listen. Your body is helping you out.

You are replacing critical nutrients in your body when you follow your cravings at these times. Good nutrition and weight loss can come later. Do what you need to balance your chemistry NOW and let go of judgments.

*"Wisdom is knowing what to do next, virtue is doing it."*
*David Starr Jordan*

## October 23

## What Are Your Options?

What haven't you tried yet as a way to change your chemistry?

Are you adding more whole grains and other healthy carbohydrates to your diet every day?

Are you making certain that you maintain adequate sleep every single twenty-four hour cycle?

Are you exploring the various amino acid and other supplement choices that are available for depression?

Is there a stressor in your life that keeps tension ever-present that you are not addressing?

Do you season your day with random moments of joy, a belly laugh, a moment with a friend or hobby?

Have you enlisted the very best professionals to aid you?

There are 300 plus ideas in this book and I have not exhausted all the options. Discover some for yourself.

I am going to use two quotes that refer to cancer but have EVERYTHING to do with depression as well:

*"We have two options, medically and emotionally: give up or fight like hell."*

*Lance Armstrong*

*"Cancer* (depression for us) *is a word, not a sentence."*

*John Diamond*

*October 24*

## An Exceptional Book

I will list a partial bibliography at the end of the book (partial only because I have written this book over a period of fifteen years and have lost some of my early reference work), and I am certain that educating yourself (so as not to be totally dependent on others' opinion of what is best for you - only YOU know that) is absolutely critical to turning your life around.

But, you don't need to be overwhelmed with information when you are struggling just to survive. So, if there was one book that would clearly and easily help you discover what is not working efficiently in your body, I would tell you that *The Mood Cure* (Julia Ross, Penguin Books, 2004 - Viking Penguin edition 2002) is a must-read.

Ms. Ross approaches chemical dysfunction through four major imbalances: thyroid, adrenal, sex hormones and food cravings. At the end of the book she includes four separate chapters addressing each of these with simple questionnaires so that you can decipher for yourself what is out of whack in your body.

She also includes chapters called "Your Master Supplement Plan" and "Nutritional Rehab". She will walk you through assessing some of the fundamental - and easily remedied - problems that create our havoc.

No book can substitute for a good physician, but this one will move you forward light-years in self-knowledge.

"The respected neurophysiologist Ralph Gerard said, 'Behind every crooked thought there lies a crooked molecule.'...Great strides are being made relative to how the chemical balance in our bodies changes with feelings of fear, anger, pain, love, joy, etc..."

Beatrice Sparks and Aron Flare in
*Almost Lost: The True Story of an Anonymous Teenager's Life on the Streets*

*October 25*

## Nature Abhors a Vacuum

If you are deleting something from your life - a smoking habit let's say - then, you will have to replace the money, time and focus you gave smoking with something else. There are no blank spaces in nature.

So, if I could replace all the time and money and energy that I had used in pursuing good health, what would I replace it with?

I have spent hours of my 'bottom time' fantasizing about what I would do with all the money I had spent on overcoming this illness. If I hadn't spent tens of thousands on medications that did not work and doctors that could not help, I could look like Cindy Crawford with all the plastic surgery this wasted money could buy! I could not only go on an extended vacation - I could rent an exquisite villa on the Italian Riviera for a whole summer!

I could feed and clothe a handful of children. I could shelter dozens of homeless.

I would mentally add up all the hours spent waiting in doctor's offices that I could have spent watercoloring. I would take the energy spent on recovery and consider instead if I could have been researching money-making opportunities.

This mental trick may not work for you. But, when I was too sick to move anything but the molecules of my thoughts, I could begin to turn the corner with this wishful thinking. Invariably, I would create some image in my mind that brought a smile to my face. And some times the inspiration to actually LIVE some of my fantasies was the catalyst I needed at that moment to get me out of bed - to the phone to make an appointment or call in a refill for my meds or to talk to someone in my support circle.

Believe me. There is or was nothing too foolish - too simple - too ludicrous that I wouldn't try if I thought even for a second that it might help me. So, if I all I could muster on a bad day was my imagination, then I made it work FOR me - not against me. Maybe it was just one more brick in my path, but at least I would be going forward and not backward. And momentum is what recovery is all about.

*"Mountains cannot be surmounted except by winding paths."*
*Johann Wolfgang Von Goethe*

## *October 26*

## Pre-Planning

Take some time on your good days to plan for your bad days.

Much of what I advocate as tools for recovery require some forethought on your part. In your functioning cycles, you will need to:

1. Write down the name and phone number of your primary doctor and the names and phone numbers of your support team. Keep this list taped to the front of the phone or inside your bathroom cabinet door or on the refrigerator. This needs to be easily located. Your brain will be too foggy when you need this list to have to search to find it.

2. Explain your policy of survival to others. Tell those who need to know that during your depressions, you may not return phone calls or answer your door, etc... If you are working and have not disclosed your illness to a superior, you will need to adopt a strategy for when depression strikes.

3. Never let your medications get low. I never get within three or four days of my last pill without refilling.

4. Stock your cabinets with necessities. Always have extra toothpaste, toilet paper and for me, coffee, on hand. I need to keep a carbohydrate and sugar supply at the ready. I always have starches of various forms in my cupboards. There will always be peanut butter, soup and a loaf of bread in my house.

5. Make sure your telephone system has an answering device and a ringer that you can turn off.

Take time to pre-plan what you will need in the rough spots.

These are simple tasks. They must be in place for a successful 'time out'. Picking back up the pieces of your life will be considerably smoother.

*"Be willing to accept a temporary inconvenience for a permanent improvement."*

*Unknown*

*October 27*

## Odd Symptoms

Do you have a really bizarre symptom that accompanies your depressions? I have two odd symptoms. In some depressions, I feel a crushing head 'pressure'. It feels like I am a hydrocephalic and I just need someone to drill a hole in my skull and let some of the excess fluid out.

I also get a weird feeling of sickening 'nausea' about the size of a half-dollar at the base of my skull at times. Boy, I get some funny looks when I try to describe this one.

Do you have symptoms that are too embarrassing to mention?

I do not discuss these symptoms but with one very trusted physician, although I KNOW that they are real for me. What has helped enormously though is to listen at support group meetings when others describe unusual problems associated with their depressions and then to use various Internet search engines to look up the symptoms.

I can't say that I have ever found a remedy for these oddities, but I sure feel better knowing that I am not alone.

*"God gives every bird it's food, but He doesn't throw it into the nest."*

*www.indianchild.com*

*October 28*

## Surviving

This is a survival guide. Just as there are books explaining how to survive in the wilderness, this is a book of simple, yet effective ways to cope when you are depressed.

Although I do mention some changes I made that helped shift my chemistry, primarily this is about surviving the pain of depression.

All of these coping skills are ones that I developed in order to save my own life or that I learned of through others who suffer depression.

These tools will work for all forms of depression: from the depression caused by the temporary hormonal imbalance of Post-partum Depression to the suicidal cycle of clinical depression.

These are tools for those who are experiencing a transitory depression caused by a life trauma such as divorce or unemployment or for those like me, who have a genetically-predetermined neurobiological predisposition to depression and cannot find the proper anti-depressant relief.

These are not all the answers. Be alert and open to options that may work for YOU. I have tried to be as thorough as I could with coping techniques, but this book certainly is not an exhaustive list.

Some of my suggestions cover exactly how NOT to go backward during a depression.

This was a duel to the death. I never saw myself as just getting better. I always envisioned a return to my former robust and vigorous life. Just 'getting by' was not an option. I was going to not only conquer this demon, I was going to thrive!

I had the determination of the fiercest of rugged mountain men when I 'went into the woods'. I promise that if you can find even a handful of the suggestions I offer to be effective for you, you can beat this. I have and you can, too.

*"An invincible determination can accomplish almost anything and in this lies the great distinction between great men and little men."*

*Thomas Fuller*

*October 29*

## What I Owe Barbara Streisand

At first this may not appear to be relative to depression and how to cope with the dark days, but bear with me. And for the men who may be reading this, substitute someone else (possibly Billy Crystal ?!) but, use the same theory.

When I was a junior in high school, all the 'pretty girls' - at least those elected to positions of supposed beauty: the Homecoming Queen and Her Court, the cheerleaders and majorettes - had long, straight, flowing blond hair. My hair is dark, coarse and naturally curly. Of course, I knew that this single feature damned me to ugliness. The one single similarity of the chosen few was that gorgeous, Surfer Girl hair.

I was not allowed to dye my hair, but I sure ironed it, straightened it chemically, wrapped it around my head at night - tortured it into submission for a few hours at a time. But, I damaged it so much that it remained short and most assuredly, coarse. Hats were not cool and I simply could not hide my disgusting flaw.

About this time Barbra Streisand starred in the film, *Funny Girl*. I owe Ms. Streisand a huge debt. Not only are her eyes slightly crossed, she has a huge nose AND this enormous honker has a slight bump in it. And yet she was being paid millions as the featured beauty opposite that handsome guy, Omar Sharif!

I was flabbergasted. How could this be? Over the next two years, I paid a lot of attention to Ms. Streisand - and I learned one of the greatest lessons ever. We thought she was beautiful, because SHE thought she was gorgeous. I watched how she carried herself, how she flirted with the very best looking men with complete confidence, and how her ego was undaunted in any circumstance.

She was adamant in NOT having plastic surgery on her considerable nose (and certainly, this is at least in part due to the changes surgery would make in her voice). But, everything about her screamed 'let me tell you how terrific I am'.

So, if it was good for her, it would work for me. And as I saw myself through Barbra Streisand eyes, I learned to play my hair up. My hair is an asset and I act like it now.

Here is the point as it relates to depression. If we can change our perspective - of ourselves and our illness - we can change how others see us as well. I never tell new people in my life that I am living with the handicap of a form of bipolar disorder. They get to know me as an exuberant, verbal, outgoing individual with enormous curiosity and zest for life. If they eventually become a part of my life, they get to know the diagnosis. But, I have yet to have someone see me as 'ill' then. The perspective I see of myself is what they see, because that is the ME I believe in and display to the world.

You can do this. Decide who you are and show the world that person. One recommendation I might include here is to peruse the several hundred adjectives for self-description that Richard Bolles lists in his book, *WHAT COLOR IS YOUR PARACHUTE? A Job Hunters Manual*. Choose twenty or thirty of these adjectives for yourself. Write them down on an index card and tape it to your mirror. Ingrain these in your mind and you will exude them.

If Barbra Streisand can convince the harshest critics in the world to pay her millions for her 'beauty', then certainly we can believe in our uniqueness. If you believe in your inherent worth, others will believe in it, too.

"No one can make you feel inferior without your consent."
Eleanor Roosevelt

## *October 30*

## Vigilance

This is one of those tedious parts of our recovery, but one that is mandatory for us. Not only do we have to make numerous changes in our lifestyle and ingest more pharmaceuticals than most, we have to always be on the alert for those insidious triggers that push us back to square one.

Here are some examples of what I am talking about:
Seafood is a real treat to me - I love shellfish, fresh fish, any fish. But, after a particularly wonderful meal of grouper, I was really ill. In only a few hours, I was in a dark funk. I did not make the connection between fish and the mercury I was ingesting until after another festive meal, this time of shrimp. It dawned on me that I was particularly sensitive to mercury now that I had removed the amalgams from my teeth, and that even a few ounces of seafood could trigger a depression.

So, seafood-avoidance is now a part of what I do to insure my recovery.

Some other things I have to be vigilant about are:

I avoid the nightly news.

I avoid those people who seem to have it all and live a perfect life.

I avoid missing sleep.

I am conscious of the weather and prepare for fronts that lower the barometric pressure.

I avoid high protein diets.

There is no point in getting our medications balanced and then undoing all that good with a preventable slip. Be vigilant about how you feel. It is a critical part of our recovery.

*"To wait for someone else, or to expect someone else to make my life richer, or fuller, or more satisfying, puts me in a constant state of suspension."*

*Kathleen Tierney Andrus*

*October 31*

## The Icebergs of Life

*"People are a lot like icebergs;*
*there's always so much more under the surface."*
*Andy Entwistle*

How good is your intuitive radar? Mothers are inevitably tops in this department. Most women in general are. But, men have this ability, too, and I know many who have developed this skill quite well.

Use your intuition to gauge who to trust. I have met many folks over the years, that if I were to judge them solely on their appearance, I would have made superficial contact and dismissed them from my life. Big mistake!

These were 'iceberg' folks. Very little of their true worth was visible on the surface. Little by little I discovered huge segments of talent, compassion, intellect, etc... in these otherwise plain vanilla individuals.

On the other hand, I have met some of the most image-conscious, 'pretty-people' who irked me with their abundance of label-display and purported wealth. I have met some folks who were slovenly and I immediately parallel this with unintelligent and lazy. Wrong again.

Some inner nudge - an emotional twitch I call it - tells me that below the surface of some of these people is a deep and abiding wisdom, spiritual strength, a huge and loving heart. And I am the poorer for not getting to share some time and conversation with them.

I find that if I look deeply into a person's eyes, I will find my 'depth-sounder' there. Let your gut be your guide.

Some of the most inspirational people who have changed my life came in the plainest wrappers.

*"Each person we welcome into our lives blesses us in ways that only the passage of time can validate."*
*Unknown*

# NOVEMBER

# *November 1*

## Weight Swings

Rare is the depressive who does not have unexplained weight changes as they cycle through periods of depression and normalcy.

It used to be thought that depression caused such weakness and fatigue that lack of appetite automatically caused weight loss. Or that the extended periods of sleep eclipsed normal eating habits.

Current medical thought is that weight gain or weight loss can be a symptom of depression. Because I have atypical depression, my appetite evaporates but my basal metabolism is so 'depressed' that I could eat five hundred calories a day and still gain roughly twenty pounds in a depression cycle.

I really feel we have to ignore this issue. And, yes, I am just as vain as the next person. But, I have actually forced myself to log every calorie and bit of exercise during some dark days and it made not a whit of difference if I ate less than five hundred calories a day. During a depression cycle, I gained weight and when the depression passed the weight fell off. And my eating and exercising would remain static throughout both periods.

Most depressives lose fifteen or twenty pounds during their depression cycles.

This is not about the side effects of some anti-depressants. I am talking here about a fundamental change in our chemistry that no one has an answer for at this time.

Most of us have some clothing in several sizes to get us through these hills and valleys. Try to focus on your recovery and ignore the scale when it is futile to try and fight this.

*"Standards of beauty are arbitrary. Body shame exists only to the extent that our physiques don't match our own beliefs about how we should look."*

*Martha Beck*

## *November 2*

### Sleep During Our Balanced Times

When I am going through a cycle of normalcy, I subconsciously think that I am well - period. Before long I am overextending myself. Getting run down to me means not getting enough sleep.

I can be perfectly in balance for a period of time and then, lack of sleep automatically will put me on the edge of a depression again. And it doesn't have to be missing a lot of sleep. It can be just missing an hour two nights in a row. It can be just changing my sleep pattern. If I go to bed several hours later than normal, no matter how long I sleep, I am 'off' the next day.

One of the oddest aspects of this is if I have to get up early - before eight a.m. - I am sick the rest of the day. Ironically, I used to be a 'morning' person, accomplishing more between five and nine a.m. than most people accomplished all day. I really don't understand this. But, the results are consistent and I have to honor this quirk.

So, I accept this shift in my chemistry and schedule appointments, etc.. after noon. I have also been fortunate to be able to work on this schedule.

I have learned to be extremely protective of my sleep. I do not go to the late movie anymore - I make sure the show starts before 8 p.m., I don't start to watch television shows that end after eleven o'clock. I unplug my phone or turn the ringer off as I go to bed. I let friends know what I am doing and why.

You will learn your sleep requirements if you do not already know them. Become very aware of your limits and honor them. Why jeopardize some really good days because we are careless?

*"Sleep, nature's rest, divine tranquility. That brings peace to the mind..."*

*Ovid*

## *November 3*

## Pleasing Others at Our Expense

Have you ever felt forced to accept an invitation or honor an obligation and then been miserable because of it? I'm sure that this happens to everyone. But, not everyone can potentially provoke an illness by being 'nice'. But, with depression, the added stress can, in fact, make us ill.

I am not saying to be rude. But, you know your limits. Stick by them. It's especially difficult if there are several of 'them' and just one of you having this discussion. Do not argue. Do not defend yourself. 'I'm sorry' is sufficient. If saying this as a response several times is not accepted, you may have to terminate the conversation. If the other person or persons do not understand and you are in a bad place, it is not your responsibility to educate others. (At least not now.) Let it go. Take care of yourself. Educating them eventually will resolve these problems for the next time. Pushing past your healthy limits in order to appease others will make you ill. Every single time.

*"Self-respect is a question of recognizing that anything worth having has a price."*

*Joan Didion*

## *November 4*

## Rudeness

Rudeness can go two ways. Others may be rude to us. They may ask inappropriate questions, they may not honor our boundaries, they may demand more of us than we are capable of giving.

But, more often I found that I was the one being rude. I was irritable and abrupt (to my family, to clerks, to anyone in my path when I was in a nasty depression). I cut people off in conversation or traffic. I was demanding.

I couldn't change those feelings or behaviors at the time. But, I could remove myself from situations that I might be rude in. If that meant avoiding people (in person or on the phone), that's what I did. It wasn't them to begin with. It was just my illness talking.

Irritability is just part of the territory of depression. Be aware of it. Work around it. Do as little damage as possible.

*"Through pride we are ever deceiving ourselves. But, deep down below the surface of the average conscience, a still, small voice says to us, "Something is out of tune."*
*Carl Jung*

## *November 5*

### Psychotherapy

Because I have a chemical imbalance, it took chemicals to get me back together. All the talking in this lifetime wouldn't make me well.

But, psychotherapy gave me the emotional outlet necessary to handle the pain and frustration that goes with brain illnesses.

Use it if it helps.

It is not unusual in current American society for you to need to see a psychiatrist for your medications and a psychologist for counseling and therapy. Once you are stabilized, you will usually only have fifteen minute 'med checks' with the psychiatrist. Be well prepared for these appointments because if you are having severe side effects from one of your anti-depressants, you will need to get to the heart of the matter and will need time to discuss what your other options are.

Certainly any of the problems in work or relationships or money are not going to get covered. A strong support group can be wonderful in this area and it is free. A minister can be another option.

But, there were definite times in my struggle with depression that the problems needed professional help. Get recommendations from people you trust. This is a time not to hesitate. Rather than dissolve and go away on their own, these issues and problems can build and undermine your medications.

Just getting them out in the open can be enormously healing.

*"Even though you may want to move forward in your life, you may have one foot on the brakes. In order to be free, we must learn how to let go. Release the hurt. Release the fear. Refuse to entertain your old pain. The energy it takes to hang onto pain is holding you back from a new life. What is it you need to let go of today?"*

*Mary Manin Morrissey*

## *November 6*

## 'Layers of the Onion'

Do you tend to see the world in extremes? Are most areas strictly black or white? Are there any grey areas of 'maybe', 'somewhat', 'average'?

Realizing that our recovery comes in layers helps to accept the progress we are making. If we see our lives as 'good days' and 'bad days', we will miss the 'okay' days. These are valuable days too. Everyone has them. They add a lot to our inventory of life.

The mundane and the mediocre are not just the filler part of life to be trudged through and overlooked. The real meat of life can be found in the ordinary.

Try to track your days on a scale of 1 to 10 (1 being suicidal and 10 being euphoria) allowing plenty of room for those 'average' days of 4, 5 and 6. Remembering that our recovery from depression usually comes in fits and starts will allow us to acknowledge and celebrate every step closer to good health we achieve. Almost never does recovery happen in one isolated swoop.

Journaling allows you to look back from time to time and see your progress. Pictures do the same. Feedback from friends and family can remind you of how far you have come.

The greatest adventure in the world always takes place one step at a time.

*"Start living now. Stop saving the good china for that special occasion. Stop withholding your love until that special person materializes. Every day you are alive is a special occasion."*

*Mary Manin Morrissey*

*November 7*

## Adrenaline

Adrenaline is what seems to make my functional days good and what seems to be missing on my off days.

Adrenaline is produced from either pair of endocrine organs that manufacture epinephrine or norepinephrine. And we already know that these are two of the six most important chemicals in affecting mood in our brain.

Adrenaline feels good. It energizes. We feel buoyant and optimistic when adequate adrenaline is in our systems.

I have only found one way to create adrenaline. That is through aerobic exercise. Pushing the oxygen level up in my bloodstream for twenty minutes minimum was a prescription that never failed. 'Runner's high' is known to be a very high level of epinephrine circulating in the bloodstream at that time.

If you are not able to exercise, try laying on your back and doing 'jumping jacks' in that position. Just the amount of activity this produces makes a difference. If you can walk briskly (I used to pretend I was getting away from a fire to motivate me), this will do the trick as well. The correlation is exact in that the more you do, the better you feel. But, doing anything is a guarantee for an improved mood. This is one of the things that is worth forcing yourself to do.

And adrenaline creates more adrenaline. If you can just get started a bit, it is an escalating process. The hardest part is getting started. Everything from there on is a breeze.

*"Striving for excellence motivates you; striving for perfection is demoralizing."*

*Harriet Braiker*

## *November 8*

# Alcoholism

If you are not able to detect a history of depression or manic-depression on either side of your family, look for alcoholism. The overlap between the two illnesses is huge. Upward of seventy per cent either way you look at it.

Scientists have proven the hereditary predisposition theory now. In fact, multiple genes appear to be involved. *Reuters* announced in October 2003 that nineteen chromosomes appear to be related to depression.

Use this in several ways. See your illness as a chemical problem. See that you didn't cause it; you inherited it. Understand that recovery is possible. Be glad that both of these are 'invisible' illnesses. You are not disfigured nor carry the signs of your trauma outwardly.

Some of us carry both genetic traits. Do not despair. Of all the ailments in the world, these are two of the most treatable. You can be well.

*"Thinkers do not accept the inevitable; they turn their efforts toward changing it."*

*Paramhansa Yogananda*

## *November 9*

# Prayer

There is no time or place or circumstance that prayer is not available to you. Prayers can be silent. Prayers can be sung or shouted. No matter how severe your isolation feels, prayer will link you to another. It guarantees that someone hears you and is connected to you.

There is no overdoing prayer or using it up. Ask questions, demand answers, plead for help, request guidance. There is no limit to the resources of prayer. If God is not a part of your spiritual beliefs, use Higher Power, the Source, something. Let a power greater than yourself be there for you.

Every society on earth in all times have had a belief system of some sort. The Native Americans have used Mother Earth as the elements of wind, water, fire and earth for direction and guidance.

Let Someone Else or Something Else give you strength when you are weak.

*"Thinking back over my life, it seems to me that there are different ways of looking out and trying to understand the world around us. There's a very clear scientific window. And it does enable us to understand an awful lot about what's out there. There's another window, it's the window through which the wise men, the holy men, the masters of the different and great religions look as they try to understand the meaning in the world. My own preference is the window of the mystic."*
*Jane Goodal in Reason for Hope*

## *November 10*

## Abusing Your Support

You will probably vent your anger and powerlessness at someone. Usually it is someone very close to you. Someone you trust not to go away - no matter what you say. Part of you will probably feel wretched at your behavior. Part of you will probably pray that this person will not abandon you, no matter how unlovable you act.

It is most likely that this individual will be a professional who is trained to deal with this. Sometimes it is a relative.

If you are able, say to them in the good times what it is you feel. Or say it in a note. These folks are probably there in the first place because of their unconditional love for you. Give back to them your love and your support when you are able. Replenish this source as you can. Let them know your 'boiling over' is not personal nor do you wish to hurt them. Ask them to understand and forgive you.

*"I get by with a little help from my friends."*
*John Lennon*

*November 11*

## Exercise

When I was in high school and college, the girls who were active - who sweat - were jocks. And this was not good. It was not until my thirties that jogging and aerobics became important to me (about the time that the rest of the world took up the trend, too). Now it is a form of addiction that I embrace.

Men take this for granted. Women usually don't have access to Little League and pee-wee football when they are in elementary school. So, women generally have a later start. That is not important. It doesn't matter when you begin. Just that you do begin.

Try tennis. Get an aerobics tape from the library and throw yourself into that. Walk regularly in your neighborhood. Swim. Go dancing. Hike. Tune into your favorite television show and rebound away in front of that. Bike - inside or outside. Find your activity. Alternate. Have fun.

Exercise is free and guaranteed to make you feel better. All those endorphins you create are phenomenal pain-fighters.

*"Movement is a medicine for creating change in a person's physical, emotional and mental states."*
*Carol Welch*

*November 12*

## Stress

It seems like this word has become vogue in the past decade. It is the catch-all for undiagnosed issues. Do not let the overuse of this term lull you into ignoring the reality of it.

Stress is too much to do in too little time. Too many obligations and not enough money. Too many demands and not enough energy. It is an imbalance of 'too much' and 'not enough'.

The side of the equation that you have the greatest power to influence is the first part. You can reduce the tasks, but you cannot create more hours in the day. You can reduce your obligations, but you cannot give yourself a raise. You can lessen or eliminate many of the demands upon you, but you cannot produce energy out of exhaustion.

You will never eliminate stress from your life. There will always be the red light when you are late, the illness or problem of a family member, insecurity in your job and more. But, you are capable of minimizing these. This is where an objective opinion, maybe your therapist or a good friend, can help put your worries in perspective. It may be uncomfortable at first to give up some monetary pleasures, or to say 'no', or to take a nap when there are calls to be returned.

But, stress can and will undo our progress. It doesn't have to.

*"The time to relax is when you don't have time for it."*
*attributed to both Jim Goodwin*
*and Sydney J. Harris*

## *November 13*

## Distraction

I discovered this little miracle quite by accident. Intuitively, I was using distraction to get me through the blackest part of the depression cycles. In hindsight, I became aware of the *necessity* of this coping skill.

For me, there were three ways to survive the very bottom of my depression. All of them were a form of distracting myself from the reality of my life at that moment. This might seem like a weak way of dealing with a critical issue. But, for me, ignoring the pain until it passed worked. I jokingly refer to this as my 'ostrich approach'. Bury your head in the sand and stick your butt in the air.

My distractions were to sleep my way through the dark days, read through them or watch movies (television) until my brain was functional again. The level of my debilitation determined which of these tools was dominant.

I did nothing else, but eat and use the bathroom.

I was always prepared. There were unread books and magazines in my home continually and I had spare video tapes from friend's libraries on hand.

The darkness will pass. You just need to pass the time until it does.

*"Sometimes it is important to work for that pot of gold. But other times it is essential to take time off and to make sure that your most important decision in a day simply consists of choosing which color to slide down on the rainbow."*
Douglas Pagels,
*These are the Gifts I'd Like to Give You*

## November 14

### In Partnership with your Doctor

This is a power that we should carry into all our relationships with professionals. We hire doctors, attorneys, and accountants to serve our needs. To be fifty percent of all the decisions is your part. The consequences are always yours. Keep this in mind.

Do you have a doctor (psychiatrist) who hears you? Do you feel comfortable asking your doctor lots of questions? Do you tell him/her when the side effects become intolerable and you need to re-evaluate your medication? Can your pain be discussed on your terms?

Envision yourself as half of the team. Take responsibility for getting your needs fulfilled. There are doctors who are not threatened by an assertive patient. Be sure that you have one.

*"Never be bullied in silence. Never allow yourself to be made a victim. Accept no one's definition of your life; define yourself."*
Harvey Fierstein

*November 15*

## Non-traditional Medicine

Acupuncture. Acupressure. Amino acids. Massage therapy. Vitamins. Herbs. Chiropractic. Reflexology.

If you are having trouble getting stabilized, you may want to explore alternatives to traditional medicine. Not as a substitute, but as an adjunct.

Some or all may be powerful components of your recovery and on-going health.

I especially like the term 'complementary' medicine. Webster's New Riverside Dictionary defines complementary as: something that completes, perfects or makes up a whole.

Experiment and use other modalities and protocols that complete the picture of your recovery. These needs will change as you heal, but some of these practices are thousands of years older than Western medicine and have served mankind well.

I do not ask my doctor's permission to try some of these alternatives. I remind myself constantly that I alone am the one living in the laboratory and I am able to make these decisions for myself. I do not hide what works for me, but I do not feel the need to defend it either.

Use your judgment. Not all practitioners (whether traditional or non-traditional) are competent.

*"Every time you don't follow your inner guidance, you feel a loss of energy, a loss of power, a sense of spiritual deadness."*
*Shakti Gawain*

*November 16*

## Married or Dating

Some of you are married. This is either a bond that will strengthen and mobilize you or can be an albatross that pulls you further into depression.

Some of you will be in a committed relationship or casually dating. But, whether the other person is a support or a detriment will greatly affect the quality of your life. (Needless to say, this is true of every relationship for every person in life.)

You will learn the best ways to maximize the relationships in your life. And due to the endless variables involved, I will only state that you must protect your health as your first priority. No matter what. You will be no good to your children (or anyone else) if you are unable to function or are hospitalized.

If there is recurring stress from your relationship, you must find a way to minimize that before you will heal.

Now, if you are single and dating... Men, you have the option to quit asking. Women, you have the option to decline a date. Do this when necessary. Without guilt. But, every life is enriched by the people who are part of our path. The more people - the richer you are. Just be wise in choosing who you spend your precious free time with.

Take advantage of what others have to give you. Give them of your resources as well. Dating casually or building a relationship takes time and energy. You will know your limits here. Honor them.

It may be prudent to not reveal your brain imbalance at first in a new relationship. I delayed this in all new circumstances ~ for several reasons. Sometimes the other person was in my life for a brief moment. It was futile to expose myself unnecessarily. Or more frequently, I let the other person get to know me - the wit, the professional, the caring friend. Then, my illness became just another part of me. It seemed if I told someone immediately, my diagnosis overshadowed all the other aspects of my personality.

Some people you will never tell.

But, if you are able to build a loving, supportive relationship and incorporate that into your life, it can be the very foundation you exist on. A good partner is a best friend. Building a life filled with love is what all of us need to thrive. Giving and receiving love is priceless.

Let all your relationships be nurturing ones.

*"The hunger for love is much more difficult to remove than the hunger for bread."*
*Mother Teresa*

## *November 17*

### Two Different People in the Mirror

I distinctly saw two different people looking back from my reflection in the mirror.

I liked the person who looked back at me on my good days. Nothing special to look at, but acceptable.

I despised the person I saw in the dark days. There was nothing redeeming in her. I saw glazed, lifeless eyes, a bloated face and pasty, dull skin.

So, I avoided mirrors when I felt bad.

Simplistic, but it worked.

*"What is a face, really? Its own photo? Its makeup? Or is it a face as painted by such or such painter? That which is in front? Inside? Behind? And the rest? Doesn't everyone look at himself in his own particular way? Deformations simply do not exist."*
*Pablo Picasso*

## *November 18*

### Polypharmacy

This is one of the relatively new words created to describe the vast knowledge being discovered about the brain and its breakdowns. Polypharmacy is taking more than one medication for the same illness at the same time. Heart patients do it all the time. It is not that unusual.

But, only recently have physicians begun to utilize polypharmacy in the treatment of depression and related illnesses.

Most of us are on an anti-depressant (or two), a stabilizer, possibly an anti-psychotic medication, a thyroid supplement and/or hormonal replacement.

This is nothing to fear or avoid. It is wonderful that we have these options available to us.

*"The art of medicine is in amusing the patient while nature cures the disease."*

*Voltaire*

## *November 19*

## Bloating

I do not know the underlying medical reason for the swelling that takes place for me during every depressive cycle. My face swells. My feet and hands swell. Nothing fits around my waist anymore.

But, I believe to try to alleviate this is harmful. The body is using this extra fluid to dilute something. The overload is serving some purpose. To live with this temporary problem is better than the possible consequences of diuretics. Most prescription diuretics create a rebound affect.

Keep some 'big' clothes around to accommodate these days. The body in its own miraculous way is healing itself. Allow the process to happen.

For some odd reason, it feels like even my head is swollen during some depressions. I will eat parsley (or use Solaray Parsley supplements) or eat asparagus as a natural diuretic.

Not everyone has bloating as a factor in their depression. But, if you do, adding another medication is not the best solution.

*"In order to change we must be sick and tired of being sick and tired."*

*Unknown*

## November 20

# Reading

If reading is not a pleasurable activity to you, ignore this. It would be like trying to learn to love oysters because you were forced to.

If you are a reader ~ or even a voracious reader like I am ~ you may read only certain types of material. Whether that be business journals, or romance novels or mysteries or historical texts, if reading is a pleasurable pastime for you and already a part of your lifestyle, expand it. Read more to learn about your illness. Read for fun. Read for distraction. Read to help you go to sleep. Or as an activity when insomnia strikes. If your brain isn't strong enough to concentrate on books, read magazines. The *Reader's Digest* can be a lifesaver. *People* magazine relies on lots of pictures to fill its pages. If you are having trouble concentrating, these are the best types of material for those times.

I do not recommend reading the newspaper however. *USA Today* publishes informative articles. Otherwise, newsprint is usually catastrophe, misery or trauma in its ugliest detail. Leave it alone. There is plenty of other uplifting material available.

Reading will remove your thought process from the misery of depression. It is a proven distraction for me and for many.

*"Man's mind, once stretched by a new idea, never regains its original dimensions."*

*Oliver Wendell Holmes*

## November 21

# Sex Drive

Considering that brain illnesses affect behavior and mood and that neurotransmitters have strong hormonal affects, it is reasonable that our sensitive sexual nature would be disturbed, too, during cycles of depression.

Mania and hypomania can create periods of hypersexuality. In the beginning of mania and through most of hypomania, it can make us feel like we are Mel Gibson or Kim Basinger. There's a delightfulness in pure pleasure during these cycles.

Full-blown mania can move us over the edge to promiscuity. The consequences here may affect us professionally, maritally and financially.

Sex takes energy and we have none in our depressions. The last thing that crosses our thoughts during these times are sexual activities.

Some anti-depressants dampen your sex drive as a side effect.

This is an individual thing. Balance is what we all are working toward. My feeling is that if we focus on balancing chemistry, our sexual needs fall into balance then, too.

*"Love is the answer, but while you are waiting for the answer, sex raises some pretty good questions."*

*Woody Allen*

## *November 22*

## Church and Organized Religion in General

What did the church mean to you as a child? This is probably what you will revert back to during your tough days.

If going to church was an obligation in your childhood, you will probably not be motivated to seek out religious guidance at this time.

If worship, sanctuary, calm, stillness, 'getting centered' come to mind, then church may offer you some solace. At the height of my isolation and desperation, I would slip in the back of the sanctuary late and slip out during the last hymn. But, that hour of fellowship left me warmer and stronger. Even singing lifted me up.

Discover where God is for you and go there.

*"God understands our prayers even when we can't find the words to say them."*

*Unknown*

## *November 23*

# Concentration and Loss of Memory

It would infuriate me to dial a phone number and by the time the other party answered, I'd forgotten who I'd called! Or to be talking to someone and in the middle of a sentence forget what I was saying. I would find myself reading the same paragraph over and over again. It was as if my brain was a light and suddenly someone unplugged it.

This will pass. There are several herbs and amino acids that I found definitely helped. They may be of some help to you or you may find your own solution. I will use amino acids - especially DL- phenylalanine or tyrosine (but not both at the same time as one is the precursor to the other) for help during the tough times.

Humor is useful here. People can identify with you if you acknowledge you've just lost your train of thought. "I must have Alzheimer's very early" works, as does "Brain cramp! Hold on just a minute". It really is no big deal if you don't make it one.

*"The existence of forgetting has never been proved: We know only that some things don't come to mind when we want them."*
*Friedrich Nietzsche*

## *November 24*

# Hospitalization

People with brain illnesses go to hospitals now just like other people with other ailments. Institutions have disappeared. Being hospitalized sounds lots less demeaning than being institutionalized.

Sometimes hospitalization is necessary. Facilities today are modern and clean with a zealous program of activities to facilitate a speedy return home.

Sometimes multiple hospitalizations are required. If you can approach this with the attitude of this being a little rest and relaxation rather than a forced hospitalization, it can be bearable and even a bit pleasurable. I enjoyed someone being in charge of meals, cleaning, scheduling when I was beyond even taking care of the basics of daily life. See yourself lifted out of your dark place and held in gentle, loving arms for a while. You can relax as if angel's wings support and protect you.

Let me be quick to note all hospitals are not havens of rest. Some are notorious for unsympathetic care. But, there are reputable hospitals available and most insurance will cover a brief stay.

If there are times in your healing that you need to let go and let someone else take over for awhile, find a good treatment center or hospital and get yourself there.

*"An illness is like a journey into a far country; it sifts all ones experience and removes it to a point so remote that it appears like a vision."*

*Sholem Asch*

## *November 25*

## Letting Things Go

Other than eating and using the bathroom, there's really nothing that can't be put off until tomorrow. Or the next day or the week after that.

Nothing is going to happen if you just let everything slide. Guilt is unwarranted. Take it easy. Be good to you.

When I was depressed, I didn't even have the luxury of choice. I simply couldn't keep up with chores or deadlines or anything else. Neither can anyone else when they are ill.

We automatically excuse someone else suffering from the flu or a migraine or recuperating from surgery. Why should we expect any more from ourselves?

*"Drag your thoughts away from your troubles...by the ears, by the heels or by any other way you can manage it."*

*Mark Twain*

## *November 26*

# Tolerating Side Effects

There are a host of symptoms that may or may not accompany your medication. Almost all of these disappear within a matter of weeks after a new medication is introduced. There are times when side effects are uncomfortable enough to be medicated on their own.

If a side effect cannot be tolerated, you need to feel free to be honest about this with your psychiatrist. If the symptom cannot be alleviated, your dosage can sometimes be lowered or an alternate medication be substituted. Being inconvenienced is understandable, but being miserable is not.

This can be sticky sometimes. There will be times when the medication offers such tangible benefits that a few mild side effects can be tolerated. Some side effects are quite serious and must be addressed. Some may just personally not be worth it to you. Some physicians will dismiss any side effect complaints. This is not acceptable.

However, if at all possible, try to grin and bear it through the two or three weeks most new medications require to begin to feel the benefits.

*"Reality is a crutch for people who can't cope with drugs."*
*Lily Tomlin*

## *November 27*

# In the Company of Others

This is tough to get a handle on at first. If I was marginally well, I often pushed myself to get out with others rather than isolate. But, there were times when I returned home feeling much worse than I felt when I left.

It took me a while to figure out what was happening. The common factor in these occasions was that some of the people in these groups made me feel good about myself and others made me feel terrible about myself. I realized that it wasn't important for me to know the underlying reason for this, but it was important for me to be aware of these feelings. I learned not to expose myself to potential damage. Your intuitive self will be your guide here.

There are definitely those occasions when you are better off staying home with a good book. There will be times when the outing started well but, you may need to depart early.

Watch how you are feeling when out socially. Don't wait until the end of the evening if you are not benefiting from being in the company of others. Excuse yourself early and go home to some great self-care like a bubble bath or favorite ice cream.

There will be times you are better off not pushing yourself.

*"Cocktail party: A gathering to enable forty people to talk about themselves at the same time. The man who remains after the liquor is gone is the host."*

*Fred Allen*

## *November 28*

## The National Institute of Mental Health

The largest and finest research center in the world is in Bethesda, Maryland. What this means to you is that you may use this resource free of charge (if you don't count all the taxes you have paid), but, unfortunately not many people know this. Actually, until October 1992, there were two separate facilities - the National Institute for Health and the National Institute for Mental Health.

Originally N.I.M.H. was a part of the National Institute of Health, until scientists and surprisingly, the government, acknowledged that the mental health field was still behind the times and must be addressed separately. Then, in October 1992, the two institutes were again combined so as not to duplicate research efforts and waste funding.

There are five research facilities in the world that are noteworthy. The number two institute is in France and has a relatively small budget, whereas the NIMH 2003 budget for Extramural and Intramural Research was $1.3 billion dollars. Our tax dollars pay for both NIH and NIMH.

If you have not found an answer to your depression or cannot get stabilized, you have access to this fabulous work. Not many people are aware that the general public is allowed to participate in their studies.

If you are accepted to participate in their program, the only cost to you will be your first airline ticket to Washington, D.C.. Your subsequent airfare, hospital facilities, meals, doctors, medications, tests, blood work-ups are of no charge to you.

The requirement on your part is to be a part of their ongoing research. Constant monitoring of blood and urine, as well as other tests would be expected. Trips outside the hospital are included so that you are not a patient the entire time. The average length of stay is between three and six months but, can be a year in duration. This would be their decision and not yours.

There is no promise of any help or solution to your problem by participating in this work. But, you will be helping others in the future with hope that the information will be helpful to you, too.

But, if you have exhausted ALL avenues and resources - as I did at one point - then, being part of an in-house research study would at least provide you with the finest medical care in the world and the very brightest doctors on the cusp of the latest research at no cost to you.

Be aware though that you would essentially be the guinea pig in the laboratory. I did not mind this when I applied as I had no other options at that point.

I was turned down after all the application process and numerous calls between my psychiatrist and the psychiatrist/researcher assigned to me at NIMH and even the visit I paid for to meet with the committee. This was a profound disappointment. Unfortunately, my prior history of hormonal imbalances would have clouded their research and I would not benefit their current research programs.

This is an extreme measure but certainly one that can be utilized under certain circumstances. But, if there comes a time when this option might work for you, NIH.gov would be the place to start.

"Getting out of the hospital is a lot like getting out of a book club. You're not out of it until the computer says you're out of it."

Erma Bombeck

## *November 29*

### Barometric Pressure

Quite by accident, I discovered that a change in weather and particularly, low pressure fronts, were sometimes a trigger to my low cycles. The National Weather Service has documents from four European countries on this phenomenon. To date, I know of no studies that have been done in the US.

A 1999 study by the Canadian Psychiatric Association concluded that low barometric pressure increased impulsive behavior (as indicated by emergency psychiatric visits and violent crimes). Be aware of this catalyst and remember that it is only temporary.

If you are a weather watcher, you may want to plan important commitments around low pressure fronts.

One of my primary symptoms during cycles of low barometric was also one of my oddest symptoms. I have only met two other folks who suffer from periods of depression who also suffered from what I call 'head pressure'. I could not call the feeling a headache. It was more like I was a hydrocephalic and my swollen brain was waterlogged.

Once I could identify this symptom with weather changes, I knew to take parsley supplements or eat asparagus for natural diuretics.

For me, relief was this simple. If you identify with any of these thoughts, you might find an answer this way, too.

*"It is only in sorrow bad weather masters us; in joy we face the storm and defy it."*

*Amelia Barr*

## *November 30*

### Accurate Diagnosis

The only accurate way for a correct diagnosis is a thorough and exhaustive intake interview of two to three hours. Symptoms that present themselves at an emergency hospitalization or other crisis interventions may mimic another brain illness. For example, an individual who is manic may appear delusional and be incorrectly diagnosed as schizophrenic. Medications would be then prescribed that would be inappropriate.

Unless a doctor probes diligently into our past, the right information may be missed. When asked "have you ever felt high like this before?", we are apt to selectively forget other episodes (this is not intentional). Questions about our genealogy and family are critical and again can be overlooked unless we are prompted by specific queries. It is the "was there ever a time in your past when you were unable to perform for a length of time?", "have you ever been accused of being lazy or irresponsible by an employer because of significant periods of missed work?", "have you ever felt suicidal and tried to act on it?", etc... that will eventually give the most reliable diagnosis of our illness.

Did you know that the DSM IV (the Fourth Edition of the *Diagnostic and Statistical Manual of Mental Disorders*) lists fifteen separate numerical classifications for major depressive order alone?

Of all the appointments we will ever have with our psychiatrist, this is by far the most important. If you feel you have been misdiagnosed, get a second opinion. Recovery depends on appropriate medication and appropriate medication depends on the correct diagnosis.

"Diagnosis: The physician's art of determining the condition of the patient's purse in order to find out how sick to make him."
Ambrose Bierce

# DECEMBER

## December 1

### Scar Tissue Really IS the Strongest Part of the Body

One of the mental mantras I use when things are pretty bleak is the old saw of scar tissue being the strongest tissue in the body.

I make myself think of Daniel of *Bible* fame, going through the fiery furnace. And his survival all but made him invincible.

I can do anything if I survive this. Depression is a fiery furnace AND icy death and everything in between. If I can survive this, I can survive anything else life might throw my way.

Haven't you felt this?

I feel that every cycle of depression that I have survived creates another layer of indomitable strength and character in my deepest being. I may not wear my scars visibly, but I am a survivor and a success both.

*"The human mind is driven to understand as the body is driven to survive."*

*Hugh Gilmore*

## December 2

### The Brain is the Most Complex Organ of the Human Body

I am adamant that I have a brain illness - NOT a mental illness. There is a world of difference in the two connotations. The brain is the largest organ of the ten major organ systems of the body - weighing in at approximately three pounds.

But, here are the statistics that will give you some perspective of this miraculous organ:

* the human brain is capable of over a hundred trillion possible connections
* the hundred trillion connections are capable of simultaneous calculation
* the human brain holds the equivalent of twelve hundred terabytes of computer memory
(likened to six million years of The Wall Street Journal)

*the human brain interacts with the world through a biological body with five senses
* the brain is super efficient; it uses only approximately ten watts of electricity

Greg Iles, *The Footprints of God*

And we expect something this powerful and complex to work perfectly all the time??

So, if some of your wires are crossed, it is understandable. Anything this intricate will have malfunctions. Do not belittle how much we have going right for us at any given moment.

If you are sitting in complete stillness while you read this, you have several thousand commands working in unison in your body. The messages from your brain to your heart alone as to when and how to beat is staggering. What about the eye messages? Blinking is something we never even think about. Or the fluid levels in our eyes. Or the muscles that move your vision across the page while you read. Or your lungs - or liver - or kidneys - and on and on.

The brain sends every single message to every single cell in the body to perform multiple tasks in a certain order in certain time frames according to particular circumstances.

Whew! It really is impossible for me to comprehend the vast miracle of the human body.

But, our brains are the ultimate CPU's. How can we be shocked if the system is 'down' from time to time?

Depression is no more than a chemical imbalance in some of the signaling sites in certain regions of the brain. And we can add back in what we need - just like diabetics learn to regulate their insulin.

So, we can appreciate the beauty of the organ that gives us our life and objectively see our depression as a small flaw in the overall system. And this glitch can be repaired.

Sometimes I just need to see my problem from this perspective. I feel much more gratitude and far less self-pity when I do.

"The brain is a monstrous, beautiful mess. Its billions of nerve cells – called neurons – lie in a tangled web that displays cognitive powers far exceeding any of the silicon machines we have built to mimic it."

William F. Allman

*December 3*

## Side Effects

Anti-depressant medications come with some of the more serious side effect profiles. Always read the package insert that comes with your medications and follow suggested guidelines. Knowing to take all pills with a full eight ounces - not just a swallow - of water is key to the medication not being too concentrated in our bloodstreams.

Some side effects are mild and most all will disappear after a few weeks.

But, there will be some side effects that cannot be ignored. It is up to you and your doctor to decide if the benefits outweigh the problems of any given pill. And sometimes you have the option of taking a second medication to overcome the side effects of the anti-depressant.

This is a very important area of your recovery. And only with frank discussions with an empathetic physician will you be able to make the decisions that are best for you.

Every package insert clearly states what the life-threatening signs of a serious reaction to the medication are. Know these signs for each anti-depressant. If you experience any of these, it is the time to call your doctor - no matter the time of day or night.

It has also been proven that the same medication will not cause the same reactions at different times in our lives. I wish I could give some standard simple solution for you here, but your unique chemistry will determine what medications you can tolerate and what you cannot.

*"It is easy to get one thousand prescriptions but hard to get one single remedy."*
*Chinese proverb*

*December 4*

## Some Helpful Definitions

I want to list some of the more common terms that are associated with depression as a kind of easy reference guide for you. By no means is this list inclusive.

AGITATED DEPRESSION -

Defined generally as a major depressive disorder with restlessness and motor excitement. The patient exhibits irritability. Often occurs in middle-aged and elderly population.

ANHEDONIA -

This is usually melancholy characterized with a loss of pleasure. A failure of reactivity to most or all activities including pleasurable stimuli.

CLINICAL DEPRESSION -

This usually refers to acute or chronic depression severe enough to need treatment.

MINOR DEPRESSION -

This term is not used often but refers to a subclinical depression that does not meet the criteria for major depression but where there are at least two symptoms present for two consecutive weeks.

RAPID CYCLING -

Rapid cycling is used in reference to patients with one of the bipolar illnesses wherein there are at least four major cycles in any twelve month period. Ultra-rapid cycling refers to those few patients who cycle through highs and lows within a twenty-four hour period.

DYSTHYMIA -

This comes from a Greek word meaning "ill" or "bad" ('dys'-) and "emotion" or "feelings" ('-thymia')

Dysthymia refers to a mild to moderate chronic state of depression. People who suffer from dysthymia rarely seek treatment as they have experienced this mood for most of their life and often do not realize they are depressed.

ATYPICAL DEPRESSION -

This is a deceptive name as this condition occurs more frequently than one would expect. The symptoms that a patient with atypical depression has are often the antithesis of 'normal' depression - i.e. excessive sleep and increased appetite. However, other symptoms such as heaviness of limbs, ability to experience joy and heightened energy for short periods within a major depressive cycle and inappropriate sensitivity to rejection may be present.

Atypical depression often presents in adolescence and can also be present with social phobia and/or body dysmorphic syndrome.

It is important to note that medications that are often successful with major clinical depression, are not those used to treat atypical depression.

CYCLOTHYMIA -

This actually falls under the Bipolar Illnesses but is included here as cyclothymia is defined as cycles of mild to moderate depression with mild to moderate highs. Because these mood swings are generally mild, they are often not recognized and treated.

*"Depression – when one feels a pessimistic sense of inadequacy."*

*December 5*

## Mercury Sensitivities

As odd as it may sound, in a last ditch effort at recovery, I decided to have the six visible fillings in my teeth replaced with non-mercury fillings. I had talked to several people who had - again as the very last resort - gone through the expense and aggravation of having old fillings replaced to heal ailments ranging from a prostate infection to severe eczema.

The odd aspect is that I had absolutely no pain in my mouth or anything that related to my teeth. And I didn't think six was a whole lot of silver amalgam fillings anyway. But, as I had no other options - and the depression was unbearable - SOMETHING had to be done - I researched the process and found a specialist in mercury removal and began.

There are a number of guidelines that must be followed and one is that only one quadrant of the mouth is done at a time - even if that involves just one filling - and there must be eight days minimum before going to the next quadrant.

I did not notice any difference whatsoever until the completion of the third quadrant. And walking out of the dentists' office that day, I felt drastically better. There had been the initial setback from the added mercury in my bloodstream as it vaporized and re-entered through my lungs, but after that third visit I felt 'lighter' and less toxic.

And far more importantly, I began responding to all the medications that had failed to work for me in the past. The very same prescriptions that had no effect on me prior to this were now suddenly effective! My thinking was noticeably sharper and clearer. I felt greater initiative and got more done. I was 'undepressed'!

This is strictly a matter to discuss with your physician before undertaking dental mercury removal. I did this because all else had failed. I had been on every medication available in the United States and two from Canada - some meds I was prescribed seventeen times in the hopes that maybe THIS TIME they would work; I had been to the Mayo Clinic in Minnesota; I had tried every cognitive, experiential, humanistic/ transpersonal therapy; there wasn't an alternative treatment that I hadn't tried, etc... You probably have been here. You might know the frustration of having nothing work.

So, in utter desperation I gave mercury removal a shot. It was a huge factor I attribute to being able to turn the corner and begin rebuilding my life.

It was getting the toxic metal out of my mouth that changed everything for me. Everyone does not respond this positively. I have talked to many people whose results have been as dramatic - if not more - than mine, and to some who found no relief. But, you will not know if your old silver amalgam fillings are toxic to you until you go through the removal process. If you are at your wit's end like I was, the expense and inconvenience is worth it.

Also, very few dentists will support this approach (they would be leaving themselves open to lawsuits for continuing to imbed patients with a poisonous material - see http://www.amalgam.org, http://www.mercuryfreenow.com or http://www.mercuryexposure.org for more mercury toxicity information). There are reference sites on Google on how to find a competent dentist for mercury removal in your area.

In my case, it was the beginning of a new beginning for me. And I found that as I rid the mercury from my system, not only did I respond to medications that had failed in the past, but that eventually, I even could halve dosages! But, the inverse of this was that I also became ultra-sensitive to mercury in any form. Certain contact lens solutions were unbearable now and I ultimately had to give up all the cold-water fish that I loved to eat due to mercury levels.

Again, Google can lead you to reference sites of how insidious mercury is in our environment and the products we use.

Because this is not a universal solution, but a critical one for many, I address this option for you.

*"I'm as old as my tongue and a little older than my teeth."*
*Jonathan Swift*

*December 6*

## The Mercury Connection or Looking at the Mercury Issue from Another Angle

In the seventh and eighth years after my diagnosis, I became really resourceful in my search for recovery and healing. I read constantly and did not disregard any option - no matter how far-out it seemed.

One of the options that I read about that had helped others' with chemical imbalances - not necessarily depression - was having the mercury removed from their old dental work. I read as much as I could find - both medical and anecdotal - and then spoke to some folks who had gone through this procedure. In theory, this made sense to me. I knew not to ever touch the pretty silver balls that eluded capture when the thermometer broke and I knew that mercury is a poison and is always carefully regulated by government agencies.

And although the fillings in my teeth were considered 'silver' fillings, I knew mercury was one of the components. All silver amalgams contain mercury. So, if this was a carefully monitored poison, what was it doing in my mouth?

Then I read that every time we chew - the simple act of biting down - released a tiny amount of mercury vapor or gas- both into our bloodstream and the cavity of our mouth to be inhaled.

So, we are constantly re-exposing ourselves to this toxin hundreds of times a day. And the cumulative damage is what hurts some of us. I believe now, that anyone with a compromised chemistry - anyone who suffers from food sensitivities or allergies, who has kidney problems, AIDS, cancer, etc... - will benefit from mercury removal. It can be the straw that eventually breaks the healthy balance within our delicately balanced bodies.

Of the individuals I spoke to, one woman had felt no relief, most had felt it worthwhile, but one particular individual provided information that made up my mind for me. This man is very orthodox and mainstream. However, he had suffered from a prostate infection for a period of approximately two years and in his desperation for relief, he had turned to mercury/amalgam removal. It worked. Nothing the traditional medical services offered him had produced any benefit. But, it seems that the poison of the mercury in his teeth was congregating in his prostate gland.

If something this esoteric would produce such dramatic results, then it was worth a try for me. I also had absolutely NO other options at this point and couldn't bear to accept that I could get no better than the hell where I was then.

Having no dental insurance was not an issue, as mercury removal is an elective procedure, so all costs are out of pocket. But, it is expensive. And I had decided that if I was going to go through the discomfort and expense of doing this, then I was going to do it right the first time. I was fortunate in that one of the best specialists was available to me - right in Atlanta.

And it worked! It was a sunny afternoon in May 1995 that the work on the third quadrant was done and I felt relief immediately. I can remember walking out of the dentists' office feeling like a five hundred pound weight had been lifted off my torso. And I truly believe that was the turning point in my recovery.

Not that there haven't been setbacks along the way. But, from that day on, the trajectory of my recovery has been on a steady upward incline.

If this is an area you would like more information on, please research for yourself a listing of mercury sources that sneak into our every day lives. Because there is a wide diversity in the costs of mercury removal, what is acceptable as substitutes for the silver amalgams and specialists who will perform this procedure, you will need to research these areas as well.

I do not feel that mercury removal is a panacea. But, I do know that I had been prescribed Prozac six times in prior years and after I had replaced the silver amalgams in my mouth, I was not only able to tolerate Prozac, but finally had a therapeutic response to it. Other medications also began to work for me that had never been helpful in the past (primarily hormone replacement and adjunct depression medications).

This is a very personal decision. But, if you fit some of this profile and have exhausted every other option in your recovery, it might prove to be your turning point as well.

*"My life is one long curve, full of turning points."*
*Pierre Trudeau*

*December 7*

## The Human Spirit – Whatever That Is

I truly believe an important factor in my remaining above ground - as opposed to being underground, i.e. dead/buried - during some of the crushing depressions I experienced was the strength of the will to live that I have no control over.

I have come to believe we are born with a dose of personal will - it is engineered into our fiber and our being just as irrefutably as our genetic blueprint. Some of us get a huge portion. Some of us don't.

This has absolutely nothing to do with personal attributes - we are neither better nor worse people because of this aspect. We don't get to choose this. I believe we can alter it - a bit, not too much - to the good. But, I also believe we have no power at all to diminish it.

This personal will cannot be deciphered on a physical level. Yet, time and again when an individual survives against the prognosis of all medical opinion, it is this spirit at work. Medical science cannot explain or define it. Philosophers have tried for ages to clarify it. We can't see it, touch it, hear it, feel it. But, you know exactly what I am talking about.

We can cognitively choose to fight - to win - to be better. And if suicidal thoughts plague us during some depressions, we have to choose again and again moment by moment to live. To stay above ground is how I see it, because in deep depressions I do not feel like I am living - only existing. I am not dead ... I just feel that way.

Do you know this inner spark I am speaking of? You are a fighter if you are reading this. Your thoughts may run to suicide and giving up - maybe you think these thoughts a lot - but, you are still seeking relief and recovery, or you wouldn't be seeking answers here.

I feel that if I were to mentally choose death at times, I would ultimately be unsuccessful at suicide because of this intangible, indomitable human spirit/will. I believe that those who survive the nightmare conditions of imprisonment have that extra dose of this human spirit. Those who recover from impossible ailments have more than most. You have more than most. That is why you - and I - are still fighting and seeking. And we are still trying one more new medication, one more treatment option, one more procedure - because our spirit burns brighter than our will to put that flame out. We couldn't be successful at suicide - even if we wanted to. We are at odds with our own highest and greatest nature - that essence of who we are. That super-powerful, intangible part of us that is without protoplasm or form.

So, when you are tempted to give up, instead lean on this aid built miraculously into us. Rest and let your spirit fight for you when you have no more strength to beat down the depression. Our inner light is the very best part of our humanness. Let it bring you back to health.

*"What he yearned to embrace was not the flesh, but a downy spirit, a spark, the impalpable angel that inhabits the flesh."*
*Antoine de Saint-Exupery*

## December 8

## How To Recognize Depression

Now this may sound pretty ludicrous. You will know you are depressed because you feel like Hell. But, one of the very best resources I can offer you is to be able to recognize and acknowledge your depressions as early as possible in the cycle. The quicker you can pick up on your initial symptoms, the sooner you can stop this cycle of depression in its tracks.

Here is what clued me in to my days of impending darkness: my handwriting changed dramatically - it was larger, wild, unformed, sloppy; I could not sleep enough or I couldn't sleep but two or three hours a night; my cravings for carbohydrates were an incessant itch that demanded to be scratched; I would catch myself repeating "I don't care" in response to consequences that I normally would avoid.

The importance of knowing the warning signs of impending depression was that the earlier in the cycle I could 'catch' the illness, the shorter the duration of the cycle and the weakening of the pain.

What are your signs? What will alert you that your chemistry has shifted and you need to take immediate action to rebalance yourself? Find these pronouncements and you have gained a measure of control over your illness.

*"Every patient carries her or his own doctor inside."*
*Albert Schweitzer*

## *December 9*

# Who Can You Count On?

Name them. Right now. The first two or three names that come to your mind - that's them. The family or friends, colleagues or neighbors, college roommates or childhood friends that you have the relationship with, that they are there for you - no matter what.

And, hopefully, this is a two-way street and your name would come to mind for them. You have to be a friend, to have a friend.

Here is something that will tell you about me and what it takes for someone to be my friend. When I cry, I sob. Sometimes this includes hiccupping. My face gets red and my eyes are squinched up and snot runs out my nose. I am in awe of Hollywood actresses who can cry so beautifully. A delicate little tear will trickle down their flawless cheek. If anyone ever took a picture of me when I am crying, it would be fabulous decor for a Halloween Fright Night.

So those folks I count on, are not people who will say "Oh, it will be okay. Don't cry now." Or shudder at the hideous sight of me. They won't minimize my pain or put a time limit on my dealing with it.

These are folks - I am so fortunate to have male and female friends of this caliber - that I can call and say, "I need to talk" and they say, when and where - not why.

Who are these people in your life? They are your core support group. And you are probably the same for them.

Treasure them. Tell them - often - that they mean the world to you.

Some friends will be with you like family (some of us are lucky enough to have relatives who are our best friends, too) to share holidays and special occasions. Some of these friends live far away and it takes effort to plan them into your life. Their support may be mainly verbal.

Some might be people you would vacation with. Some would only have a passion for pets in common with you. These extraneous factors are nothing when it comes to the mutual respect and 'in your bones' kind of love that connects you.

Having these people in your life is as important as getting your chemistry right.

"Friendship isn't a big thing. It is a million little things."

*December 10*

## Exogenous versus Endogenous

Only ten or fifteen years ago, physicians and scientists were still classifying depression according to a simplistic, dualistic method:
a. exogenous - a depression that was precipitated by events (loss of job, divorce, health crisis, etc..) in a person's life; at this time, cognitive therapy was thought to be adequate treatment
OR
b. endogenous - a chemical imbalance severe enough to require clinical intervention

Due to the vast improvement in brain imaging (PET, SPECT, MRI and EEG), the current theory is that all depressions are treated clinically (i.e. with medical and pharmaceutical intervention) regardless of the reason for onset if major depression is diagnosed according to: severity of symptoms (intensity) and duration of symptoms (usually more than two or three consecutive weeks).

If a person portrays five or more symptoms of depression for that extended period of time, it is believed that normal levels of neurotransmitters have been eroded to the point that pharmaceutical replacement is needed.

In common terms, this means that if a widow is still losing weight, not attending normal activities, struggling with insomnia, feeling unsubstantiated guilt, and is not returning to work two months after her husband's death, she would be treated with anti-depressant medication. The duration of the treatment would depend on her response to it.

No matter the catalyst, if the miraculous - yet fragile - balance of neurotransmitters in the brain is disrupted for an extended period of time, they are not able to replenish themselves and external supplementation is needed.

What this means to you, is that if you meet the criteria of clinical depression according to Beck's Depression Inventory - you will need medication. No amount of talk therapy will replace the depleted neurotransmitters in your brain.

*This is my depressive stance. When you're depressed, it makes a lot of difference how you stand. The worst thing you can do is to stand straight up and hold your head high, because then you'll start to feel better. If you're going to get any joy out of being depressed, you've got to stand like this."*

*Charlie Brown, Peanuts character*

## December 11

### The Weather and You - Part One

The weather is a strong factor in our sense of well-being. It is evident in how it affects everyone in our common terms like "I am under the weather", "the dog days of summer", "spring fever", etc...

The field of science that deals with climate and health is called bioclimatology. The field of science that deals with weather and health is called biometeorology. Bioclimatology emphasizes long-term influences and biometeorology refers to everyday, short-term influences.

The acknowledgment of how we are affected by our weather environment can be traced to 400 B.C. when Hippocrates, the Greek physician, wrote in his book, *On Airs, Water and Places*, about the affect of hot and cold winds on individuals. After World War II, scientific equipment was developed that could measure and quantify much of this data.

Mortality rates increase during severe summer heat. People tend to be sluggish, irritable and generally uncomfortable.

Besides, temperature, winds strongly affect us as people. It appears that our tolerance level for comfort is when winds are under twenty mph. Anything over that transmits distress signals from our skin to our brain. For certain very sensitive people, the strong winds of a Chinook or other major wind force can cause emotional disorientation. It is obvious that even moderate winds would stir up dust and pollens that would be damaging to asthma, allergy and other respiratory illness sufferers.

Ironically, as distressing as high winds are, people also find calm wind uncomfortable. The calmness of the atmosphere that precedes a storm, for instance, affects most people psychologically and even, some people, physically (Palmer, 1976).

Climatotherapy is the field of treating certain illnesses by climate conditions. For example, the symptoms of bronchial asthma and emphysema are alleviated in climates of pure air and low humidities. Asthma sufferers find the lee side of mountains or the lower mountainous areas of the southwestern United States are beneficial. Due to travel and lifestyle restrictions, climatic chambers are being used to treat noninfectious respiratory ailments (Landsberg, 1969).

How does this help you face and deal with your depression? Foremost, knowledge is a powerful weapon. Being aware that just taking a brief break on a bench in the direct sunlight will lighten your mood is medicine. Unfortunately, we know that it is status within the organization that will land us an office with a window. Barring that, making it a point to get outside - as frequently as possible - is good medicine. Walk your dog, walk to the mailbox, sweep your driveway, bike to your grocery store, etc... Sunlight is fabulous medicine and free to boot!

Become aware of your own reactions to various weather conditions and decipher what you need to do to remedy the situation. You are your own best physician here.

From *Health and Climate*; Nicodemus, N.L., Hodge, W.T., and Weiner, L.J.; pp. 470-477.

*"Climate helps to shape the character of peoples, certainly no peoples more than the English. The uncertainty of their climate has helped to make the English, a long-suffering, phlegmatic, patient people rather insensitive to surprise, stoical against storms, slightly incredulous at every appearance of the sun, touched by the lyrical gratitude of someone who expects nothing and suddenly receives more than he dreamed."*

H. E. Bates

## December 12

## Mini-Cycles

Be aware of little dips and speed bumps in your path. Adjust accordingly. These are small mini-cycles within the larger cycles of life. This is what everyone experiences. It is called LIFE.

As always, being vigilant about your symptoms is key.

Just be sure to make the minor tune-ups that will get your motor running properly again. Don't let a molehill become a mountain of pain for you.

*"This grand show is eternal. It is always sunrise somewhere; the dew is never dried all at once; a shower is forever falling; vapor is ever rising. Eternal sunshine, eternal sunset, eternal dawn glowing on seas and continues on islands, each in its turn as the round earth rolls."*

*John Muir*

## *December 13*

## EDUCATING OTHERS - Part 2

This an ongoing and often trying issue.

There are times when you will be able to educate others about the mysteries and complexities of this ambiguous disease. There will be other times when you need to protect your energy and accept the ignorance about depression of those around you.

Learn to be able to tell the difference between these two times.

It is self-destructive to spend your last shreds of energy in a depressive cycle trying to explain this often-contradictory illness. If the wires in your brain are crossed so that being coherent is an issue, much less being patient and logical, walk away. If someone cannot understand your experience and you are not in a place to help them understand, let it go until you are feeling better.

You might want to give some of the free literature from the Depression and Bipolar Alliance to those who are in a 'need to know' relationship with you. This is often a wonderful format for opening the dialogue in building the understanding and support that you must have from those you live and work with.

*"Authentic and clear requests generate the possibilities for new futures."*

*Sylvia Sultenfuss*
*from www.sylviasays.com*

## *December 14*

# Sunshine

Dogs just so instinctively know what to do. Both of my little terrier-types are sunbathers. It is hilarious to watch them on their backs, spread-eagled in the bright daylight. They will get just toasty warm and refreshed and head back into the air-conditioning.

It doesn't matter that scientists can link the benefits of sunshine to everything from Vitamin D that helps our immune system to stimulating the pineal gland which produces tryptamines that are mood-elevators. Dogs just know that sunshine feels good.

Do you have any way to spend a few minutes outside when the sun is shining? I just swept the small sidewalk in front of my home. Walk to your mailbox, trim a few bushes, return something to a neighbor.

This takes only a minute and doesn't cost you a thing. Guaranteed to work. Every single time.

*"Keep your face to the sunshine and you cannot see a shadow."*
*Helen Keller*

## *December 15*

# The Need for Vitamin B-12

"A deficiency in Vitamin B-12 increases the risk for depression. Because this nutrient plays a central role in the production of norepinephrine and serotonin - those neurotransmitters that are crucial to maintaining enthusiasm and an upbeat outlook - it is critical to get your minimum daily requirements either through your diet or through supplements. The best food sources are: yogurt, Swiss cheese, tuna on whole-wheat crackers, fortified cereals."

*First*, March 9, 2004

B-12 is critical to the maintenance of our nerve sheaths and to make the red blood cells in our bodies. It is also necessary for processing carbohydrates, proteins and fats from our diet. Severe depletion is called pernicious anemia.

Vitamin B-12 (cyanocobalamin) is not found in plant sources, but, is abundant in meat, liver, egg yolk, poultry and milk. Unfortunately, some people do not absorb this vitamin when taken orally as a supplement (and people over age sixty often lack the mucoprotein made in the stomach that creates the intrinsic factor that is necessary for assimilation) and, so, there is often a need for B-12 shots.

Scientists have established that B-6, B-12 and folic acid are all involved in mood and adequate levels must be maintained for mental energy. B-vitamins are not stored well in the body and are quickly depleted by dieters and caffeine and alcohol drinkers. Your doctor has three lab tests he can run to ascertain if you have low B-12 levels in your bloodstream. These tests are: an antibodies test, a methylmalonic acid test and a Schilling test. He can decipher which is necessary.

Because B-12 is important for healthy brain function and to prevent confusion and forgetfulness, this is a good area to explore (or at least eliminate) as part of your depression profile.

*"The first wealth is health."*

*Ralph Waldo Emerson*

## December 16

## The Wisdom of Francis Lear

This truly remarkable woman was married to a legend - the creator of the Lear jet - and yet, made impressive contributions to society in her own right. She was the founder of the first magazine focused on the needs and interests of women over forty, *Lear's*. And her battle over alcoholism and bipolar disorder is chronicled in her book, *The Second Seduction.*

Listen to how absolutely perfectly she nails the description of depression:
"As a patient, I have described, countless numbers of times, to all the doctors who have treated me, the particular pain that comes in a depression. The details of my story are the same each time, with the same intensity, the same hopelessness, but something was always missing in the communication. I could not catch the link that was not there between us. Did they not understand when I said that I felt the pain in my soul? It is different from physical pain and is not knowable to someone who has not felt it.

Dr. R has patients with manic-depressive illness who explain their suffering to him. He went into a depression himself for the first time in his life while I was seeing him. He asked, "Why didn't you tell me there was actual pain in depression?" I thought I had made it clear many times."

This is so eloquent. How hard it is to explain hell when the person you are talking to lives in the land of peace - the land without depression.

Do whatever you can to make your doctor understand your experience. To a lesser extent, those closest to you need to understand the depth of your pain. But, if they cannot hear you, find other sufferers who can.

It is critical to know that you are heard.

*"When women are depressed, they eat or go shopping. Men invade another country. It's a whole different way of thinking."*
*Elayne Boosler*

## *December 17*

## **Meeting Your Humor Quotient**

Everyone needs one. A bare minimum of grins - that barrel of laughs to get them through life. We who know depression intimately need laughter probably more than the average person to balance the dark days of depression.

Do you have friends that you are always chuckling or giggling or teasing with? Do you share a love of the absurd with some people in your life? Some folks are silly addicts. Some live for practical jokes.

I have two women friends that require a year-long quest to find the most outrageous, hilarious birthday card possible. Every year the bar gets raised just a little bit higher. I look forward to their cards to me but, the fun of finding their cards is a challenge that adds light and laughs to lots of my days throughout the year.

My nieces will not sit with me at a funny movie. I don't laugh casually. I am screaming laughing. And the ninth time I saw "Dumb and Dumber", I laughed just as hard.

Whatever your minimum daily requirement is - find those smiles and laughs. Laughter really IS the best medicine.

A Redneck Joke:

A small Alabama Wild Animal Park acquired a very rare species of gorilla. Within a few weeks, the gorilla, who was female, became very difficult to handle. Upon examination, the park veterinarian determined the problem. The gorilla was in heat. To make matters worse, there was no male gorilla available.

Reflecting on their problem, the park administrator thought of Eddie, a part-time redneck intern, who was responsible for cleaning the animal's cages.

Eddie, like most rednecks, had little sense but possessed ample ability to satisfy a female of any species. The park administrator thought they might have a solution. Eddie was approached with a proposition. Would he be willing to mate with the gorilla for $500.00?

Eddie showed some interest, but said he would have to think the matter over carefully. The following day, Eddie announced that he would accept their offer, but only under the following four conditions.

"First," he said, "I don't want to have to kiss her on the lips." The park administrator quickly agreed to this condition.

"Second." Eddie said, " You must never tell anyone about this." This was readily agreed to.

"Third," Eddie said, "I want all the offspring to be raised Southern Baptist." Again, they agreed.

And last of all Eddie stated "You've got to give me another week to come up with the $500.00."

And two blonde jokes:

A married couple was asleep when the telephone rang at two in the morning. The (blonde) wife picked up the phone and listened a moment and said, "How should I know? That is two hundred miles from here!" and hung up.

The husband said, "Who was that?"

The wife responded, "I don't know; some woman wanting to know if the coast was clear."

And:

Two blondes are walking down the street. One notices a compact on the sidewalk and leans down to pick it up. She opens it and looks in the mirror and says, "Hmmm, this person looks familiar."

She hands it to the second blonde who looks in the mirror and says, "You dummy, it's me!"

*Now don't you feel better?*

## *December 18*

## Sex

This is easy.

Forget it.

Well, although that is exactly what a depressed person usually feels like, sometimes there is a place for sex in depression.

Letting your intuitive self be your guide, you may find that the touching, tenderness and physical contact with another individual on an intimate level may be extremely healing. *The Health Benefits of Sex* by D. Zimmer states that oxytocin levels increase during intercourse which translates into lowered pain in everything from headaches and cramps to overall body aches. The March/April 2001 issue of *Psychology Today* says a team of researchers from the Queen's University in Belfast and the University of Bristol studied a group of men and found that an active sex life reduced heart attacks by fifty percent.

Be aware of medications that can sabotage your sex life though. Here are some common ones: Xanax, Valium, Tegretol, Dilantin, Mysolin (Primidone), Elavil, Ascendin, Anafranil, Norpramin, Prozac, Tofranil, Paxil, Nardil, Zoloft, Desyrel, Effexor, Tenormin, Lopressor, Inderal, Aldactone, Proscar, Tagamet, Pepcid, Axid, Zantac, Lioresal and Cordarone. (from *Healing Edge Sciences*)

Never let yourself feel pressured into physical intimacy. But, if you can exert yourself enough while depressed, you may find the endorphins have done their work! You may not feel euphoric, but you might feel a whole lot better.

Sex has a place in our lives - just not always in our depressions.

I have to break my pattern here and veer away from wise sayings to some base - and often hilarious - quotes:

"Condoms aren't completely safe. A friend of mine was wearing one the other day and got hit by a bus."

Bob Rubin

"Remember, if you smoke after sex, you are doing it too fast."

Woody Allen

"Sex on television can't hurt you unless you fall off."

Unknown

"Sex is not the answer. Sex is the question. "Yes" is the answer."

Swami X

"Life in Lubbock, Texas taught me two things: one is that God loves you and you are going to burn in Hell. The other that sex is the most awful, filthy thing on earth and you should save it for someone you love."

Butch Hancock

"Contraceptives should be used on every conceivable occasion."

Spike Milligan

"No matter how much cats fight, there always seem to be plenty of kittens."

Abraham Lincoln

"There is nothing wrong with going to bed with someone of your own sex. People should be very free with sex; they should draw the line at goats."

Elton John

"Sex between a man and a woman can be absolutely wonderful. Provided that you get between the right man and woman."

Woody Allen

"The hypothalamus is one of the most important parts of the brain, involved in many kinds of motivation, among other functions. The hypothalamus controls the Four F's- fighting, fleeing, feeding and mating."

Unknown psychology professor in neuropsychology class

"There are a number of mechanical devices which increase sexual arousal, particularly in women. Chief among these is the Mercedes-Benz 380 SL convertible."

P.J. O'Rourke

*December 19*

## Cards, calls and letters

It seems that regardless of whether I was receiving or sending mail or calls, it was vital for my mental health to keep committing to communicating. Much as I wanted to completely isolate in the days of the greatest pain, I knew I could not.

I found that at the very bottom of my depression, I could do virtually no reaching out to others (and I mean days of the 'sleep eighteen hours at a time' days). But, even in a profoundly low period, if I *could* "reach out and touch someone" I would feel better instantly. I cheated some here. I often knew friend's schedules well enough that, although I was incapable of formulating my thoughts coherently enough to hold up my end of a two-way conversation, I could leave a message on their answering machine that I was thinking about them. And this provided a double benefit as it removed me temporarily from the self-centeredness of my misery and it left a pleasant message for my friend to find.

I personally like to shop for greeting cards. In fact, it is one of my favorite (free) things to do. I have been known to stand in a card section of a store and just howl laughing - much to the amusement of other patrons. So, it is normal for me to have a supply of cards on hand. And it lets me feel connected to others - even in my isolation - to drop them a note. These notes were always short. Sometimes the pain though would just start to spill out through my pen and the writing would turn into a journaling experience. This was always a great catharsis. And I never mailed these ramblings.

I didn't feel the need to be brilliant. I just wrote what came naturally. My handwriting usually worsened during my dark times and I didn't fret about that either.

I hated the loneliness of those suffering days and yet, I could not contribute more than one-sided communication much of the time. I understand how controlling this may seem. I never meant it to serve that purpose.

And for those who ached to lessen my pain but felt impotent, I let them know that to be on the receiving end of an answering machine message or a greeting card was ultra-beneficial. This could be a cheap, easy two-way street of healing.

This is not an available option at all levels of depression - there are some phases just too dark for this to be a tool for you to use. But, utilize it as much as you can. I can't number the times it has turned my whole day around.

*"The way we communicate with others and with ourselves ultimately determines the quality of our lives."*
*Tony Robbins*

## December 20

# Those Who Can and Those Who Can't

Without a doubt, this has been one of the most surprising and baffling of all the elements of dealing with depression. And it seems I am not alone in experiencing this aspect of our illness.

What I am speaking about is this: those people who were most connected to me (family, colleagues, friends I saw on a daily or at least, frequent, basis) and those who were the most educated - and ironically, some whose careers were in the fields of psychology or even mental health - were almost invariably the people who could not grasp or deal with my depression. And yet, these were the same people who had been supportive through all other - positive and negative - experiences we had shared.

It never failed that the very people that I counted on - and assumed, dangerous as that was - to understand my illness were the people who were at a complete loss as to how to deal with me or to know what to say to me.

Usually the response was not to respond at all. Either silence or a blank look would replace what would have been concern or help in other circumstances.

And those that I thought would never grasp the nature of neurological imbalances would astound me with their candor and intuitive wisdom. I have often wished I had written down some of the wonderful, spontaneous things that were said to me by these strangers (or at least folks that were not in my immediate circle of friends) - so that I might say them to others.

And I am talking about an offhand remark one day to a grocery store cashier in response to the generic 'how is your day?'. I must have mumbled that my day was not too terrific and the comment she made was jaw-dropping in its insight and warmth. And there were other similar casual encounters that were eerie in their perception and support.

Do not be dismayed by this irony. I soon learned that it had nothing to do with whether the other person cared for me or not. In some cases, I just needed to help them understand that although I was normally a high-energy personality, depression dampened my enthusiasm, skewed my attitude and generally replaced my sunniness with a grump. Or in some cases, I had to learn to discern that some of these folks were the epitome of fair-weather friends.

I hope you learn not to take it personally when those you count on just cannot figure out what to say to you when you are depressed. I figured out that my expectations of others was creating a lot of my dismay and expectations were something I had the power to change.

*"You never really understand a person until you consider things from his point of view."*

Harper Lee, *To Kill a Mockingbird*

## December 21

### N. B. D.

This is really important stuff. Everybody needs to pay attention here.

I was introduced to the N.B.D. way of life in 1983. Steve gave me this gem of wisdom and I continue to be grateful.

If you can adopt this philosophy in the context of your life, I can guarantee that you will never suffer from ulcers. And your day to day life will be so much smoother.

N. B. D. is just the short version of the Serenity Prayer: "God grant me the serenity to accept the things I cannot change, courage to change the things I can and the wisdom to know the difference."

N. B. D. stands for No Big Deal.

If something or someone rubs you the wrong way, just say "N.B.D." Say it to yourself. Say it out loud (this can often diffuse a tense situation).

Some things ARE a big deal (missing your meds, hurting other folks, etc...). But, it is simply amazing when you really get things in perspective, how little much of it really matters after all.

I have let so much aggravation and tension slide effortlessly away with this tool. Problems never got beyond the mole hill stage with the N.B.D. technique.

Try this. It works.

N. B. D.

*"A positive attitude may not solve all your problems, but it will annoy enough people to be worth your effort."*
*Herm Albright*

*December 22*

## The Contradictions to Depression Recovery

Just when I felt that I was getting a strong sense of myself, undoing a lifetime of co-dependent behaviors and finally feeling at peace with my place in the world, my depression increased to the point that I was forced to quit working.

Suddenly with this new lifestyle, much of what I knew about independence and self-care went out the window. I was forced to trust other people and admit that I needed help. I had to learn this was far from a black and white situation.

There were times when I needed other people to do some tasks for me. If I could not drive because the wires in my brain had broken circuitry at that time, someone else had to go pick up my prescriptions.

The same was true for groceries. Or getting to a doctor's appointment.

I was afraid that I had reverted back to an infantile helplessness. I was ashamed of how much I had to have at times and how little I was able to give back in return. Gratefully, this was an occasional situation - not a constant. But, I initially felt I had taken a step backward.

A wise friend asked me if I felt that the people I had done favors for in times past were being infantile. Of course not! Therefore, I was not infantile either.

This was just the part of the journey where I received. I was not giving up any personal growth or power. I was just on the other end of the give-take continuum.

*"Depression defies description – taking place on a plane not only beyond words, but an abyss where all language fails."*
Martha Manning, *Undercurrents*

*December 23*

## Generics Are NOT the Same As Standard Prescriptions

I have been told over and again by doctors and pharmacists alike that the medicine I was taking in generic form was EXACTLY the same as the higher-priced, brand name prescription. I can only tell you that I did NOT react the same.

The fillers and binders in the pills may cause differences. The method by which the generics are processed is different. Some medications have been shown to have a difference in bio-availability. When doctors say generics are the chemical equivalent of standard brands, they are speaking only of the active ingredients. The size or color in binders, dilutents, excipients and preservatives may vary.

The point is - listen to YOUR body. If you feel different on generic medications, insist on taking the name brand prescription.

*"Medicine is not only a science; it is also an art.*
*It does not consist of compounding pills and plasters;*
*it deals with the very processes of life,*
*which must be understood before they can be guided."*
Paracelsus

*December 24*

## You Are Not Alone

In 1990, The Global Burden of Disease published their findings. The number one cause of disability throughout the world was unipolar major depression. At that time, depression affected twice as many people as the next highest cause of disability.

Depression is a chemical imbalance of the complex and fragile mechanics of our brain. And it is now getting the research attention that is long overdue. The abundance of medication options that have become available just since Prozac was introduced in 1987 is reason for hope. And the alternative ways to overcome this illness is another growing field.

There is strength in numbers.

*"Knowledge is an antidote to fear."*
*Ralph Waldo Emerson*

## *December 25*

## Making the Most of Christmas

It doesn't matter if every other person in the world is celebratory and joyous today. Take your "emotional temperature" when you get up and make today one that is right for YOU. If you have made plans that aren't appealing at this moment, cancel them. You need give no explanation. "I am unable to ...(whatever) and just wanted to wish you a Merry Christmas. I'll talk to you soon."

Or if your mood is too low for even this brief exchange, simply skip the occasion and give your apologies later.

If you feel that the best way for you to see this day through is to be in the warm embrace of family and loved ones, then participate as you are able and let the exuberance, laughter and good food nourish you.

If you need to save your energy and just allow yourself to wallow in personal pampering, then so be it. Keep taking your emotional pulse and do what is best for that moment. If watching all the holiday specials on television helps, do that. If you cannot bear to hear one more seasonal carol, leave the television and radio off.

Maybe calling two or three old friends and just reminiscing can make your day. What works in the morning, may not be refreshing in the afternoon. Be vigilant in assessing your needs and meeting those needs.

This day can be a great day. However you spend it. But, above all, allow this day to acknowledge your needs that only YOU can provide.

*"To free us from the expectations of others, to give us back to ourselves – there lies the great, singular power of self-respect."*
*Joan Didion*

## *December 26*

## Talk Therapy

Everyone in life uses this tool at some point. How many times have you found that just by discussing a problem with a trusted friend, the answer reveals itself to you during the conversation? "Hashing it out" is what we called this in our family.

Suddenly an option that you had not thought of is so apparent. The light bulb goes on in your mind and the solution is evident.

Not only is this therapy free, but in the worst case scenario, you feel your burden is lessened simply by sharing it.

So rather than ruminate and obsess about an issue, call a friend. Worrying alone never solved a problem.

*"Everything becomes a little different as soon as it is spoken out loud."*
*Hermann Hesse*

## *December 27*

## The Rescue Me Syndrome

I consider myself to be a strong - willful, even - independent woman. Why is it then, at times, I would do virtually ANYTHING to have a caretaker in my life?

I guess this fantasy person would kind of be a MOM. I feel at times that I NEED to have all my needs met, just like a Mom would do for me. It gets so bad that I want someone to: make my bed, wash my clothes, decide on menus, buy groceries, prepare the food, set the table , clean the dishes, go the post office for stamps, walk the dog,...... In short, I want to be taken care of. Just like a baby.

Sad, isn't it? I can be so competent. I can juggle domestic, corporate and personal segments of my life, performing at peak levels in all these areas. But, sometimes it is too much. Sometimes the world is just too much.

And then I don't just slow down. I simply stop.

I seem to work only in high gear or I'm in idle. And when the resting stage has been reached, I want to be waited on, pampered, coddled.

These phases don't last very long. My batteries recharge at a remarkable rate. But, oh, how I long for this magical entity when I am out of internal resources.

Sometimes these intervals correspond with depression and sometimes I just am tired of doing it all myself.

Whatever the catalyst, it really is okay to appreciate the need for pampering and seek it. Whether this takes the form of a massage, hiring someone to clean your home, or resigning from a committee. The Rescue Me syndrome is born from *overwhelm*. You will no longer feel the need for rescue when your life is at a manageable pace.

*"Instead of saying that man is the creature of circumstance, it would be nearer the mark to say that man is the architect of circumstance."*

*Thomas Carlyle*

## December 28

## Getting Insurance Coverage

Not just depression, but any illness today is exorbitantly expensive. From the doctor visits themselves, to the lab tests and imaging procedures, to actual medications - costs can be prohibitive.

There are ways around this.

If you need to bypass the physical examination and screening for pre-existing illness, join a large organization for employment. Any government position, school system, large corporation will skip this step.

Sometimes you can be covered from your first day of employment.

Another way to insure yourself is to work for some of the large organizations that will pay (as of this writing at least) full benefits for part-time work. Both United Parcel Service and J.C. Penney will pay medical benefits if you work only twenty hours a week.

If you are unable to work, but have worked in the past, you can collect Social Security Disability insurance and get Medicare coverage that way. However, medication is not covered under this plan.

If you have a spouse that has coverage, elect to join their plan or see if you qualify to be a dependent to some family member who can add you to their coverage.

When I lived in Atlanta, there was psychiatric care available for free and prescriptions for only a copay of $3.00 at one of the general hospitals that treated some indigents.

Be innovative and relentless. You need not be paying for your treatment out of pocket in our society.

"Some patients feel guilty about achieving recovery with medication. They have been thoroughly indoctrinated in the idea that emotional disturbance must reflect psychic ills, and they expect treatment to require a prolonged, painful search of their unconscious."

Nathan S. Klinie, M. D.

## December 29

## Such a Little Thing

It seems we have to supplement our diets now because of the nutrient erosion of farmland. And an often neglected little factor in depression is low folate levels.

Harvard conducted a study in which they added adequate folate to antidepressant medications for patients. The Recommended Daily Allowance (RDA) is 400 mcg. Of those seventy-one people, forty-three percent relapsed into depression who had inadequate levels of folate in their blood, compared to only three percent who received adequate amounts.

From *Prevention* magazine, February 2005

Folic acid (folate) is a B-vitamin found in our diet when we eat green leafy vegetables, dried beans and legumes, citrus fruit and fruit juice, wheat bran and whole grains, liver, poultry, pork and shellfish. Do not exceed 1,000 mcg per day.

*"He that takes medicine and neglects the diet, wastes the skills of the physician."*

*Chinese proverb*

## December 30

# Why You Need Alpha-lactalbumin

Now here is a term you probably aren't familiar with but, it is critical to mood and coping skills.

"Alpha-lactalbumin is a whey protein that makes up about eighty percent of the protein in cow's milk. This chemical raises blood levels of tryptophan (an essential amino acid that stimulates production of serotonin which plays a role in soothing frazzled nerves). And because stress depletes serotonin, it is not a bad idea to indulge in a protein-rich milk shake from time to time."

*First*, March 9, 2004

Our diets can work for or against us. And any diet that eliminates a food group or is not diversified will lead to chemical imbalances and that is a guaranteed recipe for depression.

If you crave a milk shake, your body is signaling that it needs some powerful nutrient that these ingredients can provide. As always, make sure you use high quality products (and this is not the time to go low-carb/low fat either). Carbohydrates and fats play important roles in our chemistry and if you deprive yourself of these, you are likely to spiral into a bad mood.

These are low moods that we can control. If milk products are difficult for you to digest and process, there are multitudes of products available in any drugstore to combat this. Be aware that milk - and all milk products like cheese, ice cream, yogurt, etc... - is important to brain health and alpha-lactalbumin is a vital part of a good diet.

*"Let food be your medicine and medicine your food."*

*Hippocrates*

*December 31*

## New Year's Eve – YOUR Way

How do you end your year?

I found boisterous, alcohol-fused New Year's Eve celebrations painful, even when I was in a fabulous mood. My husband and I had particularly found the midnight stranger-kissing segment to be an uncomfortable way to start a new year.

But, I devised a ritual that makes New Year's Eve one of the highlights of the year for me. Invitations are not accepted unless the circumstances are a far cry from the above scenario. Dinner is whatever I most desire. Usually lobster. If a candle-lit bubble bath fits my mood, then I spend a tranquil hour pampering myself. If it is having someone earlier in the day do the whole massage/facial/manicure/pedicure routine, that is part of my plan.

Yet the very best part of the night is to sit down with my Daytimer, address book and a journal. I review the year that is ending and write down all the people who have entered my life and left my life in the preceding twelve months. I reflect on each of these people.

Then I write down all I have accomplished that year. Even in my very worst years, I have been able to acknowledge dozens of successes. I not only take the time to cherish my life but, to savor my growth as well.

Why not give yourself credit for a year well-lived and create your own ritual?

*"Be always at war with your vices, at peace with your neighbors, and let each new year find you a better man."*
*Benjamin Franklin*

# Desperate Days Checklist

1. Cancel all plans

If you are unable to make the necessary phone calls, hopefully you have a person already 'trained' to know what to do for you in this case and you need only make one phone call - to them.

2. Look at your options - lecithin, DL-phenylalanine, tyrosine

3. If changing your chemistry will not work, distract yourself (from the misery until your chemistry shifts out of the depression naturally). This will be sleep, television or reading.

Do whatever it takes to get through today.

Tomorrow is a fresh start.

# Partial Bibliography

Abbey Press. Carenotes. St. Meinrad, Indiana: St. Meinrad Archabbey.

Ackerman, Diane. *An Alchemy of Mind: The Marvel and Mystery of the Mind.* New York: Scribner, 2004.

*A Course in Miracles.* Temecula, CA: Foundation for Inner Peace, 1996.

Allen, James. *As A Man Thinketh.* New York: G. P. Putnam & Sons, 1987.

Allman, Wm. F. *Apprentices of Wonder: Inside the Neural Network Revolution.* New York: Bantam Books, 1989.

Andreason, Nancy. *The Broken Brain: The Biological Revolution in Psychiatry.* New York: Perennial Library, 1985.

Anderson, Joan. *A Year by the Sea: Thoughts of an Unfinished Woman.* New York: Doubleday, 1999.

Anderson, Walter. *The Confidence Course. Seven Steps to Self-Fulfillment.* New York: Harper Publishers, 1997.

A Parent's Guide to Internet Safety. <www.indianchild.com>

Barnard, Neal. *Breaking the Food Seduction: The Hidden Reasons Behind Food Cravings and the 7 Steps to Ending Them Naturally.* New York: St. Martin's Press, 2003.

Belensky, Mary, Blanche Clinchy, Mary Goldberger and Jill Tarule. *Women's Way of Knowing:The Development of Self, Voice and Mind.* New York: Harper Collins, 1996.

Berg, Elizabeth. *Talk Before Sleep.* New York: Dell Publishing, 1994.

---. *The Year of Pleasures.* New York: Random House, 2005.

Berry, Wendell. *The Peace of Wild Things.* Berkeley: Black Oak Books, 1991.

Bolles, Richard. *What Color Is Your Parachute?: A Manual for Job-Hunters and Career-Changers.* Berkeley: Ten Speed Press, 1972.

Brody, Lora. *Growing Up on the Chocolate Diet. A Memoir With Recipes.* Manchester, NH: Olympic Marketing Corporation, 1985.

Broyles, Stephen E. *The Wind That Destroys and Heals: Trusting the God of Sorrow and Joy.* Colorado Springs: Waterbrook Press/A Shaw Book, 2003.

Conroy, Pat. *My Losing Season*. New York: Nan Talese/Doubleday, 2002.

Cousins, Norman. *Anatomy of an Illness as Perceived by the Patient: Reflections on Healing and Regeneration*. New York: W.W. Norton, 1979.

---. *The Healing Heart: Antidotes to Panic and Helplessness*. New York: Random House, 1986.

Depression and Bipolar Support Alliance < www.dbsalliance.com>

*Diagnostic and Statistical Manual of Mental Disorders IV.* Washington, D. C.: American Psychiatric Association, 2000.

Duke, Patty and Gloria Hochman. *A Brilliant Madness: Living With Manic Depressive Illness.* New York: Bantam Books, 1992.

Emerson, Ralph Waldo. *Self-Reliance*. New York: Thomas Nelson and Sons, 1841.

Frank, Anne. *The Diary of a Young Girl*. New York: Random House, 1956.

Goldberg, Natalie. *Wild Mind: Living the Writer's Life*. New York: Bantam Books, 1990.

Goodal, Jane and Phillip Berman. *Reason for Hope: A Spiritual Journey*. New York: Warner Books, 2005.

Gorman, Jack M. *The Essential Guide to Psychiatric Drugs*. New York: St. Martin's Press, 1990.

Gregory, Phillipa. *Zelda's Cut*. London: Book Club Associates, 2000.

Grodin, Charles. *How I Get Through Life: A Wise and Witty Guide*. New York: Wm. Morrow and Company, 1992.

Groom, Winston. *Gump and Company*. New York: Washington Square Press, 1997.

Groopman, Jerome. *The Anatomy of Hope: How People Prevail in the Face of Illness*. New York : Random House, 2003.

Hippocrates. *On Airs, Water and Places.*

Iles, Greg. *The Footprints of God*. New York: Scribner, 2003.

Indigent Prescription Programs <www.edhayes.com/indigent.html>

iVillage: The Website for Women <www.iVillage.co.uk>

Jamison, Kay Redfield. *An Unquiet Mind.* New York: Alfred A. Knopf, 1995.

---. *Touched with Fire: Manic-Depressive Illness and the Artistic Temperament*. New York: Free Press, 1993.

Job Hunters Bible <www.jobhuntersbible.com>

Jordan, Hamilton. *No Such Thing as a Bad Day*. Atlanta: Longstreet Press, 2001.

Kaminsky, Howard and Alexandra Penney. *Magic Words: 101 Ways to Talk Yourself Through Life's Challenges*. Louisville: Broadway Press, 2002.

Lear, Frances. *The Second Seduction.* New York: Random House, 1994.

Lee, Nelle Harper. *To Kill a Mockingbird.* Philadelphia: J. B. Lipincott, 1960.

Lewis, Dennis. *The Tao of Natural Breathing*. Berkeley: Rodmell Press, 2006.

Manning, Martha. *Undercurrents. A Life Beneath the Surface*. New York: Harper Collins, 1995.

Mays, John Bentley. *In the Jaws of the Black Dogs: A Memoir of Depression.* Canada: Penguin Press, 1996.

Mental Health Matters <www.mental-health-matters.com >

Mercury Free and Healthy <www.amalgam.org>

Mercury Exposure <www.mercuryexposure.org >

Mercury Free Now <www.mercuryfreenow.com>

*Merriam-Webster Dictionary*. Springfield, MA: Merriam Webster Publishers, 2004.

Millman, Dan. *No Ordinary Moments: A Peaceful Warrior's Guide to Daily Life*. Tiburon, CA: H.J. Kramer, Inc. 1992.

Nicodemus, N.L., W.T. Hodge and L.J. Weiner. *Health and Climate*. Asheville, NC: National Climate Data Center, 1973.

Pagels, Douglas. *These Are the Gifts I'd Like to Give You: A Sourcebook of Joy and Encouragement*. Boulder, CO: SPS Studios, 1999.

Partnership for Prescription Assistance Programs <www.pparx.org>

Peale, Norman Vincent. *The Power of Positive Thinking*. Saddle River, NJ: Prentice-Hall, Inc, 1952.

Peck, M. Scott. *The Road Less Traveled: A New Psychology of Love, Traditional Values and Spiritual Growth*. New York: Touchstone/Simon & Schuster,1978.

Roberts, Nora. *Sanctuary*. New York: G.P. Putnam and Sons, 1997.

Ross, Julia. *The Mood Cure:The 4-Step Program to Take Charge of Your Emotions - Today*. New York: Penguin, 2002.

Seaward, Brain Luke. *Stressed Is Desserts Spelled Backwards: Rising Above Life's Challenges with Humor, Hope and Courage*. New York: Barnes and Noble, 1999.

Shakespeare, Wm. *Othello*. 1603.

Sherman, Elaine. *Book of Divine Indulgences*. New York: McGraw-Hill/ Contemporary, 1987.

Solomon, Andrew. *The Noonday Demon: An Atlas of Depression*. New York: Scribner, 2001.

Sparks, Beatrice and Aron Flare, eds. *Almost Lost: The True Story of an Anonymous Teenager's Life on the Streets*. New York:Avon Flare/Harper Collins, 1996.

Styron, Wm. *Darkness Visible: A Memoir of Madness*. New York: Random House, 1990.

The Joy of Adulthood. <www.sylviasays.com> <www.joyofadulthood.com>

The National Pain Foundation <www.nationalpainfoundation.org>

Thyroid Power <www.thyroidpower.com>

van Roden, Caldwell, ed. *Thoughts When Caught Between a Rock and a Hard Place*. York, PA : Wellspring, 1987.

*Webster's New Riverside Dictionary*. Boston:Houghton Mifflin, 1984.

Williams, Margery. *The Velveteen Rabbit*. Garden City, NY: Doubleday & Company, 1922.

Yoga Holistic-online <www.holistic-online.com/Yoga/hol_yoga_pos_sunsal.htm>

Zig Ziglar. *Something Else to Smile About. :More Encouragement and Inspiration for Life's Ups and Downs*. Nashville: Nelson Books, 1999.

Order Information
Saving Your LIFE:
One Day at a Time
$19.95 plus $5.95 S&H
1-800-730-3194
www.savingyourlife.org

Order Information
Saving Your LIFE:
One Day at a Time
$19.95 plus $5.95 S&H
1-800-730-3194
www.savingyourlife.org

Order Information
Saving Your LIFE:
One Day at a Time
$19.95 plus $5.95 S&H
1-800-730-3194
www.savingyourlife.org